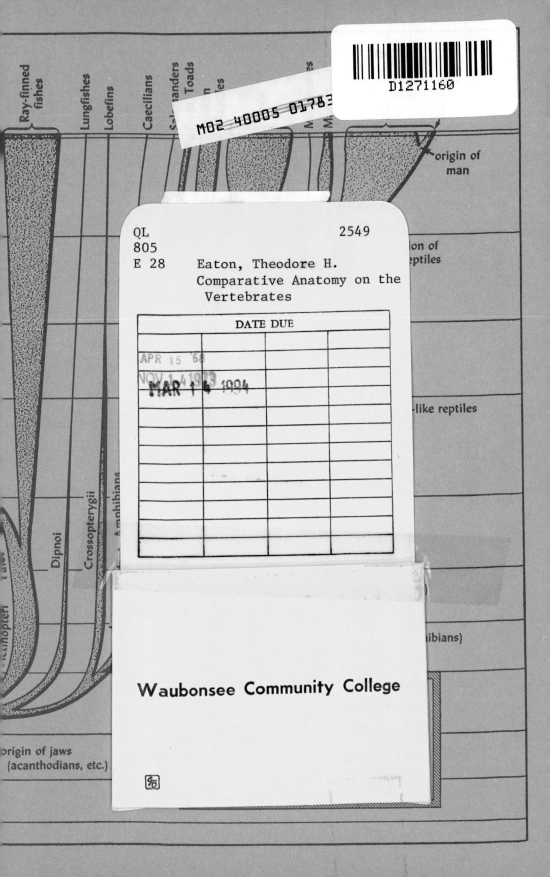

Ray-finned fishes

Lungfishes

Lobefins

Caecilians

Salamanders

Toads

origin of man

ion of eptiles

-like reptiles

ibians)

Dipnoi

Crossopterygii

Amphibians

inopteri

origin of jaws
(acanthodians, etc.)

COMPARATIVE ANATOMY OF THE VERTEBRATES

THEODORE H. EATON, JR.

Associate Professor of Zoology
University of Kansas

COMPARATIVE ANATOMY OF THE VERTEBRATES

SECOND EDITION

HARPER & ROW, PUBLISHERS

NEW YORK, EVANSTON, AND LONDON

Contents

PREFACE TO THE SECOND EDITION   vii

I. The Kind of Chordates   1
Subphylum *Hemichorda*—Subphylum *Cephalochorda*—Subphylum *Urochorda*—Subphylum *Vertebrata*

II. Development   52
Gametes, Fertilization, Cleavage—Development of a Frog—Development of *Branchiostoma* (Amphioxus)—Development of Amniota—Cells and Tissues

III. Integument   79
General Nature of Integument—Color—Glands—Epidermal Structures—Special Armor—Dermal Armor—Teeth

IV. Skeleton   110
Comparative Anatomy of the Skull

V. Skeleton (*Continued*)   141
Notochord—Ribs and Sternum—Tail and Median Fins—Paired Limbs and Girdles

VI. Muscles   180
What Muscles Are and What They Do—Arrangement and Divisions of the Skeletal Muscles—Comparative Anatomy of the

Segmental Muscles—Comparative Anatomy of the Branchiomeric Muscles

VII.   Digestive and Respiratory Systems, and Coelom   **200**

Digestive and Respiratory Organs of Protochordates—"Ammocoetes" and the Thyroid Gland—Digestive Organs of Gnathostomes—Gills in Fishes and Amphibians—Lungs and Air Bladders—Coelom and Mesenteries

VIII.   Circulatory System   **229**

Protochordates and Cyclostomes; The Vertebrate Plan—Heart —Arteries—Veins—Lymphatic System

IX.   Urinary and Genital Systems, and Endocrine Organs   **252**

Excretory and Genital Organs of Protochordates—The Vertebrate Kidney—Reproductive Organs of Vertebrates—Secondary Sex Characters—Endocrine Organs

X.   Sense Organs   **287**

Organs of Chemical Sense—Organs Detecting Pressure Change and the Movement of the Medium (Neuromast System)—Organs of Vision, the Median and Paired Eyes

XI.   Nervous System   **305**

Central Nervous System—Brain and Spinal Cord—Spinal Nerves—Cranial Nerves—Autonomic System

XII.   Panorama   **332**

The Rise of Comparative Anatomy—Origin of the Vertebrates —Panorama of the Vertebrates—Man Among Mammals

BIBLIOGRAPHY   **357**

INDEX   **363**

Preface to the Second Edition

STUDENTS of comparative anatomy need to appreciate the fundamentals of classification, something of the ways of life among vertebrate animals, elements of embryology and physiology, and especially the place of evolution in modern biology. They may then use the course to equip them for advanced study in zoology, for teaching, or for medical school. By interpreting the structure of a great host of animals, comparative anatomy gives a framework in which we can place our ideas of function, of embryonic development, and of man's origin and relationships. It is a study of the consequences of half a billion years of evolution, primarily emphasizing that of the phylum to which men belong. It is, and always will be, a rich and fertile field of inquiry, quite apart from its use as professional training.

The plan followed in this second edition is like that of the first, but numerous additions and improvements have enlarged for text. For suggestions made by users of the first edition the author is grateful. As always in an active scientific field, the lapse of eight years brings new evidence, new language, and an expanded bibliography. Certain illustrations are redrawn and others replaced.

A comprehensive first chapter, illustrated as fully as space permits and accompanied by an outline of classification, should enable the student to review the names, appearance, and ways of life of the animals concerned. It is necessary to be aware of the "time dimension" in two senses, for today's life is an outgrowth of different life in past ages, and the individual is formed, in time, from the undifferentiated egg. Therefore we refer, on occasion, to early vertebrate history in order to clarify the relationships of modern classes, and also include a chapter on embryonic development. Since structure without function means little, we emphasize the action of tissues, organs, and mechanisms of the body. A panoramic view in the last chapter may help in coördinating parts of the whole picture.

Here, as before, I should like to acknowledge my debt to Professor Charles L. Camp, of the University of California, under whom I received my first training in this field, and who gave me a vigorous enthusiasm for it; to Professor Alfred S. Romer, of Harvard, with whom I have had most fruitful opportunities to work; and to Professor William K. Gregory, now retired, of Columbia University and the American Museum of Natural History, who gave suggestions and encouragement on a number of occasions. Finally, I again inscribe this book to my parents.

THEODORE H. EATON, JR.

June, 1959

COMPARATIVE ANATOMY OF THE VERTEBRATES

CHAPTER I

The Kinds of Chordates

To FIND meaning in a study of comparative anatomy we must have more than a nodding acquaintance with the vertebrate animals and their poor relations, the protochordates. Together these comprise one great phylum of animals, including types as diverse as fishes, frogs, birds, and men. One might lay out on a table the disembodied parts of animals and note that our own muscles, our hearts, our bones are evidently inherited, with modifications, from more primitive muscles, hearts, and bones of our ancestors. But this method would give little conception of the whole body in which the parts live. So we must know the chordates first as living beings, must be conscious of the ability of organs to work harmoniously together and to change, through mechanisms of heredity, into something different when faced with new circumstances.

The background for comparative anatomy, therefore, is a clear-cut picture of the kinds of chordates and their ways of life. This picture will fit together most easily if we start with a few traits by which we can tell a chordate from anything else (Fig. 1).

With minor exceptions, every chordate has a **notochord**, a gristlelike rod running lengthwise in the body, during some part of its life. Usually this comes early and then disappears, to be replaced by a column of vertebrae which in turn provide a flexible but firm support for the body. But in some of the less progressive kinds, like the lamprey, the notochord remains throughout life, attended only by the most rudimentary verte-

1

brae. Of course a chordate ordinarily has a head and tail end (in anterior and posterior directions respectively), a right and left side which are mirror images of each other, and a back and belly surface (dorsal and ventral). Running along the dorsal side is a **central nervous system** which is a hollow tube, not far below the surface, usually well protected by hard parts. The brain, if there is one, and its continuation, the spinal cord, together constitute this hollow tube, the walls of which are built of great numbers of nerve cells, yet even in man the cavity within the tube remains, forming ventricles in the brain and a slim canal down through the cord.

In the walls of its throat a chordate has several pairs of **gill clefts** which open to the outside and allow water to stream out past the gills if the animal is a fish, aquatic amphibian, or lower in the scale, but if it is far enough up to have abandoned water breathing (a reptile, bird, or

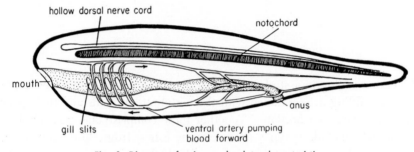

Fig. 1. Diagram of primary chordate characteristics.

mammal), the clefts show only briefly during its early development, then vanish or become converted into other structures. Finally, the blood circulates in a system of closed tubular vessels, so arranged that on the ventral side of the body a main artery transmits it toward the head, while dorsally another one carries it back toward the tail. When, as usual, a heart is present as a pumping station for the ventral vessel, blood enters the heart from behind but is then thrust forward by contraction of its muscular walls.

Separation of chordates, like other animals, into subphyla, classes, orders, families, genera, and species is necessary, first, in order to be able to think or talk about them at all, since their numbers are prodigious, and second, in order to express the real differences and real relationships which our work reveals. This is done by finding certain traits which are common to members of each particular group—or better still by using distinctive traits as the means of recognizing groups. Classification must also reflect as accurately as possible the beginnings and diverse histories of these traits or "characters" and of the animals which show them. Since we do not and perhaps never will know all we need to know in order to show relationships perfectly, it is necessary to adjust and revise and clarify as new evidence appears.

But decisions as to scientific names and the definition of each recognized group are not just matters of personal convenience. It is permissible to use either (1) classifications proposed by careful, *recent* investigators in the subject, or (2) condensed or abbreviated classifications in which some parts are left out because they are not essential to one's purpose; e.g., in this book the many orders and suborders of teleost fishes are not listed. But a writer cannot, on the spur of the moment, create a new name for an order, or divide the vertebrate animals into two or more subphyla, or decide that seals and walruses are not carnivores. Such action would result in chaos, assuming that other workers paid any attention to it. An investigator who by his own experience is well qualified to judge the evidence may, and sometimes does, propose changes of this sort, but he sets forth his reasons at the same time, and as a result is likely to have his proposals adopted by others.

ABBREVIATED CLASSIFICATION OF CHORDATA

SUBPHYLUM *Hemichorda*
    Class *Enteropneusta*. Balanoglossid worms (Fig. 2)
    Class *Pterobranchia*. *Cephalodiscus* (Fig. 5), *Rhabdopleura* (Fig. 6),
      * Graptolites (Fig. 7A)
SUBPHYLUM *Urochorda* (*Tunicata*). Ascidians, salps, etc. (Fig. 9)
SUBPHYLUM *Cephalochorda* (*Acrania*). *Branchiostoma* (Amphioxus) (Fig. 8)
SUBPHYLUM *Vertebrata* (*Craniata*)
  Superclass *Agnatha* (Fishes without jaws)
    Class *Cyclostomata* (*Marsipobranchii*)
      Subclass *Cephalaspidomorphi*
          Order * *Anaspida* (Fig. 13). Ostracoderms
          Order * *Osteostraci* (Fig. 12). Ostracoderms
          Order *Petromyzontia*. Lampreys (Fig. 10)
      Subclass *Pteraspidomorphi*
          Order * *Heterostraci* (Fig. 332A). Ostracoderms
          Order *Myxinoidea*. Hagfishes (Fig. 11)
  Superclass *Gnathostomata* (Fishes with jaws)
    Class * *Placodermi* (*Aphetohyoidea*)
          Order * *Acanthodii* (Figs. 14, 186)
          Order * *Arthrodira* (Fig. 138)
          Order * *Antiarchi* (Fig. 189)
    Class *Chondrichthyes*
      Subclass *Elasmobranchii*
          Order * *Cladoselachii* (Fig. 187). Sharks
          Order *Selachii* (Fig. 15). Sharks
          Order *Batoidei* (Fig. 16). Rays

Subclass *Holocephali*
    Order *Chimaerae* (Fig. 17). Chimaeras
Class *Osteichthyes*
  Subclass *Actinopteri* (Ray-finned fishes)
    Superorder *Chondrostei.* ° Paleoniscids (Fig. 18), *Polypterus* (Fig. 19), sturgeons (Fig. 20)
    Superorder *Holostei.* Gars (Fig. 21), bowfins
    Superorder *Teleostei* (Figs. 22–24, 99, 116, 143, 188, 194, 280, 285)
  Subclass *Choanichthyes*
    Order *Dipnoi.* Lungfishes (Fig. 25)
    Order *Crossopterygii.* Lobefinned fishes
     Suborder ° *Rhipidistia*
     Suborder *Coelacanthini* (Fig. 26)
Superclass *Tetrapoda*
  Class *Amphibia*
  Subclass *Apsidospondyli*
    Superorder ° *Labyrinthodontia* (Fig. 27)
    Superorder *Salientia*
     Order *Anura.* Frogs, toads (Figs. 30, 31, 77, 279, 287)
    Superorder *Caudata*
     Order *Urodela.* Salamanders (Figs. 29, 286)
  Subclass *Lepospondyli*
    Order ° *Microsauria*
    Order *Apoda* (*Gymnophiona*). Caecilians (Fig. 28)
  Class *Reptilia*
  Subclass *Anapsida*
    Order ° *Cotylosauria* (Fig. 37)
    Order *Chelonia* (*Testudinata*). Turtles (Fig. 35)
  Subclass *Lepidosauria*
    Order *Rhynchocephalia.* Sphenodon (Fig. 34)
    Order *Squamata.* Lizards (Fig. 32), snakes (Fig. 33), ° mosasaurs.
  Subclass ° *Ichthyopterygia*
    Order ° *Ichthyosauria* (Fig. 44)
  Subclass *Archosauria.* "Ruling reptiles"
    Order ° *Thecodontia* (Fig. 38)
    Order *Crocodilia* (Fig. 36)
    Order ° *Saurischia* (Figs. 39, 40). Dinosaurs
    Order ° *Ornithischia* (Figs. 41–43). Dinosaurs
    Order ° *Pterosauria* (Fig. 45)
  Subclass ° *Synapsida*
    Order ° *Pelycosauria*
    Order ° *Therapsida.* Mammal-like reptiles
  Class *Aves.* Birds
  Subclass ° *Archaeornithes* (Fig. 46)
  Subclass *Neornithes*
    Superorder ° *Odontognathae* (Fig. 47)
    Superorder *Palaeognathae.* Ostrich (Fig. 48), emu, tinamou, etc.

Superorder *Impennae*. Penguins
Superorder *Neognathae* (Figs. 49–51, 105)
    Order *Gaviiformes*. Loons
    Order *Colymbiformes*. Grebes
    Order *Procellariiformes*. Petrels
    Order *Pelecaniformes*. Cormorants, pelicans, and gannets
    Order *Ciconiiformes*. Storks and herons
    Order *Anseriformes*. Ducks
    Order *Falconiformes*. Hawks
    Order *Galliformes*. Game birds
    Order *Gruiformes*. Rails and cranes
    Order *Charadriiformes*. Waders and gulls
    Order *Columbiformes*. Pigeons
    Order *Cuculiformes*. Cuckoos
    Order *Psittaciformes*. Parrots
    Order *Strigiformes*. Owls
    Order *Caprimulgiformes*. Nightjars
    Order *Micropodiiformes*. Swifts and hummingbirds
    Order *Coraciiformes*. Bee-eaters and kingfishers
    Order *Piciformes*. Woodpeckers
    Order *Passeriformes*. Perching birds
Class *Mammalia*
  Subclass *Prototheria*
    Order *Monotremata* (Figs. 52, 103C)
  Subclass ° *Allotheria*
  Subclass *Theria*
   Infraclass ° *Pantotheria*
    Order ° *Pantotheria*
    Order ° *Symmetrodonta*
   Infraclass *Metatheria*
    Order *Marsupialia* (Figs. 53, 54)
   Infraclass *Eutheria* (*Placentalia*)
    Cohort *Unguiculata*
    Order *Insectivora* (Fig. 55)
    Order *Dermoptera*
    Order *Chiroptera*
      Suborder *Microchiroptera*. Insect-eating and vampire bats
      Suborder *Megachiroptera*. Fruit bats (Fig. 56)
    Order *Primates*
      Suborder *Prosimii*
        Infraorder *Lemuriformes*. Tree shrews, lemurs (Fig. 57)
        Infraorder *Tarsiiformes*. Tarsiers (Fig. 58)
      Suborder *Anthropoidea*
        Superfamily *Ceboidea* (*Platyrrhina*). New World monkeys (Fig. 59)
        Superfamily *Cercopithecoidea*. Old World monkeys (Fig. 60)

Superfamily *Hominoidea*
    Family *Pongidae*. Apes (Fig. 61)
    Family *Hominidae*. Man (Fig. 62)
Order *Edentata* (Figs. 67, 113)
Order *Pholidota*. Pangolins
Cohort *Glires*
    Order *Lagomorpha*. Rabbits, pikas
    Order *Rodentia*. Mice, squirrels, beavers, etc.
Cohort *Mutica*
    Order *Cetacea* (Figs. 63C, 66)
Cohort *Ferungulata*
    Order *Carnivora* (Figs. 63B, 64, 65)
    Order ° *Condylarthra* (Fig. 63A)
    Order *Proboscidea* (Fig. 74)
    Order *Hyracoidea*. Conies
    Order *Sirenia* (Fig. 73)
    Order *Perissodactyla*. Rhinoceros (Fig. 68), tapir (Fig. 69), horse (Fig. 70)
    Order *Artiodactyla*. Pig (Fig. 71), deer (Fig. 72), etc.

NOTE: ° before a term means "extinct."

Subphylum *Hemichorda*

Hemichordates are the first of three subphyla of small marine animals, commonly called protochordates because they seem to show the beginnings of characters familiar to us in the vertebrates. Actually this is misleading, for in most respects all three groups are too specialized to represent vertebrate ancestors. Most hemichordates are worms, burrowing in mud which they swallow and then emit in spiral castings over

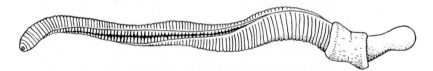

Fig. 2. A wormlike hemichordate, *Ptychodera*.

their holes. *Balanoglossus* and *Ptychodera* (Fig. 2) are familiar examples of this wormlike class *Enteropneusta*.

The body is not segmented, for they have no relationship to annelid worms, but it has three obvious divisions: a distensible **proboscis,** a short, thick **collar,** and a **trunk.** The mouth is under the base of the proboscis (Figs. 3, 4). It opens through a short **oral cavity** to the **pharynx,** which runs back into the first part of the trunk. Here a long series of paired U-shaped *gill slits* open dorsally in the sides of a groove. The oral cavity and pharynx, as well as the outer surfaces of proboscis and collar, are covered with *cilia* that sweep a current of water into the mouth and out the gill slits. This is primarily a feeding, not a breathing, mechanism, for mucus secreted by cells on the proboscis entangles microscopic food and it is thus carried to the hind end of the pharynx in little lumps that presently drop into the intestine. The animal uses this way of feeding when it protrudes from its burrow and explores with its proboscis; no doubt it digests some organic matter too from the mud swallowed during burrowing.

The *notochord* is nothing but a short, stiff projection forward from the roof of the mouth, acting as a support for the neck of the proboscis. The *central nervous system* is a tube in the dorsal side of the collar, very short, open at the ends. From it branching nerves spread to superficial parts of the body and to a median ventral nerve; the latter is not found in other chordates. The blood system has dorsal and ventral vessels. The paired *gonads,* in series in the dorsal side of the trunk, release their gametes through pores in the body wall. The sexes are separate.

Besides the wormlike Enteropneusta, there is another class, **Ptero-branchia,** containing minute deep-sea animals that are typically sessile (fixed to the substratum, like plants). Their anatomy is an extreme travesty on that of *Balanoglossus.* They feed by a ciliary-mucus mechanism carried on tentacles. The notochord is pos-

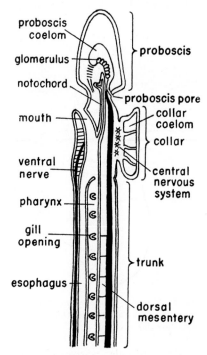

Fig. 3. Longitudinal section of a hemichordate, *Balanoglossus.* (After MacBride in *Encyclopædia Britannica.*)

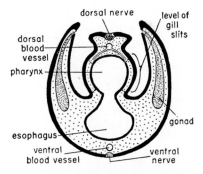

Fig. 4. Cross section of a hemichordate through pharynx, diagrammatic.

sibly represented by a pair of stiffened patches of epithelial cells that serve to fit the shape of the pharynx to the current produced by the cilia. The central nervous system is absent except as a neural plate on the

dorsal surface, comparable to that in the early embryo of other chordates.

In one genus, *Cephalodiscus* (Fig. 5), there are only two gill slits, while another, *Rhabdopleura* (Fig. 6) has none; they are simply an outlet for water, not a respiratory device. The animals are colonial, each individual living in a chitinous tube which is a branch of the coenicium (external "skeleton" of the colony). But some species of *Cephalodiscus* can leave the tube, and in the genus *Atubaria* there apparently is no tube at all.

Fig. 5. A sessile hemichordate, *Cephalodiscus*, removed from its tube. (After Parker and Haswell.)

In recent years it has been shown (Kozlowski, 1947) that the graptolites, an extinct group of colonial marine animals, possessed a coenicium essentially identical with that of *Rhabdopleura,* and they should be included in the hemichordates (Figs. 6, 7).

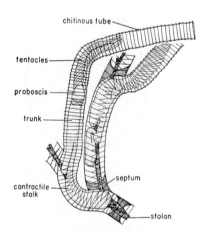

Fig. 6. Two individuals of a colony of *Rhabdopleura normani,* living in jointed, chitinous tubes. (After Thomas and Davis.)

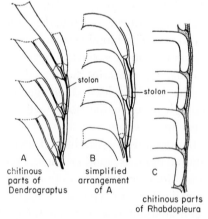

Fig. 7. Comparison of the tubes of *Rhabdopleura* (C) with those of a graptolite (A and B). (After Kozlowski.)

Subphylum *Cephalochorda*

Two genera, *Branchiostoma* (Amphioxus, Fig. 8) and *Asymmetron*, make the subphylum Cephalochordata. The first has been studied in great detail because its structure and development illuminate many points in chordate evolution. Like *Balanoglossus* it hides in the sea sand and feeds by cilia, but there the resemblance stops, for Amphioxus is not wormlike, but swims with a rapid irregular darting, and has a streamlined body pointed at both ends, with a small fin on the tail. It is not over four inches long, and is common in warm shallow seas.

The **notochord** runs from the projecting anterior tip (**rostrum**) to the tail end, hence the name of the subphylum, "head cord." V-shaped muscle segments (**myomeres**) run in series, alternately instead of opposite, along both sides of the notochord. Their contraction on one side and then the other makes the notochord and the body bend in rhythmic S-shaped curves, and the flattened tail fin therefore thrusts the animal forward. The **dorsal nerve cord** runs lengthwise above the notochord, and from it two nerves in each segment run out on each side, one dorsal, the other ventral. These correspond to the dorsal and ventral roots of the spinal

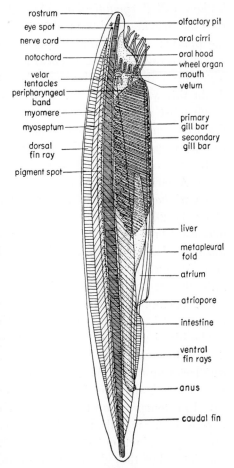

Fig. 8. A cephalochordate, *Branchiostoma* (Amphioxus), immature.

nerves in vertebrates. There is no brain, but anteriorly a nerve leads to a small pit opening to the left of the middorsal line, supposedly an **olfactory organ;** and along the nerve cord itself are small spots of black pigment, thought to be sensitive to light.

The feeding apparatus is of most interest, for none more elaborate occurs in any chordate. It is essentially a ciliary funnel and sieve. The cuplike *oral hood,* fringed by fingerlike *cirri,* admits a current of water into the *mouth,* which is a hole in a circular membrane, the *velum.* This in turn has a lobed fringe, the *wheel organ,* covered with beating cilia that draw the current into the *pharynx,* a long deep chamber. The sides of this are perforated by a great many (up to 200) pairs of oblique narrow *gill slits,* and the delicate *gill bars* between are braced by small bridges called *synapticulae.* Through the slits, of course, the current runs out, leaving food trapped inside, to be carried into the intestine. But the pharynx is not exposed directly to the outside world, for an outer wall has grown around it, enclosing it in a space, the *atrium,* and the water must then leave by a small posterior opening, the *atriopore.* No doubt this wall protects the fragile gill basket.

We must return to the pharynx for a moment, however, to look at the arrangement of *ciliated bands* that catch and carry the food. A narrow deep groove, the *endostyle,* runs the whole length of the pharynx in the midventral line; it secretes mucus, which cilia then propel forward. Anteriorly this band of cilia divides, just behind the velum, into two *peripharyngeal bands.* They (with the help of cilia sweeping up along the gill bars) carry the mucus and food entangled in it up to the middorsal line, where they unite in a ciliated *epipharyngeal groove,* and this is the last lap, for it leads back to the opening of the *esophagus.* The latter is much smaller in diameter than the pharynx, and continues with little change to the straight *intestine.* From this a finger-shaped blind pouch reaches forward for a variable distance along the right side of the pharynx. It is probably equivalent to the *liver* of vertebrates.

The blood system has a ventral artery with a pulsating enlargement in it, a rudimentary *heart,* so that it pumps blood forward and then through capillaries up the gill bars to the dorsal artery, where it flows back to the rest of the body. Above the pharynx lie microscopic excretory organs called *protonephridia* (Fig. 267), the functioning units of which are *solenocytes* or flame cells, so called because of the flickering cilia that wash excretory products out of their ducts. No such organs are known in other chordates, but they do occur in several invertebrate phyla; hence *Branchiostoma* is doubtless primitive in this character at least. The *gonads* are paired sacs below the myomeres, bulging into the atrium, and they burst to release gametes, which then escape by the atriopore. A related genus, *Asymmetron,* has only a single row of gonads, and differs in other minor ways.

Subphylum *Urochorda*

This subphylum, the ***tunicates*** or ***sea squirts,*** numbers several hundred kinds, most of which have not the faintest outward resemblance to any other chordates. The simple tunicates live attached to a solid substratum, and produce buds as well as gametes. The compound tunicates may be attached or may float in chains or clusters in the open sea; frequently they are transparent, and some are luminous at night. We may take as an example one of the simple sessile tunicates (Fig. 9).

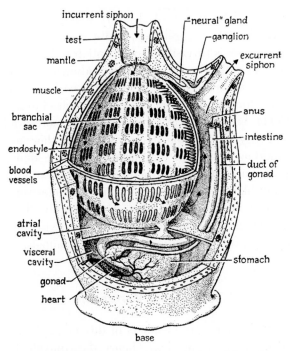

Fig. 9. Diagram of structure of a simple ascidian. (From *General Zoology* by Storer.)

The animal resembles a sac with two openings at its upper end, the ***mouth*** and ***atriopore.*** The body is covered by a ***tunic*** of about the same composition as cellulose in plants; through its oral and atrial siphons water will squirt out when the disturbed animal contracts. This accounts for two of the names, sea squirt and tunicate, used for members of this subphylum. Another name, Urochorda, means "tail rod," for there is, in the swimming larval stage, a ***notochord*** in the tail. The larva is shaped like a tadpole, but is usually only two or three millimeters in length. Its tail contains muscles and a tubular nerve cord. After a short period of swimming it becomes attached to a surface by adhesive papillae below the mouth, loses the entire tail, and transforms into the adult.

The pharynx and feeding mechanism are much the same as in *Branchiostoma*. Imagine the latter fixed with its head up, and with the atriopore brought forward dorsally to lie not far from the mouth. Water now pours into the mouth, diffuses through the pharyngeal basket and out into the atrium. The intestine is expanded into a pouchlike **stomach,** and the **anus** enters the atrium. Here too enter ducts from the **gonads** (**ovary** and **testis**). Tunicates are **hermaphroditic,** having both sexes in the same individual.

There is a ventral **heart,** a ventral artery that parallels the endostyle and sends branches into the gill bars, and a dorsal artery that receives these. The blood flow is reversible, an exception to the rule among chordates. Dorsally there is also an extremely rudimentary **brain,** simply a ganglion (cluster of nerve cells). **Endostyle, peri-** and **epipharyngeal bands** are as in *Branchiostoma*, but there is no wheel organ.

Branchiostoma, while close to tunicates, seems more primitive in certain ways, and may be near the stock from which they arose. After the sessile and budding habit was established in simple tunicates they diverged more and more from the structure described until it becomes difficult to see any likeness whatever. The tunicates offer some marvellous examples of "degenerative" evolution. Undoubtedly they are a side branch from early chordates, which was able to survive by withdrawing quite adroitly from competition with most other animals.

Subphylum Vertebrata

All remaining chordates are members of this subphylum, in which the most distinctive feature is the **skull** (hence the equivalent name **Craniata**). A **vertebral column,** to which the usual name of the subphylum refers, is by no means universal, however. For example lampreys and hagfishes, and many of the older extinct fishes, are without complete vertebrae. But a skull is always present, associated with a **brain;** and no adult vertebrate feeds by means of cilia, a character of all protochordates. There is a **heart,** of at least two chambers, and the blood contains erythrocytes with the respiratory pigment hemoglobin.

In discussing each class of vertebrates we shall say something of the kinds which are no longer living. This is not simply to add to the information which might be gained from the modern ones, important as that may be. But comparative anatomy based only on the study of existing animals (the twigs of the family tree) would be full of misinformation, unnecessary errors, and hopeless puzzles, as is shown whenever one tries to teach it without reference to our knowledge of ancestral forms. Many early groups are very well known, and a glimpse of them will go far toward unfolding a clear picture of the evolution of vertebrates toward mammals and man. (See end leaves for Chart of the Relationships of Vertebrate Groups; also refer to Abbreviated Classification, p. 3. Both of these sources are greatly oversimplified, many minor branches or divisions being omitted.)

SUPERCLASS *AGNATHA*: FISHES WITHOUT JAWS

The lampreys (order *Petromyzontia,* Fig. 10) and hagfishes (order *Myxinoidea,* Fig. 11) are the modern members of the *Agnatha,* while at

Fig. 10. Lamprey, *Entosphenus tridentatus.*

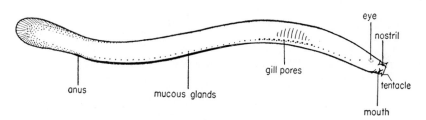

Fig. 11. A hagfish, *Bdellostoma.*

least five different orders of jawless, armored fishes, collectively called *ostracoderms,* constitute the earliest known stock of the vertebrates (Figs. 12, 13, 334A). Lampreys and hagfishes are descendants of these, along two apparently independent lines; both are parasitic on other fishes, although the ostracoderms obviously could not have been. Both have funnel-shaped, sucking mouths (hence the name of the class, *Cyclostomata:* "round-mouthed"), soft cartilaginous skeletons, and no paired fins. They are without scales and have only one nostril. The gills are in muscular pouches, opening by a row of pores along each side. Lampreys come up rivers during the spawning season, a few living only in fresh water, but hagfishes are wholly marine. The larval lamprey ("*Ammocoetes*") is a remarkable minnowlike animal that burrows in the sand and feeds by the same mechanism of ciliated mucus bands that we found in the protochordates. It is distantly reminiscent of Amphioxus, but when it becomes an adult it changes radically in almost every feature.

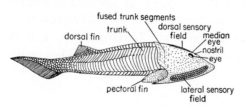

Fig. 12. An ostracoderm, *Cephalaspis*. (Modified after Abel.)

Ostracoderms had dermal scales on the trunk and tail, and bony skeletons in the anterior part of the body, in most cases; they were not parasites, although they lacked jaws. Some had a pair of pectoral fins, others no paired fins. The first known occurrence of ostracoderms comes in the Ordovician, and they vanished by the close of the Devonian, some 300 million years ago.

As yet the classification and history of the ostracoderms are obscure, although we know many kinds, representing at least five orders. Those known in greatest detail are the Cephalaspids (order **Osteostraci**, Fig. 12), from a remarkable study by Stensiö (1927). He was able to show that the internal structure of the head, except for its heavy bony shield,

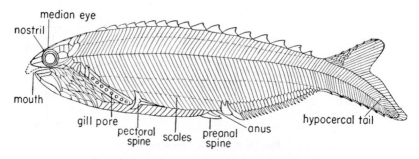

Fig. 13. An ostracoderm, *Rhyncholepis*. (After Kiaer.)

was basically the same as that of modern lampreys, especially as to the brain, olfactory organ, single nostril, and gill pouches with external openings. On the other hand some other ostracoderms, with a number of separate bony plates on the head, resemble hagfishes in the forward position of the nostril and the backwardly directed, tubular passages from the gills. These (**Heterostraci**, etc.) may represent the stock ancestral to hagfishes, although the question cannot be settled until we have more evidence. But the division of cyclostomes into two subclasses, as suggested by Stensiö, is followed here, and it should be noted that if this is correct, then the class Cyclostomata *must* include the ostracoderms as well as lampreys and hagfishes, and not be restricted to the latter two orders alone.

SUPERCLASS *GNATHOSTOMATA:* FISHES WITH JAWS

With the coming of jaws, by modification of the first gill arch of some very early ostracoderm, we enter upon a bewildering array of new forms and habits among fishes. This notable event took place in the Silurian period, and made possible for the first time the pursuit of prey, the capture and devouring of food that was more than microscopic in size; in other words, it was the "invention" of a predatory vertebrate animal. By the following period, the Devonian, we find enough profound differences among fishes with jaws to warrant recognizing three distinct classes, rather than the outmoded "class Pisces" of our older textbooks.

One class, **Placodermi,** consists of extinct fishes which had a full-sized pair of gills on the posterior margins of their jaws. The first gill arch of the series had become converted into the upper and lower jaws, and bore teeth, but had not yet forsaken its earlier function of supporting gills. This fact, first demonstrated by Watson (1937) in the acanthodians (Fig. 14), shows how the structure of typical fishes originated from that of cyclostomes, although there are many details not yet understood.

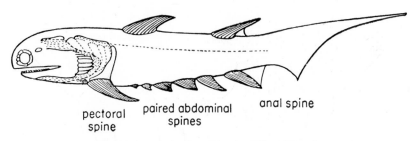

pectoral spine   paired abdominal spines   anal spine

Fig. 14. An acanthodian, *Climatius.* (After Watson.)

Placoderms ("plated-skin") were armored fishes, either with small diamond-shaped scales, as in acanthodians, or with large plates of bone, as in antiarchs and arthrodires. The latter order were the monsters of their day (the Devonian), ranging in length up to 30 feet. Their heads moved up and down against a pair of lateral pivots in the body armor, hence the name "jointed neck" (arthrodire) (see Fig. 138).

Then in the middle Devonian there arose a diverse class that has many well-known representatives today, the sharks, rays, and chimaeras

(*Chondrichthyes*). Some placoderm may have been their ancestor, but the connections are not known yet. In modern Chondrichthyes the skeleton is of cartilage only, but there was bone in some of the early kinds

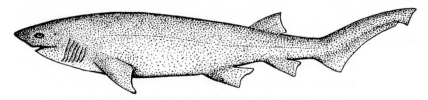

Fig. 15. Hexanchus griseus, a shark.

(Romer, 1942). The skin is generally leathery with fine embedded denticles ("placoid scales") whose points project slightly.

Sharks of many kinds flourished in the late Paleozoic, but they have declined in numbers since then, at least as compared with the bony fishes. A shark (Fig. 15) has five to seven gill clefts on each side of the

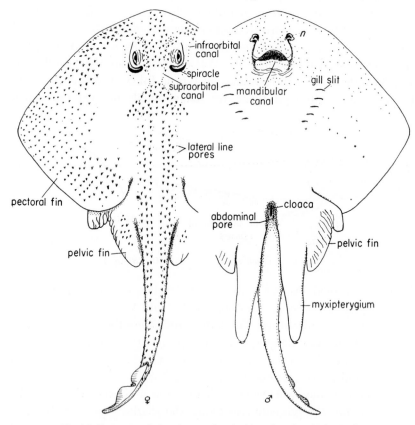

Fig. 16. Thorny ray, Raja erinacea, female (dorsal) and male (ventral).

throat, and also, as a rule, a vestigial porelike cleft, the spiracle, just above and behind the jaws. Rays (Fig. 16) appeared as bottom-dwelling, flat-bodied derivatives of the sharks in the Mesozoic; the mouth bears a pavementlike grinding mechanism of flat teeth for crushing hard-shelled molluscs. The chimaeras or ghostfishes (*Holocephali*) likewise originated from sharks in the Mesozoic; they number only half a dozen living kinds, all but one of them (Fig. 17) in the deep sea. Instead of teeth there are

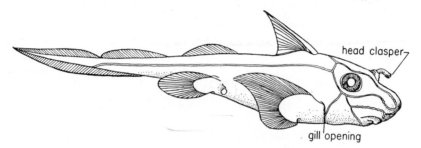

Fig. 17. *Chimaera colliei*, a ghostfish (Holocephali).

crushing plates in the mouth, and a skin flap (operculum) covers the gills on each side.

The next class, **Osteichthyes**, contains the vast majority of fishes. The name means "bony fishes," which in itself would not exclude Placoderms or Ostracoderms, but the **Osteichthyes** possess a bony operculum covering the gills on each side, so that they lie in a chamber with an exit behind the operculum. Usually the operculum is supported by a series of bones, hinged against the cranium and moving synchronously with the mouth in breathing. The great subclass **Actinopteri** contains nearly all existing species, say about 30,000. The name means "ray-finned," for the fins are membranous and supported by separate dermal rays. For convenience these fishes are placed in three superorders, several score of orders, and hundreds of families.

Superorder Chondrostei. The stem-group, called paleoniscids (Fig. 18), appeared in the middle Devonian and did not survive in its primitive

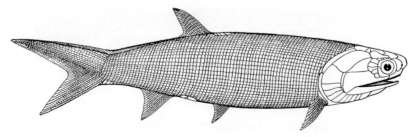

Fig. 18. A paleoniscid, *Paleoniscus macropomus*, one of the primitive ray-finned fishes.

pattern beyond the Permian. The eyes and brain, as in Acanthodians, lay far anterior to the angle of the jaw, and the tail was strongly heterocercal (its axis in the upper lobe). In Central African rivers today live two genera of sluggish, bony fishes, *Polypterus* (Fig. 19) and *Calamoichthys*,

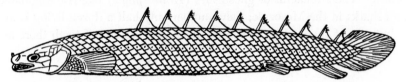

Fig. 19. *Polypterus bichir*, a primitive bony fish in the rivers of Africa. (After Parker and Haswell.)

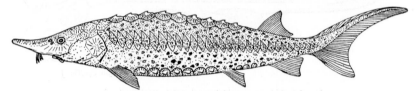

Fig. 20. Sturgeon, *Acipenser sturio*. (Redrawn from Jordan, *Fishes*, Appleton.)

which are survivors of the paleoniscid line; they can be recognized by the row of little separate finlets along the back, and the muscular, extended bases of the pectoral fins. Another persistent but more modified remnant of the paleoniscids is the small order containing sturgeons (Fig. 20) and paddlefishes. The skeleton is more cartilaginous than bony, the mouth ventral and toothless, the skin leathery. Sturgeons live in both fresh and salt water in the northern hemisphere, but the two existing kinds of paddlefish are in rivers of the United States and China.

Superorder Holostei. The United States again provides two other relicts, the bowfin (*Amia*) and garpike (*Lepisosteus*, Fig. 21), both in fresh

Fig. 21. Long-nosed gar, *Lepisosteus*. (New York Zoological Society photo.)

Fig. 22. Atlantic salmon, *Salmo salar*. (American Museum of Natural History photo.)

water. They are members of the superorder **Holostei,** which arose in the late Paleozoic from paleoniscids, and are called "bony ganoids." The tail is still slightly heterocercal, and *Amia* has a spiracle.

Superorder Teleostei. Finally the great swarming proletarian masses of fish are the teleosts, with a completely homocercal tail. This means that to outward appearances, at least, the upper and lower parts of the tail are alike. The spiracle, present in more primitive **Actinopteri,** has at last disappeared. Here belong the herring, trout, catfish, pickerel, bass, tuna, and most of the others you can call to mind (Figs. 22, 23, 24).

Since the teleosts, beginning in the Jurassic period, have become the dominant fishes of the sea and fresh waters (although they are *not* on the line leading to higher animals), it would be well to notice some of their specializations here. Very roughly we can divide them into two groups, the soft-rayed and spiny-rayed. The former, containing such fish as herring,

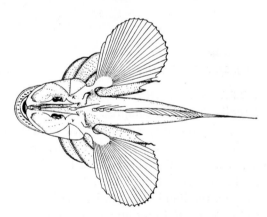

Fig. 23. Young angler fish, *Lophius americanus.*

salmon, trout, eel, minnow, carp, pickerel, and cod, is the more primitive, while the spiny-rayed group (stiff, sharp rays in the anterior part of dorsal and anal fins) is the more advanced; among these are mullet, bass, sunfish, perch, darters, mackerel, tuna, and flounder. As a rule the soft-rayed fishes also have the air-bladder connected with the esophagus by a duct, and scales of the cycloid type (round or oval, without toothed margins); their pelvic fins are back on the abdomen, as shown in Fig. 22. The spiny-rayed group have lost the connection between air-bladder and esophagus, their scales are usually ctenoid (with comblike or toothed margins), and the pelvic fins have moved forward to the level of the pectorals or even farther. But this is only a general guide to the place a given fish occupies among the teleosts; many kinds have lost their scales or their pelvic fins or even the air-bladder, and spines are found in the catfishes which in other respects are like the soft-rayed teleosts.

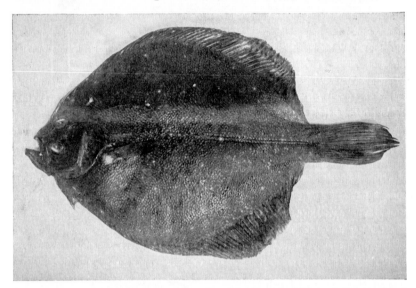

Fig. 24. A flounder, *Lophopsetta maculata*. (American Museum of Natural History photo.)

SUBCLASS CHOANICHTHYES. Lungfishes (**Dipnoi**) and lobefins (**Crossopterygii**) together comprise a small but tremendously important subclass, **Choanichthyes** ("fish with nostrils that open into the mouth"). Both orders appeared first in the lower Devonian, just as the ray-finned fishes were getting started, and both have survived, although just barely so, to the present day. Their importance lies in their evolutionary position, on the line leading to land animals (tetrapods).

Order Dipnoi. Existing lungfishes are of three genera, *Neoceratodus* (Fig. 25) in Australia, *Protopterus* in Africa, *Lepidosiren* in South America, all living in fresh water which is subject to seasonal stagnation or drying up. When this happens they burrow into the damper mud where it may be possible to survive until the return of water; the African and South American kinds make a mud case in which they lie coiled for months if necessary. A Permian lungfish, *Gnathorhiza*, was recently shown to have the same habit. Although they have gills like other fishes, these rise to the surface of the water occasionally for a breath of air, since they are provided with lungs. The nostrils, by the way, seem to have no direct connection with air-breathing, as the fish opens its mouth widely to get air, and when under water it keeps a current passing in and out through the nostrils, presumably for olfaction.

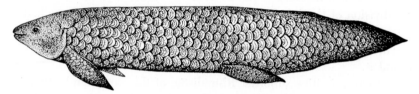

Fig. 25. *Neoceratodus forsteri,* the Australian lungfish. (Redrawn from Jordan, *Fishes,* Appleton.)

Formerly thought to be ancestral to Amphibia, the lungfishes have surrendered this honor to the lobefins because they lack, and the latter possess, the necessary combination of characters. These will be dealt with in the chapter on the skeleton and in the final chapter.

Order *Crossopterygii.*   Long known as fossils, especially from the Devonian period, the crossopterygians were thought to have become extinct at

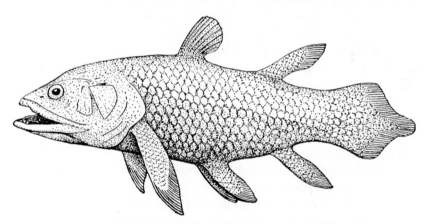

Fig. 26. The living crossopterygian, *Latimeria chalumnae.* (After Smith.)

the end of the Cretaceous, along with the dying out of the dinosaurs. Not until 1938 did anyone know that they survived to modern times. Yet a living lobefin (Fig. 26), named *Latimeria,* was then caught by fishermen trawling in fairly deep water off the east coast of South Africa, and its picture promptly appeared in magazines in this country and Europe, witnessing to the amazement of biologists that such a thing could happen. Since then other specimens, at least nine in good condition, weighing from 70 to 180 lbs., have been obtained among the Comores Islands (between Africa and Madagascar), at from 80 to 200 fathoms, on rough, rocky bottom. Their stomachs contain small fish. The single lung is degenerate, as are the nostrils, the heart is simple, the brain said to be proportionally smaller than in any other living vertebrate.

Latimeria is a member of the suborder Coelacanthini, a rather specialized division of the lobefins, in which the nostrils may not have had internal openings, the tail is three-lobed, and the paired fins, so far as known, have an enlarged basal bone and a jointed series of smaller ones beyond it.

The more primitive suborder Rhipidistia, of the Devonian to Permian, were the typical lobefins, from which, without doubt, the earliest Amphibia were derived in the upper Devonian. They were evidently lung-breathers in part, living in fresh water. Their paired fins show a jointed series of bones, smaller and more numerous distally, which provide the ground plan for the skeleton of the legs and feet of Amphibia.

Romer suggests that the transition took place, paradoxically, as an adjustment making it possible to remain in the water. After all, the lobefins were fishes and could not have survived if thrown on land all at once. The early kinds of lobefins lived in fresh water, and if, as in Australia today, the rivers seasonally dried up except for a few stagnant pools here and there, then one way for a fish to live when its own pool became dry would be to wriggle out and flop into one that had not. A more likely incentive to development of legs would be difficult to imagine, but of course we may never have direct evidence.

SUPERCLASS *TETRAPODA*

The gap, small though it was, between lobefinned fishes and the next class, **Amphibia,** has been filled by discovery of the remarkable Ichthyostegids, in Upper Devonian rocks of Greenland. Although these creatures still had a fishlike tail with fin rays, their limbs were five-toed. For this and other reasons they are placed with Amphibia.

During the Mississippian and Pennsylvanian periods (coal age) the large-headed, long-tailed and short-legged labyrinthodonts (superorder **Labyrinthodontia,** Fig. 27) became abundant. From then to the Triassic there were hundreds of kinds, the last of them eight to ten feet long, with extraordinarily flat and heavy heads. From some of the early (not the late) labyrinthodonts there arose four separate lines leading to

(1) *Apoda,* or caecilians (Fig. 28), an order of burrowing wormlike tropical Amphibia, (2) *Urodela* (Fig. 29), the order of salamanders, newts, and mud puppies, (3) *Anura* (Figs. 30, 31), the order of frogs

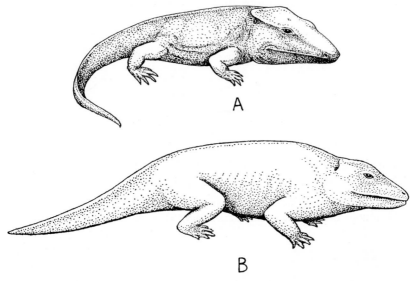

Fig. 27. Labyrinthodont amphibians, A, *Diplovertebron* (after Raymond), and B, *Eryops.*

and toads, and (4) the first *Reptilia,* to which we shall come in a moment.

Today the salamanders, frogs, and toads are the familiar examples of Amphibia, yet they give us a false idea of vertebrate evolution if we suppose that they are intermediate between fishes and reptiles. Breathing by gills during an aquatic larval stage and by lungs when adult, some of them indeed recapitulate hurriedly the change from fish to tetrapod ways of life. But frogs are extraordinarily specialized in their loss of a tail, shortening of the vertebral column, jumping mechanism of the hind legs and pelvis, reduction of skull and ribs, and the "invention" of a limbless, plant-nibbling tadpole (Fig. 31). The salamanders are perhaps less conspicuously specialized, but one glance at the skull and pectoral girdle shows striking reduction from those of labyrin-

Fig. 28. A caecilian, *Caecilia pachynema.* (Based in part on Parker and Haswell, after Boulenger.)

thodonts, and more detailed study makes it clear that scarcely any feature of their anatomy is really primitive. As for the legless Apoda of the tropics, they have a slightly more complete skull than the two previous groups, and in the skin vestigial scales are embedded. But with no trace of limbs

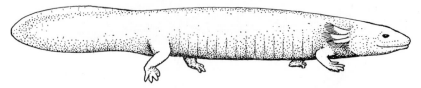

Fig. 29. *Necturus*, the mud puppy.

or girdles, and no aquatic larva, it is scarcely necessary to emphasize how far they have fallen from the high estate of their ancestors. Certainly none of these modern orders has any direct connection with reptiles.

Reptilia now living are few, modest, and retiring compared to those of Mesozoic days, when some 20 orders dominated land, sea, and sky.

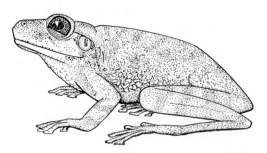

Fig. 30. A tree frog from Cuba, *Hyla septentrionalis*.

Their origin from labyrinthodont Amphibia took place much earlier, during the Pennsylvanian. We shall look first at the living, then at a few of the major extinct groups. Modern reptiles wear epidermal horny scales or plates, or both. Their skins are dry since they lack the mucous glands of Amphibia; they either lay large eggs on land or give birth to active young (viviparity); they possess, like birds and mammals, the amnion, which is a membranous sac surrounding the developing embryo, but they never breathe by gills at any stage. The aquatic habits of many reptiles are secondary, representing a return from the land rather than a persistence of amphibian ways. In size, form, and behavior the reptiles are the most diverse of all vertebrate classes, except perhaps the mammals.

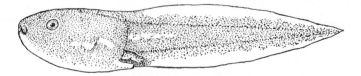

Fig. 31. Tadpole, *Gastrophryne carolinensis*. (After Noble.)

Order *Squamata.* Lizards and snakes (Figs. 32, 33) make an order, *Squamata,* containing the majority of living reptiles. A lizard (suborder *Lacertilia*) is typically coated with small scales, has four agile legs, eyelids, ear openings, a double-jointed articulation of its jaws (by way of

Fig. 32. Tegu lizard. (New York Zoological Society photo.)

Fig. 33. Southern copperhead, *Agkistrodon mokasen.* (American Museum of Natural History photo.)

the movable quadrate bone), and small teeth set on the edges of its jaw bones, not in sockets. Only two species, belonging to the genus *Heloderma* (the beaded lizards or Gila monsters) are poisonous. A few more, like the "glass snake," have no legs and may be mistaken for snakes. The

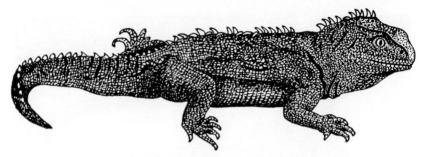

Fig. 34. *Sphenodon punctatum.* (After Gadow.)

great sea lizards (mosasaurs) of the Cretaceous period were the largest and most completely aquatic Lacertilia.

Snakes (suborder **Ophidia**) have large ventral plates (except some primitive burrowing snakes), no eyelids, no ear openings, and an exaggerated freedom of the quadrate bone, so that the mouth can be stretched immensely. In the boas and the above-mentioned burrowing snakes are found vestiges of hind limbs. The viviparous habit is common among snakes, and a substantial number are poisonous.

Fig. 35. A sea turtle, *Caretta caretta,* just hatched.

Order *Rhynchocephalia.* Probably the lowest common denominator among living reptiles is the New Zealand *Sphenodon* (Fig. 34) which looks like a lizard but belongs to the more primitive order **Rhynchocephalia.** Its principal outward peculiarity is a small parietal eye, with a lens and retina, in the top of its head. This organ occurs as a vestige in a number of kinds of vertebrates. *Sphenodon,* to the sorrow of biologists, is on the verge of extinction. Other Rhynchocephalia are known as fossils as far back as the Triassic.

Order *Chelonia.* Since we are looking only at a few terminal twigs of the reptilian family tree, the connections will remain obscure until we climb

Fig. 36. American alligator, *Alligator mississippiensis.* (New York Zoological Society photo.)

down the branches towards the trunk. Two other twigs, however, call our attention first, the orders **Crocodilia** and **Chelonia.** The latter, turtles (Fig. 35) and tortoises, date from the Triassic, in which period they looked very much as they do today. This rather contradicts the usual assumption that a slow-going, heavily armored animal is on the way to extinction. Actually the wide casket of flattened bones overlain by horny plates, and the loss of teeth (another sign of "degeneration"), have not interfered with a considerable versatility of structure and habit, ranging from the great flippered sea turtles, weighing half a ton, to the club-footed land tortoises and the little domed box-turtles. All kinds lay eggs, for which even the most completely aquatic must crawl out of water and dig in the ground.

Order Crocodilia. **Crocodilia** (Fig. 36) number only a few species, all large, all much alike in form and habits. They are aquatic or amphibious, predatory, and equipped with teeth in sockets. The skin is covered with plates, largest on trunk and tail. A bony palate separates the mouth from the nasal passages which run far back, so that the animal can breathe by putting the tip of its snout out of water, yet its mouth may be open below the surface.

Order Cotylosauria. The root of the reptilian tree was among the Carboniferous labyrinthodonts. At first no clear distinction can be made between these Amphibia and the reptilian order **Cotylosauria** (Fig. 37), the "stem" group. Cotylosaurs were bony-headed, short-legged, but pre-

Fig. 37. A cotylosaur, *Limnoscelis.*

sumably terrestrial all their lives. It should not be supposed that an "amphibian," at some particular time, evolved into a "reptile," and that the only problem is to determine when. On the contrary, characteristics of the skull, vertebrae, feet, etc., became more reptilian than amphibian at varying rates and different times, and we may never know when terrestrial egg-laying or the development of an amnion first took place.

From cotylosaurs several other orders arose before the Mesozoic era began. Rhynchocephalia, already mentioned, were on one branch, and as we shall see in connection with the skull, the **Squamata** are very closely related to these.

Turtles were another by-product of cotylosaur expansion. Still another line, containing the strange pelycosaurs and mammal-like reptiles (Therapsida), led directly to mammals during the Triassic period. We shall deal with the Therapsida elsewhere, for this transformation is of great interest.

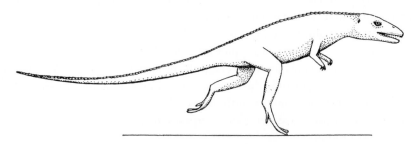

Fig. 38. A thecodont, *Saltoposuchus.*

Order *Thecodontia.* The only other branch from the prolific cotylosaur stem that we need describe now is that which produced the so-called "ruling reptiles" of the Mesozoic; this term is a gracious compliment to their numbers and size, not to their political ability. Several orders came out of this branch, with a common ancestry apparently in the **Thecodontia** (Fig. 38). This name refers to the teeth occupying sockets in the jaws (unlike those of lizards, for instance); the thecodonts looked a little like crocodiles, but often traveled on enlarged hind legs. **Crocodilia,** one of their descendant orders, long ago gave up the bipedal habit, but some of the dinosaurs did not.

Order *Saurischia.* Dinosaurs are placed in two orders which may have started separately from thecodonts back in the early Triassic. The **Saurischia** were those dinosaurs which kept a three-way pelvis, like most reptiles (see Fig. 206C); some of them, the suborder **Theropoda** (Fig. 39), remained bipedal and carnivorous, culminating much later in the fearful *Tyrannosaurus,* largest of all terrestrial flesh eaters. Others, the Sauropoda, resumed the four-legged position and became herbivorous. In the late Jurassic their line produced the gigantic *Brontosaurus* (Fig. 40), *Brachiosaurus,* and *Diplodocus,* which bore about the same relationship to the theropods that a bison has to a wolf. Whether animals so ponder-

Fig. 39. A theropod dinosaur, *Gorgosaurus.*

ous could actually carry their weight without the buoyancy of surrounding water has been disputed, but the imprints of sauropod feet on what must have been exposed mud suggest that they could. The larger ones may well have been amphibious, like the hippopotamus among mammals.

Fig. 40. A sauropod dinosaur, *Brontosaurus.*

Order *Ornithischia.* Meanwhile another order of dinosaurs appeared and branched prolifically during the Mesozoic, the **Ornithischia.** As the name implies, the pelvis was shaped like that of birds (Fig. 206D). Again the bipedal habit came first, as in the duckbill dinosaurs (Fig. 41), but was superseded in the weird *Stegosaurus* (Fig. 42), Ankylosauria, and Ceratopsia (Fig. 43) by an obviously clumsy quadrupedal posture. The entire order seems to have been herbivorous. No dinosaurs, indeed no ruling reptiles except the Crocodilia, survived beyond the end of the

Fig. 41. A duckbilled dinosaur, *Trachodon*.

Cretaceous. Extinction seems to have overtaken these and six or eight other Mesozoic orders that we have not discussed, at about the same time.

Order *Pterosauria*.   Perhaps the strangest of all reptiles that ever lived were the pterosaurs, familiarly called "pterodactyls." They belong some-

Fig. 42. *Stegosaurus*.

where among the offshoots of the thecodonts, hence were ruling reptiles. They were the only reptiles that ever accomplished real flight. Presumably they soared and skimmed much like an albatross or a pelican, and either dove for fish or snatched dead ones from the water, like a gull. But the wings of pterosaurs did not resemble those of birds, and it is important to emphasize that these creatures were not ancestors of birds, nor were they directly related to either birds or bats. Flight originated in

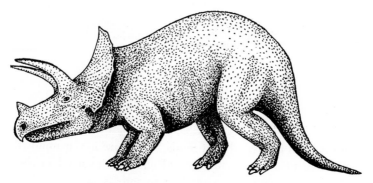

Fig. 43. A ceratopsian dinosaur, *Triceratops.*

these three groups quite independently. The last finger of a pterosaur, greatly lengthened, supported a leathery wing of skin. Some pterosaurs were little fellows, but a few, with wings outstretched, exceeded 25 feet. Their skeletons were remarkably light and compact. *Pteranodon* (Fig. 44), largest of all, was toothless, but some individuals grew a long blade-like crest on the back of the skull, which may have acted as a vane to keep the long beak to windward.

Fig. 44. One of the largest flying reptiles, *Pteranodon.* (Redrawn from Dunbar.)

Order Ichthyosauria. Before leaving the reptiles we must speak of another group that everyone has heard about, the ichthyosaurs (Fig. 45). These were porpoiselike in habits, size, and form. The feet made flippers, the nostrils migrated to the top of the head (as in whales), and these marine reptiles are known to have caught cephalopods. But the tail was unlike that of whales, being vertical instead of horizontal, and the tail vertebrae curved down abruptly into its lower lobe. Skeletons of embryos found in place in adult bodies show that ichthyosaurs were viviparous; obviously they could neither drag themselves out on land to lay eggs, nor lay viable eggs in the water.

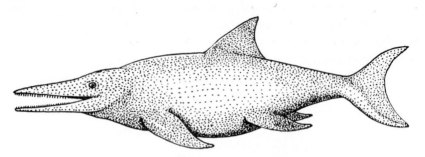

Fig. 45. *Ichthyosaurus,* a sharklike marine reptile.

Class Aves

To label a bird a "glorified reptile" emphasizes a number of points of similarity between the two, but it tends to obscure in our minds the fact that there were nearly as many radical changes involved in coming to modern birds as in coming to modern mammals. Some of these were physiological: constant temperature well above 100°F; highly special-

Fig. 46. The earliest known bird, *Archeopteryx.*

ized sense organs and brain; astonishing neuromuscular coördination associated with flying and balancing. Outwardly the most obvious characteristics of a bird are its feathers and the feather-bearing wings, in which the supporting part is an abbreviated forelimb carrying only vestiges of fingers. Birds have no connection with Pterosauria.

Bird skeletons are delicate and seldom found fossilized. Therefore extinct birds add little to our knowledge of the class. Most important of all fossil birds are the oldest, *Archeopteryx* (Fig. 46) and *Archeornis*, from the Jurassic of Bavaria. These tell us that feathers, wings, and therefore flight had already been established, but instead of a horny beak there was a reptilian mouth full of teeth in sockets (affinity with archosaurs), and the tail, unlike that of any later bird, was a long column of vertebrae with feathers projecting from both sides. By this tail we may set off the subclass **Archeornithes,** for all other known birds have shortened it to, at most, a stub, the pygostyle, from which feathers extend back; the latter subclass, **Neornithes,** numbers more than 20,000 species. Teeth, by the way, still persisted in the Cretaceous sea birds, *Hesperornis* and *Ichthyornis,* although these were modern as to tail.

Fig. 47. Hesperornis, a toothed Cretaceous bird with vestigial wings.

Among **Neornithes** are four very unequal superorders: **Odontognathae** (the Cretaceous toothed birds, Fig. 47); **Palaeognathae** (the ostrichlike flightless birds, Fig. 48, and the South American tinamous, which do not fly well); **Impennae** (the flightless, marine penguins of the southern hemisphere); **Neognathae** (all the rest). Curiously enough, the pattern of bones in the roof of the mouth, as first noted by T. H. Huxley, seems to give a better clue to broad relationships than any of the bigger, more superficial differences with which we are familiar. This is probably because, independently of one another, various bird lines have given rise to swimmers, waders, soaring or running birds, or flightless kinds, and this has affected proportion of limbs, wings, neck, beak, feathers, etc., while the bones of the palate remained conservative, having no occasion to change with every whim of adaptive evolution.

Although it has been argued that the ostrichlike birds (the Ratitae), with a primitive type of palate, are also primitively flightless (that is, that none of their ancestors ever flew), this seems quite improbable when we find that they possess feathers (albeit peculiar ones), wings (albeit vestigial), and most of the normal anatomical characters of birds. In losing the power of flight (as many others have done), the ostrich, emu, cassowary, rhea, and kiwi have emphasized powerful legs, long neck (or bill in the kiwi), a flat, keel-less sternum, and very large eggs.

Among *Neognathae,* which were well established by the Eocene pe-

Fig. 48. South African ostrich. (New York Zoological Society photo.)

Fig. 49. A shoebill stork, *Balaeniceps rex.* (New York Zoological Society photo.)

riod, we may take note of the major adaptive groups. The orders of birds, by the way, do not differ from each other as much as do the orders in most classes of vertebrates. Loons and grebes comprise two orders of diving, fish-eating birds, the sharp beak and many other features distinguishing them from ducks. Albatrosses and petrels are oceanic flying (rather than swimming) birds, although of course they may alight on the water. Pelicans and gannets dive from the air, plunging into the sea to catch fish, but cormorants, belonging to the same order, are more like loons in appearance and behavior. The herons, storks, and flamingos are longlegged waders in shallow water, whose food is fish, frogs, or crustaceans. The neck and beak together are about equal in length to the legs. Ducks, geese, and swans are another aquatic order, with more or less flattened beaks; they feed on vegetation (geese), fish (mergansers), or molluscs and other aquatic invertebrates (many other ducks).

The hawks, eagles, and vultures are well-known birds of prey and scavengers. Superficially like them in beaks and claws, but belonging to another order, are the owls, nocturnal predators. The *Galliformes* are the grouselike birds, including turkeys, pheasants, quail, and domestic chickens, mainly terrestrial seed-eaters, not well equipped for flight. In the order of cranes and rails, and in that of the sandpipers, gulls, and

Fig. 50. Black-bellied plover. (American Museum of Natural History photo.)

Fig. 51. Bluejay. (American Museum of Natural History photo.)

auks, we meet aquatic adaptations again, especially for life on beaches and in marshes. The auks have carried their specialization to the point where they superficially resemble penguins, and the great auk, now extinct, was flightless.

Several small orders may be mentioned here by name only: pigeons (including the famous extinct dodo), cuckoos, parrots, whippoorwills, hummingbirds and swifts, kingfishers, woodpeckers. Each of these has characteristic specializations of beak, feet or wings, associated with its way of living.

About half of all species of birds belong to the last order, *Passeriformes,* the perching and song birds. (This does not mean that all of them can sing—for a crow certainly cannot—nor that these are the only birds able to perch on a twig, for a hawk or a hummingbird can do this too, but nevertheless it is the best general descriptive name of the group.) Beginning with crows and jays (Fig. 51) the order contains a great variety of small familiar birds of fields and woods, some seed-eaters (as the sparrows), but the majority are insectivorous (wrens, warblers, flycatchers, swallows, etc.).

Class *Mammalia*

Mammalia are warm-blooded animals with hair, which feed their young after birth by milk produced in paired mammary glands. They usually feed the young before birth by means of a placenta, which acts as intermediary between the embryo and the blood supply of the mother's uterus; but the very primitive monotremes (duckbill and echidna) of Australia lay eggs, as the first mammals must have done. Numerous anatomical details distinguish mammals from reptiles: the four-chambered heart, the single (left) aorta, the three tiny sound-transmitting bones of the ear, the fusion of a number of reptilian skull bones to make

Fig. 52. *Tachyglossus* (*Echidna*), a monotreme, with its egg. (American Museum of Natural History photo.)

the complex mammalian temporal bone, the loss of several lower-jaw bones leaving just a dentary on either side—these mark the class that came, with birds, to share the world released from ruling reptiles at the close of the Mesozoic era. Like birds, the mammals originated long before that. They came from certain primitive reptiles of the Triassic period, the order *Therapsida*, or "mammal-like reptiles," and the stages of transition are now fairly well known.

We need not deal with these except to say that therapsid reptiles walked with their legs beneath, as mammals do, that their teeth were differentiated into incisors, canines, and molars, and that they showed the beginning of the mammalian hard palate. Of three extinct and very rare subclasses of Mesozoic mammals we shall mention none but the **Pantotheria** (*Trituberculata*), whose molar teeth bore three cusps each, in a pattern suggesting the source of the molar cusps of modern mammals. The trituberculates probably ate insects.

The order **Monotremata** (Fig. 52) is different enough from all others to warrant a subclass, **Prototheria**, containing only the duckbill (*Ornithorhynchus*) and spiny anteaters (*Tachyglossus* and *Zaglossus*). Their mammary glands lack nipples; their digestive and reproductive systems have a single opening (hence the name monotreme, "one hole"); the mouth is equipped with a beak, while the teeth are degenerate; the shoulder girdle contains bones not known otherwise in mammals; and, worst of all, no early fossil monotremes are available to tell just how the living ones accumulated their awkward combination of characters. There is a possibility that the monotremes are derived from a different group among mammal-like reptiles from those ancestral to the other mammals.

Fig. 53. Opossum and young. (American Museum of Natural History photo.)

But in any case it is clear that the transition was not accomplished in a single jump, and that the many distinctive traits of the class Mammalia did not originate at the same time or rate.

The order **Marsupialia** or pouched mammals may be placed with the placentals in the subclass *Theria.* They comprise an infraclass *Metatheria,* now restricted to the Australian and Papuan region, except for American opossums (Fig. 53). Long isolation from the other continents permitted them to evolve a large number of diverse types, superficially parallel to many orders of placental mammals. For instance, besides the familiar kangaroos and wallabies there are flesh-eaters (Tasmanian wolf), digging types (wombat, and marsupial mole), several arboreal groups (Fig. 54) including the flying phalangers, and even a huge

Fig. 54. Koala, an arboreal marsupial. (American Museum of Natural History photo.)

grazing marsupial (*Diprotodon,* of the Pleistocene epoch) analogous to the heavy ruminants. The young of marsupials are extremely small and undeveloped when born (those of a 6-foot kangaroo may be only an inch long), but they crawl unaided into the pouch and attach there to the nipples, where they remain through a sort of second embryonic phase. In view of this demonstrated capacity to evolve into many adaptive types it seems that the main encumbrance which held the marsupials back, and allowed them to be beaten or by-passed by the rising placentals, was their second-rate brains. No marsupial pretends to be intelligent; it is somewhat better off than a reptile, but has less ability to profit by experience than the average placental.

To the *Placentalia* (infraclass *Eutheria*), then, goes nearly all credit for the rise of intelligence during the Cenozoic era. Increasing size of the forebrain and complexity of the cortex can be traced independently in several lines of advanced mammals, for example the horses, elephants, carnivores, and especially the monkey-ape-man order, Primates. The earliest known members of most of the living orders are found in deposits of the Eocene (e.g., horses, whales, elephants) or Paleocene (carnivores, rodents, primates), but there were insectivores and marsupials in the late Cretaceous. Many orders, no longer in existence (as the *Condylarthra, Dinocerata, Tillodonta, Notoungulata,* etc.) also arose during the

Fig. 55. Elephant shrew, *Elephantulus rufescens.* (New York Zoological Society photo.)

early Cenozoic, persisted with moderate or great success for a while, and finally vanished.

Feet and teeth are perhaps the best indicators of mammal specialization, but obviously other structures show great modification in particular cases, and if we were to pick out a few common evolutionary trends they would include increasing size, reduction in tooth number, reduction of toes, enlargement of the brain, and increased folding of the cerebral cortex.

The order **Insectivora** (moles, shrews, Fig. 55) is probably at the base of the whole subclass, although our common kinds are specialized in some respects. It is thought that the earliest placentals were small, arboreal, nocturnal animals, perhaps not very different from the elephant shrew here pictured. Some insectivores today retain the ancestral number of teeth, 44 (3 incisors, 1 canine, 4 premolars, 3 molars, on each side of each jaw), and the feet have 5 digits with simple claws.

Bats (order **Chiroptera**) are close to insectivores, but have modified the forelegs into wings; each wing is a thin sheet of skin spread between

Fig. 56. Indian fruit bat, *Pteropus giganteus*. (New York Zoological Society photo.)

the delicate, elongated fingers (except the thumb), and of course reaching the side of the body, hind leg, and tail. Most bats are small and catch insects in flight, using their remarkable "sonar" system, by which high-pitched squeaks emitted by the bat are echoed back to its ears from nearby objects. In the tropics of the eastern hemisphere there are much larger fruit-eating bats, the "flying foxes" (Fig. 56).

Unquestionably the order *Primates* also arose from very early arboreal insectivores. Tree shrews are now considered Primates. The fossil record of Primates is poor, however, and we shall simply review the kinds now living.

1. Suborder Prosimii. A lemur (Fig. 57) looks like a cross between a squirrel and a monkey. To see lemurs in the wild go to Madagascar; a very few occur in Africa and India. Lemurs live in trees, feeding mainly on insects. They show the beginning of flattened nails, in contrast to

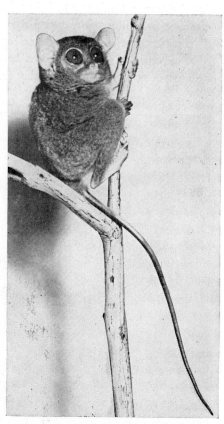

Fig. 57. Ring-tailed lemur, *Lemur catta*. (New York Zoological Society photo.)

Fig. 58. Tarsier. (New York Zoological Society photo.)

Fig. 59. Spider monkey, *Ateles ater.* (New York Zoological Society photo.)

Fig. 60. Hamadryas baboon, *Papio hama-dryas.* (New York Zoological Society photo.)

pointed claws, a tendency to bring the eyes forward on the face so that vision is partly binocular, and a certain amount of brain enlargement. But, compared with monkeys and apes, they are not intelligent. The tarsier or specter (Fig. 58) is a harmless little arboreal animal with enormous eyes, living in the Malay jungle. It is active at night, and its

Fig. 61. Chimpanzee, *Pan troglodytes.* (New York Zoological Society photo.)

fingers and toes bear expanded tips like those of a tree frog, to help in climbing.

2. Suborder Anthropoidea. Here we must use another category (superfamily), since the monkeys of the New World are distinct from, and more primitive than, those of the Old World. The South and Central American monkeys constitute a superfamily Ceboidea (or Platyrrhina), characterized by a broad nasal septum, usually 36 teeth, and (often) a prehensile tail. Of these the marmosets (*Hapalidae*) are most primitive, having claws on every digit except the hallux, and bushy, squirrel-like tails. Cebidae are the spider monkeys (Fig. 59), howlers, capuchins, and a few others, most of them with prehensile tails.

Old World monkeys (superfamily Cercopithecoidea) are of many kinds, in Africa, southern Asia, and the East Indies as far as Borneo. The short-tailed, doglike baboons (Fig. 60) are a terrestrial group, and the so-called Barbary ape (living at the strait of Gibraltar) is a tailless monkey. The true apes and man belong in another superfamily (Hominoidea), and both of these superfamilies, agreeing in the narrow nasal septum, 32 teeth, and lack of a prehensile tail, are collectively known as Catarrhina.

Apes (family Pongidae), like men, have no tail, and are generally larger than any monkey (Fig. 61). Their arms are much longer than their legs, in correlation with the habit of brachiating or arm-swinging from branch to branch. They approach quite closely in structure and intelligence to man. The modern apes are: gorilla (largest) and chimpanzee, in Africa; gibbon (smallest, several species), and orangutan, in the Indomalayan region.

The human stock (family Hominidae) most probably arose five to ten million years ago in Asia or Africa. We shall speak of the early types of man in our last chapter. Although man is, both physically and mentally, a giant among Primates (Fig. 62), most of his peculiarities are distinctly foreshadowed in the apes. The brain in the earliest known

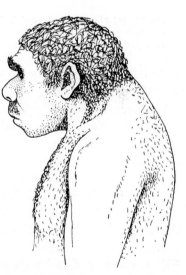

Fig. 62. Restoration of Neanderthal man. (Draw from bust in Chicago Natural History Museum.)

men was not larger than that in apes of comparable size, but the upright posture was already established, with accompanying specializations of the skeleton. Among anatomists there is little doubt of our arboreal ancestry, remote though it was. And there is no doubt that the ability of the hand to grasp objects by opposing the thumb to the fingers (as most Primates do) contributed more than any other single factor to developing the brain, for Primates constantly explore their environment

Fig. 63. (A) *Phenacodus,* a condylarth, somewhat like the ancestor of modern ungulate mammals. (B) A creodont, *Sinopa.* (C) Killer whale, *Orca gladiator,* one of the Odontoceti. (Redrawn from Parker and Haswell, after True.)

by handling things, turning them over, associating touch with sight, and, sometimes, remembering the association.

We have intentionally included the Primates, with man, in the first part of the placental mammals because in many respects the order is quite primitive. Teeth, for example, and limbs, are obviously less modified than those of the majority of living orders.

Order *Carnivora.* Not very distant from ancestral insectivores were the ancestral **Carnivora,** the flesh eaters, represented today by a great many mammals: (1) Creodonta, the small-brained carnivores (Fig. 63B) of the early Tertiary; (2) Fissipedia, the cats (Fig. 64), dogs, weasels, bears, and all other terrestrial carnivores; (3) Pinnipedia, the seals (Fig. 65), sea lions and walruses. Both of the modern suborders arose from the extinct Creodonta. Compared with the latter, most living Fissipedia possess larger brains, specialized cutting teeth, greater speed and agility, and a tendency to raise the heel off the ground so as to run on the toes (**digitigrade** locomotion).

Order Cetacea. Whales and porpoises have gone so far in adjustment to marine life that it is very difficult to determine their early relationships, but there is some suggestion of a creodont connection. At any rate, their structural peculiarities are evident: loss of hind legs; conversion of fore-legs into flippers; development of horizontal flukes on the tail; migration of nostrils (in toothed whales these are combined into a single opening)

Fig. 64. Leopard. (American Museum of Natural History photo.)

Fig. 65. Fur seal, female. (American Museum of Natural History photo.)

to the top of the head, so that a whale can "blow" merely by rolling the back just above the surface; loss of differentiation among the teeth and vertebrae so that the whole series of each becomes essentially alike. The toothed whales (Odontoceti, Fig. 63C) are the majority of Cetacea, ranging from small porpoises to the 70-foot sperm whale, which dives for the giant squid to a depth of half a mile or more. But the greatest of all whales are the Mysticeti (Fig. 66), the whalebone whales, and one of

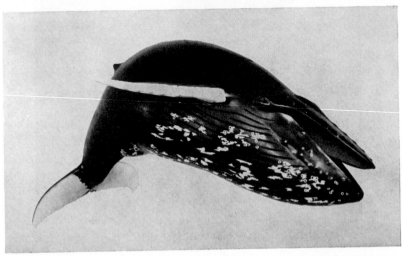

Fig. 66. Model of a humpback whale, *Megaptera nodosa,* one of the Mysticeti. (American Museum of Natural History photo.)

these, the sulphur-bottom, is probably the largest animal that ever lived. It may reach a length of 100 feet, a weight of 150 tons. Yet the food upon which these leviathans attain their bulk is mostly minute swimming Crustacea, strained out of tons of water by dangling fringes of horny "whalebone," taking the place of teeth.

Order *Edentata.* The edentates or "toothless ones" deserve notice for certain very peculiar features. Anteaters (Fig. 67), for instance, are truly edentate, feeding only on ants and termites which they mop up with a slender sticky tongue. But armadillos (Fig. 113), the animals with a flexible armor of bony plates in the skin, and sloths, which climb inverted in trees and have the wrong number of neck vertebrae, are not toothless. Edentata occur only in South and Central America, with the exception of some giant ground sloths that went as far north as Canada a few thousand years ago, glyptodonts which came into the southwestern states, and armadillos, which reach Louisiana. The order seems to be a product of the long isolation of South America from the rest of the world during the first half of the Cenozoic era.

Orders *Rodentia* and *Lagomorpha.* Much more familiar are the rodents, most numerous order of mammals, and the lagomorphs. The first contains all those mammals that gnaw by means of two upper and two lower incisor teeth: the squirrels, woodchucks, mice, rats, beaver, guinea pigs,

Fig. 67. Great anteater, *Myrmecophaga tridactyla.* (New York Zoological Society photo.)

Fig. 68. African rhinoceros, *Diceros bicornis.* (New York Zoological Society photo.)

Fig. 69. Malay tapir, *Tapirus indicus*. (New York Zoological Society photo.)

Fig. 70. Grant's zebra. (American Museum of Natural History photo.)

porcupines, and their innumerable relatives. There is little information from fossils as to their connection with other mammals. The lagomorphs (rabbits, hares, and pikas) agree in most ways with rodents, but they have four upper incisors, and the apparent relationship may actually be quite remote.

As to the odd-toed ungulates (order *Perissodactyla*), the even-toed ungulates (*Artiodactyla*), the elephants (*Proboscidea*), conies (*Hyracoidea*), and the sea cows (*Sirenia*), they all have something in common, mainly the presence of hoofs in the terrestrial kinds, but their rela-

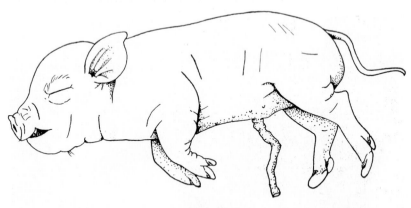

Fig. 71. Fetal pig.

tionships are not close; they have been separate since the Eocene at least. Then, and before, there existed a poorly defined ancestral stock, the order *Condylarthra* (Fig. 63A), from which radiated eight or ten different lines of hoofed, herbivorous animals. Some of these failed and died out millions of years ago; others survived through remarkable sequences of progressive evolution.

Perissodactyla today are rhinoceroses (Fig. 68) and tapirs (Fig. 69), with three toes on each foot (four on front feet in tapirs), and horses

Fig. 72. Newfoundland caribou, *Rangifer caribou.* (New York Zoological Society photo.)

Fig. 73. Manatee or sea cow. (American Museum of Natural History photo.)

THE KINDS OF CHORDATES   49

(Fig. 70), with one toe. Progress in this order has consisted of increasing size (the earliest horse could not have weighed over 25 pounds), reducing the inner and outer toes of each foot by gradual stages, and slowly improving the form of the molar teeth, to serve as grinders.

Artiodactyla are the two- or four-toed ungulates; the same rules of progress apply broadly to them, but with a great deal more leeway allowed for modification of other features. That is, a pig, deer, hippopotamus, giraffe, bison, cow, camel, and goat are all artiodactyls, and an immense variety of others are living or have lived (Figs. 71, 72).

Sea cows or manatees (order *Sirenia,* Fig. 73) interest us here because they are another example of complete aquatic adaptation, in which the front legs became flippers, the hind legs disappeared, and the tail broadened to a round, horizontal paddle. These huge and harmless animals, like the mermaid legends to which they may have given rise, are on the way out.

Order *Proboscidea*. Elephants and their extinct relatives, the mammoths and mastodons, not only show an extraordinary combination of charac-

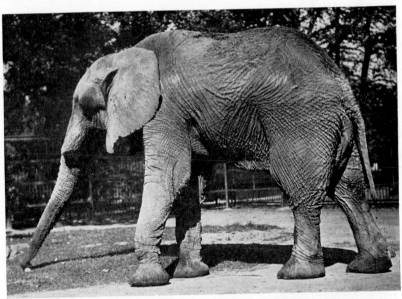

Fig. 74. African elephant, *Loxodonta africana.* (New York Zoological Society photo.)

ters, but also a wonderful array of diverging evolutionary lines that began with Eocene ancestors no larger than sheep. Some features of an elephant (Fig. 74), such as his pillarlike limbs, short neck, long and agile trunk, and thick hide (hence pachyderm), are probably correlated with his bulk; but the molar teeth, tusks, and his intelligence are equally remarkable.

A number of minor groups of mammals have gone unmentioned here, but we may have said enough to suggest how complex is the history of the class, and that the position of man is that of a twig somewhere near the top of an infinitely branching tree. The importance of that twig, of course, is not in its location on the tree, but in the kind of fruit it bears.

CHAPTER II

Development

THE ORGANISM is no less an individual in the egg or the embryonic stages than when development is finished. With many animals the processes of development occupy practically the whole life span. The changes of structure and function by which the animal reaches maturity (usually becoming capable of reproduction) constitute its development. This means that there can be no real distinction between anatomy (study of structure) and embryology (study of development).

Although the parts of an animal may look different, or may be unfinished, the study of anatomy in an early stage is just as valid as in a later one, for immature or embryonic organs often throw a flood of light on puzzling features of the adult. Sometimes ancestral traits appear vaguely and then vanish as development continues. In any case embryology shows the organism undergoing an amazingly swift and delicate transformation of parts. New tissues, new organs, new systems appear and arrange themselves as if modeled by invisible hands. Certain structures arise, working perfectly for a time, and then may disappear or transform as the way of life changes. This business of development goes most rapidly in the beginning, when a few hours may reveal tremendous advances, but it slows down gradually until at maturity the only significant changes are those of normal physiology, of healing wounds, or of wearing out.

We used the word "development" in the first chapter to express the evolutionary transformation of some structure in the history of a group of animals. We now use it in another, stricter, sense, for *the changes in structure, in composition, and in functions during the life of an individual from the beginning to maturity.* Development is not growth. Growth means increase of mass. An organism can grow without developing; more often it develops without growing; but as a rule they go together. So development means a change of form, of materials, the construction of new parts not previously present, or sometimes even loss of parts. It is the making of cells, tissues, organs, and systems from the undifferentiated substance of the egg. It is the theme of embryology.

Every kind of chordate, including those that give birth to fully formed young, goes through a developmental sequence (*ontogeny*) of which the first stage is an *egg* (Fig. 75). From this single cell, by transformation of

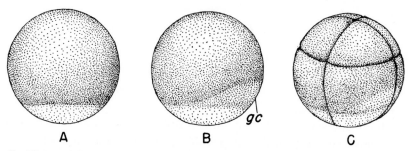

Fig. 75. Egg of frog, *Rana pipiens.* A, unfertilized; B, fertilized (zygote); C, eight-cell stage of cleavage, gc, gray crescent.

materials in it or brought to it, there follow the elaboration of parts and refinement of functions which presently make it self-sufficient, independent. Up to this time (before birth, or before hatching) it is an *embryo* (Fig. 76). Of course much development is yet to come, sometimes grad-

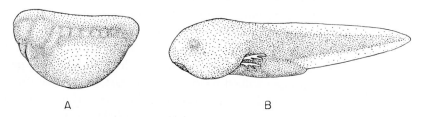

Fig. 76. Frog embryos. A, as somites appear; B, at time of hatching.

ually, as with the infancy, childhood, and adolescence of man, or sometimes with abrupt transformations which go with a radical change in the ways of life, as when a tadpole in a few days becomes a frog. *Postembryonic* development may therefore include a stage called the *larva* (Fig.

77), which may have little resemblance to the adult. Most amphibians and fishes have larvae, but reptiles, birds, and mammals do not. The abrupt change from a larva to the form of the adult is *metamorphosis*. Occasionally, as with some fishes, there is more than one larval stage.

No one will now suppose that development consists merely of making large individuals out of small ones. This idea of *preformation* was current, however, in the eighteenth century (see Chapter XII). Later when microscopes were used more widely, preformation was abandoned as a

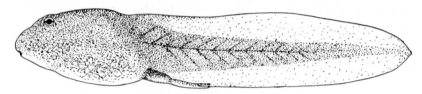

Fig. 77. Frog larva, a tadpole, Rana.

theory of development, and the more natural concept of *epigenesis* took its place. Epigenesis means simply that an individual develops by accumulating new structures, and adopting new functions, that were not there when it began.

Is there any general rule that animals follow in this epigenetic development, any "law" that makes it possible to understand embryology as a whole? The broadest generalization perhaps is von Baer's law, that different kinds of animals resemble one another more closely in earlier than in later stages of development. Karl Ernst von Baer (1792–1876) pointed out that the more general and widespread characteristics in a group of animals arise earlier during ontogeny than do the special features; for example it is possible to recognize a certain embryo as a mammal at a much earlier stage than one can decide whether it is a dog or a cat. Also embryos of one group resemble embryos of other groups rather than adults. Naturally these statements are expressions of our usual experience, rather than "laws" in the physical or mathematical sense. They are, in general, true, but exceptions occur where embryos are specially equipped, as, for example, in a large-yolked hagfish egg contrasted with the small-yolked lamprey egg. A similar generalization, subject to still more exceptions, is the "Biogenetic Law" of Ernst Haeckel (1834–1919), that animals tend to repeat, during their ontogeny, the changes undergone in evolution by their ancestors from the earliest times. This *recapitulation* would explain the close resemblance between different types in early embryonic stages, and it could (and sometimes does) shed a good deal of light on what happened in the evolution of special characters. The trouble is that larvae, embryos, and even eggs may become so much modified in adaptation to circumstances which they meet (but which the adult does not and never did meet) that they refuse to remain photostatic copies of ancient history. Another difficulty in making Haeckel's rule work is that embryos are capable of taking short cuts, wholly spoiling the effect of continuity which we would look for.

With the vast increase in knowledge of the development of animals, we are beginning to understand the relationships of development to genetics, on one hand, and evolution on the other. G. R. DeBeer (1951) has summarized much of this in an illuminating little book. For example, the characteristics of many adult animals can be understood when we see that their development has been slow or incomplete as compared with that of their relatives. The axolotl is a salamander which becomes sexually mature while remaining, in all other characteristics, a larva. *Necturus*, the mud puppy, has gone even farther, as it cannot be made to change its larval form, although the axolotl, given a little thyroid hormone, will do so. This persistence of larval structure in a sexually mature animal is **neoteny**; it is far more general in occurrence than one would at first suppose. The cartilaginous skeleton of sharks is one which has failed, through a slowing of development, to be replaced by bone as it was in the ancestral placoderms. Feathers of the loose, fluffy type seen in ostriches are like the down of nestlings, which in most birds is replaced by normal flight feathers. Now, the rate of development of organs or structures in individuals is genetically controlled, at least in part. We may therefore think of these examples of neoteny as expressing an evolutionary change in the rates at which certain genes accomplish their effects. Evidently this may be a rich source of diversity among animals, as it can apply to one characteristic, to a few, or to many.

The concept of **homology** needs a brief word here, since it reflects the facts of both embryology and phylogeny. We take for granted, without thought, a relationship between "equivalent" or "corresponding" parts in different individuals of one species; for example, a thumb is a thumb, no matter whether it is yours or mine. But evidently such a relationship depends upon (1) inheritance of the thumb from our common ancestor who also had it, and (2) the ability of each embryo, with similar materials and by similar processes, to construct this complex organ. Yet the same idea of relationship holds, necessarily, throughout the long sequence of millions of generations of our ancestry, so long as we can visualize a thumb, or something comparable to it, namely the first digit of the forelimb. Thus we will find the first digit in a reptilian front foot, the first digit in the front foot of an ancient labyrinthodont amphibian, or in the wing of *Archeopteryx,* to represent what in ourselves is called a thumb, whether it has precisely the same form or not. All this might be called ***evolutionary homology,*** the relationship existing among organs of different animals on account of common descent. Be it noted here that homology need not always imply exactly equivalent embryonic derivation of organs, in animals not closely related. For example, the ilium in some frogs articulates with the ninth vertebra, whereas in certain salamanders it is the sixteenth, and in man commonly the twenty-fifth to twenty-ninth inclusive, yet this does not imply either that the ilia are ***not*** homologous with each other, or that the sacral vertebrae ***are*** strictly homologous; obviously the position of the pelvis in relation to the vertebral column is subject to heritable variation.

A similar concept is that of ***serial homology,*** which is the relationship among organs or parts which are repeated, occurring two or more times in the same individual. The ability to reduplicate parts or wholes is a fundamental trait of living things. Among the vertebrates it is seen in the mirror-image duplication of right and left sides, in the repetition of parts in series (vertebrae, ribs, digits, teeth, etc.), and in multiple organs which lie in fields (scales, feathers, hairs, sweat glands, etc.). But, given essential similarity of such organs in a primitive animal, there is no limit to the diversity which may be brought about by evolution within the same series in some specialized descendant. For example, the incisor, canine, and molar teeth of cats have little resemblance to one another or to the simple conical teeth of a primitive reptile, from which they have been derived. Moreover, during the development of individual teeth in a cat, their first rudiments are highly similar to one another, the characteristic differences appearing gradually.

To the comparative anatomist an understanding of embryology is essential for the precious, if intermittent, light it sheds on evolution; for solving puzzling relationships of adult structures; for correct interpretation of many highly complex organs as well as some useless vestiges; and for realization of how heredity works, through epigenesis, to renew again and again the marvel of a finished organism.

Gametes, Fertilization, Cleavage

The production of spermatozoa and of eggs is described in Chapter IX. Here we need only be reminded that fertilization of the egg cell by union with the sperm is the beginning of individual development among vertebrates, as it is among most other animals. Since heredity depends upon the complement of genes in the chromosomes present in the fertilized egg, an important mechanical problem has to be solved in fertilization to make a set of chromosomes from the female parent and a corresponding set from the male parent meet in the egg nucleus. To this end, the gametes (unfertilized egg, and sperm) must bear one set of chromosomes each, the haploid or monoploid number. This is accomplished by division taking place in the maturation of the gametes, as every biology student knows. The forerunner of the sperm, a *primary spermatocyte,* divides in such a way as to reduce its double set of chromosomes to one set, the haploid or monoploid number. The resulting *secondary spermatocytes* divide again, this time without reduction (since they already have the minimum number), and produce monoploid *spermatids,* which transform in the seminiferous tubules to swimming, flagellated *spermatozoa.* Likewise a *primary oöcyte* in the ovary reduces its diploid number, but not by an equal division; it throws off a set of chromosomes as a *polar body,* and then, dividing once more (quite unnecessarily, one would think) it gives off a second polar body, but without reduction this time. This may happen either before or at the time of its release from the ovary. Now as a sperm enters in *fertilization,* two essential results are achieved, the contribution of genes from both parents, and the stimulation of the egg to form an embryo by rapid cleavage.

Thus *cleavage* simply means cell division, as applied to an egg in the early stages of forming an embryo. But the manner of this division is highly variable among different animals, depending on the extent to which the cytoplasm of the egg is crowded by the heavier, inert foodstuff of the yolk. Among vertebrates we find very small, nearly yolkless eggs in only a few cases: protochordates and the marsupial and placental mammals. Such eggs are *isolecithal,* meaning that the yolk is quite evenly distributed, and *microlecithal,* in reference to the small quantity. But where the yolk increases, so that the egg is more yolk than cytoplasm, this material, being heavier, fills the lower part of the cell, leaving the cytoplasm and nucleus floating at the top, just under the cell membrane. If this egg is still of modest size, say a couple of millimeters or a little more in diameter, we may call it *mesolecithal,* to indicate a moderate amount of yolk. This is the sort of egg laid by lampreys, by most (bony) fishes, and by amphibians. Special circumstances have brought about a third type, the *macrolecithal* egg, in hagfishes, sharks and their relatives, and in the reptiles, birds and monotreme mammals. Here the yolk is immense, making such eggs very much larger than any other animal cells, and the cytoplasm, still microscopic in quantity, lies with the nucleus at the upper pole. Since the heavy yolk concentrates toward the lower end, the term *telolecithal* is also used.

The influence of the yolk on cleavage is seen in three corresponding cleavage patterns (Fig. 78). *Holoblastic* cleavage is that in which all the early lines of division pass through the egg so that at each cleavage the yolk as well as cytoplasm divides. This occurs, of course, in the smaller

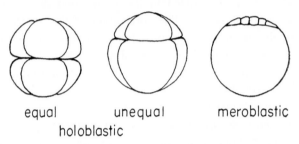

equal   unequal   meroblastic

holoblastic

Fig. 78. Three types of cleavage of vertebrate eggs.

eggs, and is called *equal* when the resulting cells are essentially alike, as in an isolecithal egg. (NOTE: Even here we may see slight differences later on between cells of the upper and lower poles.) Mesolecithal eggs have enough yolk to impose some obstruction to holoblastic cleavage, yet not prevent it; the result is *unequal* cleavage, the smaller cells being above. But a telolecithal egg can divide only at the cytoplasmic animal pole, and there is far too much yolk to allow the cleavage furrows to pass through it. Here, *meroblastic* cleavage produces a thin disk of embryonic cells floating like a raft on a sea of yolk, and only gradually does it extend around, not through, the latter. It follows that the minute holoblastic eggs of higher mammals have been reduced from the meroblastic type because, in feeding the embryo within the uterus, there was no need to retain a big yolk.

The habit of giving birth to live young instead of laying eggs is met among many classes of vertebrates. Those that do so are *viviparous;* egg-layers are *oviparous.* Many sharks are viviparous, including the common dogfish used in the laboratory. There are viviparous teleost fishes, such as the familiar guppies and other "live-bearers" kept in home aquaria. At least one salamander (*Salamandra atra,* of Europe) is viviparous. Snakes with the same habit include rattlesnakes, garter snakes, ringnecks, and others, while some of the "horned toads," among lizards, do likewise. Finally, of course, all mammals except monotremes are viviparous. Nobody has yet reported a viviparous bird, unless the Phoenix of ancient mythology meets the specifications.

Development of a Frog

We shall use the frog to illustrate the sequence of structural changes from egg to adult because it is a familiar animal, easy to observe, and shows some important phenomena, such as metamorphosis. On the other hand, frogs are not primitive or generalized vertebrates. In their development, as well as anatomy, they are a peculiar side branch of the vertebrate line, and thus do not adequately represent vertebrates as a whole. The commonest laboratory frog in this country is *Rana pipiens;* many others agree with it in most of the details that follow.

The **unfertilized egg** (Fig. 75A), as it emerges from the oviduct, has a single vertical **axis** about which its materials are arranged radially, with an upper, or **animal,** pole as the location of cytoplasm and nucleus, and the lower portion, perhaps 98 percent of the whole, filled with yolk. Pigment is darkest at the animal pole but fades downward until the lower, or **vegetal** pole, is white.

Fertilization, although external in most frogs, takes place at the instant the eggs leave the cloaca, by discharge of seminal fluid over them, for immediately afterward, in contact with the water, the membranes covering the eggs swell and will not permit entrance of sperms. The active, swimming sperm cell penetrates the cytoplasm of the egg, but its tail apparently does not. The sperm pronucleus, containing the haploid number of chromosomes (that is, a single unpaired set), moves toward the egg pronucleus, and their chromosomes form a mitotic figure containing the diploid number. Thus the gene contributions of both male and female parent are brought to the offspring. At the same time entrance of the sperm causes activation of the egg (now a **zygote**). There is a gradual concentration of cytoplasm in a crescent area lying a little below the equator on one side (Fig. 75B). This **gray crescent** obviously creates a new axis at right angles to the first, for now it is possible to say the gray crescent is **posterior,** and the opposite face **anterior.** By the same token the zygote now has a right and left side and a dorsal and ventral aspect, even though no structures have appeared yet. It has, therefore, **bilateral symmetry** as soon as the gray crescent appears.

Cleavage (Fig. 75C) is the division of the fertilized egg (zygote) into the first embryonic cells, the **blastomeres.** Cleavage in the frog is **holoblastic,** that is, the cleavage planes pass entirely through the egg including the yolk, which would not be true in an egg with larger yolk than this. Early cleavages begin with grooves that sink into the surface of the animal pole, the **first** plane across that surface through the pole, the **second** also through the pole but at right angles to the first (now there are four equal blastomeres). The *third* cleavage plane is *horizontal;* that is, a circular groove around the egg somewhat above the equator. Now there are eight blastomeres, the upper four being smaller than the lower. The fourth and succeeding cleavages lose their regularity of position, but maintain a rhythmic time sequence. Presently cleavage comes in planes parallel to the surface so that new blastomeres lie under the surface in several layers. And always cleavage is most rapid towards the animal pole, being slowed by the yolk below, with the result that the upper blastomeres become rapidly smaller and smaller, while the lower are still fairly large. The rounding-up of egg substance into cells tends to create intercellular space, so that shortly the *blastula* is formed (Fig. 79A), a

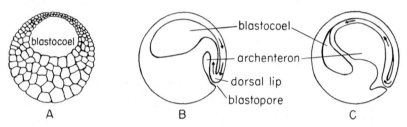

Fig. 79. Diagrams of A, blastula; B, C, movements taking place in formation of the gastrula of frog.

stage in which there is a discrete cavity lying within and somewhat above the center of the ball of cells. During this time no growth, of course, has occurred.

Recalling now the *gray crescent,* we find that it assumes a fundamental importance, for along its lower edge appears a small horizontal groove, below the equator. This thrusts deeper into the blastula, its lips remaining closed yet gradually stretching farther and farther horizontally. This slit is the *blastopore* (Fig. 79B, C). It marks the posterior aspect of the future embryo. The cells of its *dorsal lip* move slowly inward and fold back and up in a layer lying against the inner surface of those that still cover the upper half of the egg. At the same time as this involution is going on there is (1) an overthrust or pushing down of the dorsal lip towards the vegetal pole, like the dropping of a curtain over the yolk cells, and (2) a convergent movement of ectodermal cells toward the middle line. The blastopore continues to stretch sideways until it completely encircles the egg, now having moved nearly to the bottom of the yolk. At this time we see with the naked eye a round white spot beneath, which is the nearly enclosed yolk, and say that the embryo is in the yolk-plug stage. The process described above is *gastrulation;* during it, the embryo is a *gastrula.* The most important achievement of gastrulation is to make an inner layer of cells, containing a new cavity, the **archenteron** (primitive gut), whose temporary opening is the blastopore. That portion of the invaginated cells which forms the roof of the archenteron is the **chordamesoderm,** while that of the floor and sides is **endoderm.** Cells remaining on the outer surface are **ectoderm.** Strictly speaking, the gastrula has two germ layers, for chordamesoderm and endoderm are not at first distinguishable from each other.

Many years ago Spemann showed that the cells from the dorsal lip, coming in as the chordamesoderm to lie in contact with the ectoderm on its inner face, exert a controlling influence on the future development of that dorsal ectoderm, for the latter now begins to show changes leading to the development of the central nervous system (Spemann, 1938). Further, it will *not* do so if the chordamesoderm has been cut out or prevented from occupying its normal place. And finally, chordamesoderm (or dorsal lip) transplanted to a spot elsewhere beneath the ectoderm of an embryo in this stage will induce that particular area to develop a prospective central nervous system, even though such may already have been induced in the regular position. So Spemann called the dorsal lip an **organizer.** By means of a thread tied around an egg or a blastula in the sagittal plane, he was able to constrict it into equal right and left halves, and show that each half became a complete embryo. But if the constriction were horizontal, with the gray crescent (future dorsal lip) in the upper half, then only this half would make an embryo. Therefore, some organizing factor or substance must be present, even earlier than the beginning of gastrulation. Other organizers have been discovered, and one of these will be mentioned later.

Development of the central nervous system (Fig. 80) starts by the ap-

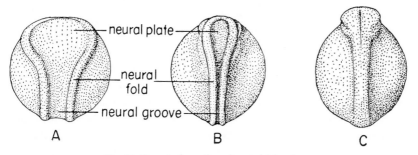

Fig. 80. Steps in formation of neural tube, frog.

pearance of a pair of low longitudinal ridges in the dorsal ectoderm, which meet in a semicircle anteriorly; these **neural folds** heighten and come closer together, assuming the shape of a tennis racket, with a deep *neural groove* down the handle. Presently this groove closes, making a tube lined with that part of the ectoderm which lay between the neural folds, as is best seen in a cross section (Fig. 81). The **neural tube,** however, closes more slowly anteriorly, leaving a much larger cavity there, where the spread part of the tennis racket lay. Finally we have a closed, tubular, central nervous system with a bulblike enlargement anteriorly,

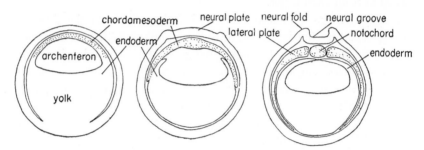

Fig. 81. Cross sections of frog embryos showing formation of mesoderm (stippled).

which, of course, is the prospective brain. **Neurulation** is this process, and the phase during which the folds and groove are patent is the **neurula.** Now the embryo begins to lengthen, and enters the **tail-bud** stage. It becomes oval and somewhat flattened on the sides, but its bulk is no greater than that of the single egg cell. The yolk is being consumed by tissue formation.

Internal changes are taking place in the roof of the archenteron (chordamesoderm) which we must sketch briefly (Fig. 81). Along the median line a rodlike organ forms, the **notochord;** its position is parallel to and just beneath the neural tube. Mesoderm cells lying to its right and left (**lateral plates**) divide in such a way as to produce two layers with a narrow space between. At the same time the endoderm of the side walls grows dorsad and mediad beneath mesoderm and notochord, making a complete endodermal roof for the archenteron. We can now say the embryo has three germ layers, for mesoderm is sandwiched between ectoderm and endoderm. The last will produce the mucosa or inner lining (only) of the digestive tract, and most of the liver and pancreas. The ectoderm will produce epidermis, lining of mouth and anus, central nervous system, and certain parts of the paired sense organs (eyes, ears, nasal cavities). The mesoderm will produce virtually all other structures in the body.

The lateral plates, extending laterad and downward, between endoderm and ectoderm, approach the midventral line as the last yolk is being used up, and thus they envelop the archenteron. The space between the inner (*splanchnic*) and outer (*parietal*) layer of mesoderm is the **coelom** (Fig. 82).

The parietal mesoderm develops a shelflike fold inward, partially and then completely separating the dorsal part (*epimere*) from the ventral (*hypomere*); henceforth the latter contains the **peritoneal cavity**, which widens, remaining undivided. The coelom of the epimere, however, nar-

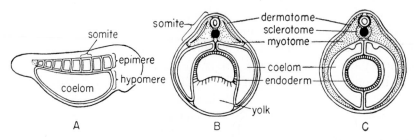

Fig. 82. Diagrams to show development of somites and myotomes in frog. A, lateral view, as transparency; B, C, cross sections.

rows on account of a great thickening of its inner wall, and becomes divided into a lengthwise series of cavities. These boxlike units are the **somites.** Their inner, thickened walls become the **myotomes** or prospective body muscle segments, while the outer layer is called the **dermatome** because it enters primarily into the formation of dermis (the deep layer of the skin). The embryo is now, in part, a segmented animal. The somites show externally as a series of slight swellings along the dorsolateral surfaces. The two-layered wall between each somite and the next is a myoseptum (later a white sheet of connective tissue separating one muscle segment from the next). Now the myotomes appear to grow laterally and down, crowding between the ectoderm and parietal peritoneum until they finally reach the midventral line. What actually happens is that mesenchyme cells associated with the hypomere contribute to the enlargement of the myotomes ventrally, for recent experimental work shows that there is no real movement of the myotomes below the midlevel of the body in animals as far apart as salamanders and birds; hence, presumably, in all tetrapods. Similarly, the dermatome contributes to dermal musculature only in the dorsal trunk; elsewhere muscles of the dermis develop from mesenchyme. The double layer of mesoderm formed along the midventral line becomes a white line of connective tissue, the **linea alba,** separating right and left portions of the body muscles. No coelom remains between myotome and dermatome.

Returning for a moment to the time at which the lateral plate mesoderm (with prospective peritoneal cavity) approaches the midventral line, we find that each splanchnic layer (next to the endoderm) thickens and meets the one opposite, then forms a groove facing the middle line. Within the groove are prospective *cardiac endothelial cells,* the fore-runners of the heart and associated blood vessels. These cells form into a pair of tubes, becoming a single tube at the level where the heart is to be, while around them the thickened wall of mesoderm closes like a sac and makes the *pericardium.* No blood forms and no heartbeat can be seen until a system of arteries, veins, and capillaries has grown sufficiently to provide a circuitous course for the blood to travel. But this is not long delayed. The ectoderm of the outer surface of the future throat grows out as three pairs of *external gills,* a short time after the embryo has hatched and become a larva. Within these gills run capillaries derived from *branchial arteries,* which in turn are branches of the *ventral aorta* running forward from the heart.

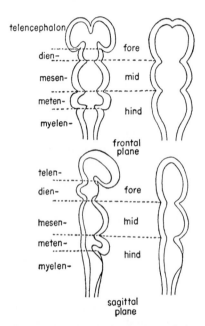

Fig. 83. Diagrams of development of the parts of a vertebrate brain. On right, earlier three-lobed stage; on left, later five-lobed stage.

The story of development of the excretory and reproductive organs is best deferred to the chapter dealing with their structure.

We left the central nervous system at the end of the neurula stage. Subsequently the brain becomes swollen at three levels (Fig. 83), anteriorly the *forebrain* (*prosencephalon*), then *midbrain* (*mesencephalon*), then *hindbrain* (*rhombencephalon*). The neural tube cavity continues through these divisions. Later the forebrain shows a new differentiation into (anteriorly) a *telencephalon,* with right and left *cerebral hemispheres,* and a smaller *diencephalon.* The midbrain develops dorsal swellings, the *optic lobes,* while the hindbrain divides into a *metencephalon* (the dorsal part of this becomes the *cerebellum*) and *myelencephalon;* this, with the remainder of the metencephalon, makes the *medulla.* Cranial nerves and other features will be treated in the chapter on the nervous system.

We should look, however, at the very interesting development of the eye, for its early stages are related directly to the development of the brain, and it is an excellent example of how an organizer works (Fig.

84). The diencephalon very early produces two hollow lateral out-growths, the *optic vesicles,* which grow toward the adjacent ectoderm and presently meet it. As they do so their swollen ends turn inward again, thus making two-layered *optic cups.* At the point where each op-tic vesicle reached the ectoderm the latter also sinks in, thickens, and becomes wholly transparent; the *lens* of the eye now lies just within the rim of the optic cup. Outside new ectoderm crosses over the lens, be-comes transparent likewise, and so makes the *cornea.*

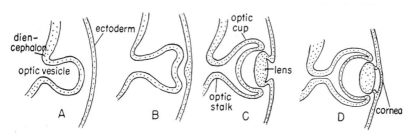

Fig. 84. Stages in the early development of a vertebrate eye, diagrammatic.

The important point is this: It has been shown that the ectoderm will *not* make lens and cornea if the optic vesicle is prevented from reaching it, and also that a transplanted optic vesicle *will* induce formation of a lens if placed beneath the ectoderm elsewhere on the body of an embryo at this stage. Hence the optic vesicle is another example of an *organizer.*

It is sufficient here to add that the invaginated lining of the optic cup will become the *retina,* while the stalk leading to the diencephalon is the forerunner of the *optic nerve.*

At the time of hatching (emergence from the jelly surrounding the embryo) the *larval* stage is reached. By now the body muscles and seg-mental nerves running to them are sufficiently complete to permit swim-ming movements. The more anterior muscle segments become capable of action first; then, in succession, those posterior to them gain this ability. But no action takes place until the spinal nerves send their fibers into the muscles and begin to transmit impulses to them. This, too, takes place in an antero-posterior succession. The first "swimming movement," then, is a contraction on one side, bending the trunk to left or right, followed by a similar bend to the opposite side. As more myomeres become active, contraction proceeds in a wave down one side, but has been reversed in the more anterior segments by the time it gets most of the way down. The body now has a sigmoid (S-shaped) bend, and actual swimming can begin. Mouth and anus open a little later, for the larva has not quite consumed its yolk; the ectoderm invaginates to meet the anterior and posterior ends of the archenteron, and when the breakthrough occurs, the mouth and anus are lined with ectoderm. A temporary sucker or adhesive organ is found at hatching just beneath the head, by which the larva clings to objects. It has, of course, no legs.

Development of the legs in frogs, unlike most tetrapods, is delayed until nearly the end of a prolonged larval stage—in *Rana pipiens*, about a month from hatching. The hind legs are apparent first because the forelegs are concealed by the operculum, a sac of skin which grew back over the external gills shortly after the latter appeared. Each leg forms as a minute **limb bud,** a pimple of ectoderm enclosing undifferentiated mesodermal cells. After a period of growth we find in the bud the rudiments of cartilages and muscles, formed in place, and presently the digits project from the tip. As soon as joints have developed and branches of appropriate spinal nerves grow into the limb muscles, the frog can begin to kick.

Other parts of the skeleton also are cartilaginous during the larval stage; bone begins to appear only a little while before **metamorphosis.** This astonishing change is much more than a mere development of legs and lungs, and loss of tail; it is a rebuilding of most of the organs of the whole body: Skull, vertebrae, mouth, tongue, pharynx, skin, eyes, muscles, circulation, intestine, excretory and reproductive systems, endocrine organs, all undergo profound and rapid readjustments. In this respect the frog is a highly exceptional animal.

Development of *Branchiostoma* (Amphioxus)

We shall follow next the earliest stages in *Branchiostoma,* the egg of which is minute and has practically no yolk, and hence is isolecithal. Cleavage is therefore holoblastic. The result of cleavage is a blastula (Fig. 85) with a relatively larger blastocoel than that of the frog, and the lower cells are slightly larger than the upper, which shows that the egg was not absolutely isolecithal. Gastrulation comes by broad invagination of the lower hemisphere of the blastula, accompanied by epiboly and involution, to make a two-layered cup with no remnant of the blastocoel. The opening of the cup is, of course, the blastopore; its lining is endoderm, its outer surface ectoderm. The blastopore then closes as the neural tube forms, but remains connected with the latter temporarily by the *neurenteric canal.*

The neural tube forms by sinking down of the medullary plate until it is closed over by more lateral ectoderm, after which it rounds into a tube. The notochord develops from the roof of the archenteron in a roughly similar way, but of course without remaining tubular.

Coelom formation is quite different from that in the frog, and the difference is important because of its bearing on the origin of body segmentation in chordates. Dorsolaterally along the sides of the archenteron

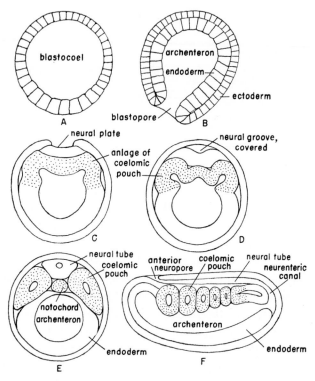

Fig. 85. Early development of *Branchiostoma* (Amphioxus). A, blastula, vertical section; B, gastrula, longitudinal section; C, D, appearance of coelomic pouches and neural tube; E, cross section after notochord forms; F, lateral view, as transparency.

there arises a paired series of pouches, commencing anteriorly and adding on behind; while the later ones are appearing, the early, anterior ones are closing and thus separating their cavities from that of the archenteron. These are *coelomic pouches;* their walls are mesoderm. As the pouches grow they extend ventrad between the endoderm and ectoderm, just as we saw with the equivalent lateral plate mesoderm in the frog, and presently the ventral part of each pouch unites with those before and behind, and on the opposite side, making a continuous coelom. The end result therefore is not unlike that in the frog, but *Branchiostoma* (more primitively) accomplishes its segmentation of mesoderm first, while the frog delays segmentation until after the coelom appears between the layers of lateral plate. The ventral coelom, formed as described, is almost obliterated anteriorly by the later expansion of the pharynx and atrium. The dorsal parts of the original pouches, remaining segmented, are the somites (or epimeres). Their inner walls, thickening, produce the myotomes (muscle segments).

The embryo has now become a larva (Fig. 86), hatching from its egg

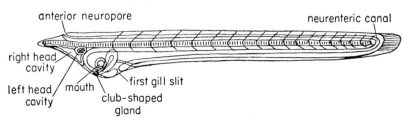

Fig. 86. Larva of Amphioxus. (After Parker and Haswell.)

membrane, and is slender and fishlike. The development of mouth, pharynx, and atrium is very curious. The mouth first opens on the left side, near the anterior end, and remains there for some time. Gill slits appear as a single row of fourteen small pores along the ventral surface (there is no atrium yet, so they open directly to the outside). They slide gradually over to the right side. But seemingly they change their minds about both number and position, for a second row of eight slits appears on the right side *above* the first, and the first row then slides back down and over to the left side, thus attaining its final position. But still the work is not completed; a bar grows downward across each gill opening from the dorsal side, dividing each slit into two; this is the secondary gill bar. Thus all the way along the finished pharynx secondary bars alternate with primary ones, which were there first. Additional slits continue to be added behind the original ones, increasing them to a hundred or more pairs.

Before this is completed, two metapleural folds arise on the outer wall of the body, running lengthwise. They lie laterally or dorsally from the gill slits, presently grow down over these, and forward from behind, so enclosing a space, the atrium. This remains open only at its posterior end, the atriopore, so that water from the gill slits can escape there.

By the time this has happened, and the mouth has moved down to the ventral side, making the animal virtually symmetrical, we can say it is no longer a larva. As we shall emphasize in the last chapter, *Branchiostoma* cannot be considered strictly ancestral to vertebrates, for much of its anatomy is open to the suspicion of being specially modified from an earlier primitive type.

Development of Amniota

The reptiles, birds, and mammals differ from amphibians and fishes in possessing a set of external membranes during their embryonic life, made by the proliferation of tissues from the body of the embryo (Fig. 87). Outermost of these is the *chorion,* an extension of ectoderm underlain by mesoderm. The second, developed simultaneously as a part of the same ectoderm and mesoderm, is the *amnion,* which gives the group name *Amniota* to reptiles, birds, and mammals. The amnion is a protective sac, enclosing the embryo in a bath of *amniotic fluid.* This is really a device to maintain the ancestral water environment on dry land, for of course no amniotes lay their eggs in the water. The embryo in reptiles, birds, and monotremes starts development on the upper surface of a large yolk. Much of the coelom extends far beyond the limits of the embryo and so is called *extraembryonic coelom* (Fig. 87B). It is roofed only by a layer of mesoderm and of ectoderm; this roof rises in a pair of *amniotic folds,* the edges of which presently meet over the body of the embryo (Fig. 87C), enclosing an *amniotic cavity,* while the outer wall of the extraembryonic coelom now is called the *chorion.* The amnion and its cavity enlarge until, as a rule, the extraembryonic coelom is obliterated, but for the sake of simplicity this is not indicated in the diagrams. In mammals (except monotremes) there is an abbreviation of this sequence, so that the amniotic cavity and extraembryonic coelom appear as spaces among the cells, rather than by the growth of folds (Fig. 90A).

The *yolk sac* is an important structure in those amniotes which have large eggs (reptiles, birds, and monotremes). It consists of endoderm which, on account of the size of the yolk, simply spreads over the surface of the latter and finally encloses it; an accompanying layer of mesoderm soon provides a system of blood vessels to absorb and transmit food to the growing embryo.

Meanwhile still another embryonic membrane, the *allantois,* grows down and outward as a pouch from the lower side of the gut of the embryo, behind the yolk sac. It is in the position of the urinary bladder, and consists of gut endoderm covered with a layer of mesoderm. It expands into the space beneath the growing amniotic fold (extraembryonic coelom), and serves, with the help of blood vessels, as an organ of respiration during embryonic life.

Among mammals, the marsupials and placentals have become viviparous and at the same time substituted a uterine food supply for that of the yolk. Consequently the yolk sac, prominent in only a few mammals, is vestigial in the embryos of most. The egg is extremely small (Fig. 88);

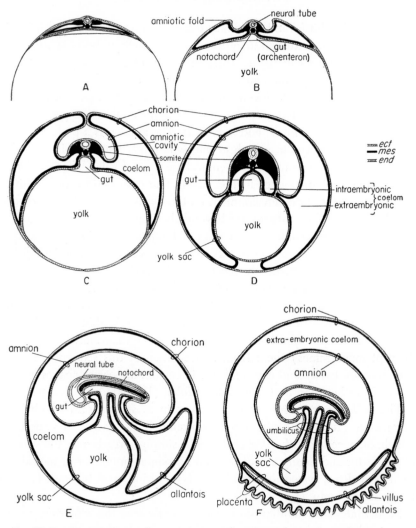

Fig. 87. Development of germ layers and extraembryonic membranes in amniote embryos. A, B, C, D, cross sections through large-yolked type (reptiles, birds); E, sagittal section of the same; F, sagittal section through embryo of a placental mammal.

cleavage is holoblastic; and the membranes external to the embryo are altered to carry on a metabolic exchange with the blood of the surrounding uterus. To see how this is done we shall trace the early stages of a mammal embryo to its establishment as a *fetus* (dependent upon the mother's blood supply) in the wall of the uterus.

The egg is fertilized in its passage down the Fallopian tube, and cleavage therefore begins considerably before its arrival in the uterus proper (Fig. 89). Instead of a blastula, the result of cleavage is a *blastocyst;* that is, a spherical ball of cells containing a cavity and also a group of inner cells; this *inner cell mass* is to be responsible for the formation of the embryo, while the outer layer, called *trophoblast,* remains in contact with the surrounding tissues of the uterus and, becoming the chorion, plays an important part in making the placenta.

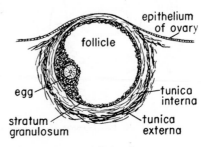

Fig. 88. Human follicle about to erupt. (After Arey.)

The blastocyst sinks into the mucosal lining of the uterus about ten days (human) after fertilization of the egg, thus becoming entirely surrounded by uterine tissue. Development now takes so many short cuts that it seems quite unlike that of primitive vertebrates, or even of other Amniota. The *amniotic cavity* (in man) appears as a space in the inner cell mass (Fig. 90A). The cells lining that space are ectodermal, and the body of the embryo presently appears on the floor of the cavity.

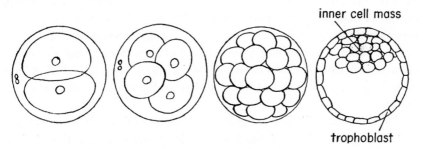

Fig. 89. Cleavage of a mammal egg.

Gastrulation, if we can call it that, comes not by any invagination but by separation of a layer of endoderm cells from the lower part of the inner cell mass, and its spreading to occupy the inside of the blastocyst. The sac so formed corresponds to both archenteron and yolk sac, for if a yolk had been present it would have been enclosed in the same layer of endoderm. (This is further demonstrated a little later by the appearance of typical yolk-sac blood vessels over the surface of the pouch of endo-

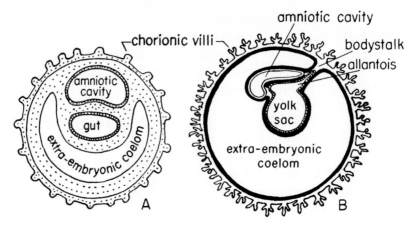

Fig. 90. Development of chorionic villi and body stalk of mammal embryo.

derm.) The endoderm with its cavity fills most of the available space within the trophoblast, below the amnion cavity.

But presently, from cells pushing in from the ectoderm (*primitive streak*) there arises mesoderm, which in turn crowds between the endoderm and surrounding trophoblast. In this mesoderm there opens the *coelom,* which soon becomes very large, and the mesoderm now makes a thin lining against (1) the inside of the trophoblast, (2) the ectoderm of the amniotic cavity, thus completing the amnion, (3) the prospective embryo itself, and (4) the yolk sac. Naturally this causes the structures already formed to float almost free in the big extra-embryonic coelom, except at one place, the *body stalk* (Fig. 90B), by which the embryo keeps continuity with its enveloping case. We can now speak of the latter as the *chorion* (trophoblast plus a lining of mesoderm), and the extra-embryonic coelom is also a *chorionic cavity.* But the amnion, during later growth, presses out against the chorion and practically eliminates its cavity.

The *allantois,* of little consequence in human embryos but a rather important organ in those of most mammals, grows out from the hindgut into the mesoderm of the body stalk. The yolk sac dwindles to a vestige. We shall not give details of the establishment of the organ systems, for these are not basically different from the corresponding stages of lower vertebrates. But for an adequate picture it is necessary to deal with the placenta and umbilical cord.

Two umbilical arteries and an umbilical vein grow out along the body stalk, and are enclosed in mesoderm and ectoderm by the spread of the amnion outward. Thus the cord is formed, carrying the embryo's own blood supply out to the chorion. In the meantime the latter has been growing branched villi out into the tissue of the uterus around it (this does not happen in marsupials). The villi form all over the chorion, but later disappear except in an area where they face the thickness of the uterus wall directly, and there they become elaborately developed. Capillaries take the embryo's blood into these villi and back again into the umbilical vein. There is no actual connection with the mother's blood system. The thick pad of chorion with villi and adjacent tissues of the uterus makes the *placenta.*

The chorion, during early stages, has been eroding away the mucosa of the uterus in which it became implanted, until the villi lie almost free in sinuses filled with maternal blood, but always the exchange of materials is through the semipermeable membrane covering these villi, and *not* by the passage of blood to or from them.

So the fetus floats in its amniotic sac, attached by a vascular cord to the placenta, until time for birth (*parturition*), when it has developed the structures and functions needed for open-air life. Several different adjustments need to be made then rather suddenly: breathing air, feeding, excreting, responding to light, sound, and touch, and a number of changes in circulation of blood. These will be mentioned in later chapters. The placenta, cord, and membranes are shed as the afterbirth, having served their purpose as embryonic adaptations.

Cells and Tissues

The most conspicuous changes undergone by an animal in its development are those of general structure, by which organs and systems appear and gradually attain their complex and functional patterns. But fundamental to all of this, though less obvious, is the transformation of "indifferent" embryonic cells into a number of special types in the course of their rapid multiplication. As these special types appear and start to function in the manner which will characterize them in the adult body, they may be called *tissues.*

At first, however, in an early stage like the neurula, we see a layer of undifferentiated cells, the *endoderm,* lining the archenteron; another, external, layer very much like this, the *ectoderm;* and a third layer between these and similar to both, the *mesoderm.* There is nothing about the mesodermal cells to suggest that they may give rise to muscle, nothing about the ectoderm to indicate that it could produce neurons, and so on. To summarize what is known about the derivation of *tissues* from the three *germ layers:*

The *endoderm* produces the mucous membrane lining the entire digestive tract and its derivatives (liver, pancreas, thyroid, pharyngeal pouches, lining of middle ear, the various digestive glands of stomach and intestine, and the lining of parts derived from the cloaca, such as urinogenital canal, urinary bladder, and allantois).

The *mesoderm* produces (1) connective tissue, present in the walls of the organs mentioned above as well as in muscles, in the deeper parts of the skin, and surrounding virtually all organs and cavities of the body, (2) skeleton, of which cartilage and bone may be considered special varieties of connective tissue, (3) muscles, including the smooth muscles of the gut walls, ureters, bladder, arteries, and dermis, the cardiac muscle of the heart, and all skeletal muscles, and (4) several other organs, such as gonads, kidneys, the adrenal cortex, blood and lymph vessels, and the red and white cells.

The *ectoderm* gives rise to the epidermis of the skin and its products (reptilian scales, hair, feathers, integumental glands), the lining of mouth and anus, nostrils, outer and inner (but not middle) ear, parts of the eye (cornea, retina), neurons of the entire nervous system, medulla of the adrenal gland, some pigment cells in the skin, and, oddly, cartilage of the gill arches (which comes from the neural crest).

Evidently there can be little correlation by form or function between the kinds of tissues and the germ layers that produced them. The relationship is simply determined by tracing the fate of particular parts of the embryo through later stages. Therefore any meaningful classification of cells and tissues must consider their finished state rather than their origin.

In the broadest view, there are four main categories of tissue: epithelial, nervous, muscular, and connective.

1. *Epithelial* cells form layers covering surfaces, or better, they themselves make the surfaces of many organs and of the body. No particular specialization characterizes all epithelia, but the cells are in contact with one another in either a single layer (*simple epithelium*) or in several (*stratified epithelium*). If the cells are flat they are called *squamous;* if elongate, standing on end, they are *columnar;* and if intermediate, about as deep as wide, they are *cuboid.* The columnar type is most frequent in glandular surfaces, as the lining of the digestive system, while the squamous is more likely to occur on an external surface or on one through which osmosis takes place (lungs, renal capsules and tubules, gill filaments). In stratified epithelium the superficial layers are generally replaced by cells being formed beneath, and the latter change from cuboid to squamous form as they move out. Glands, ciliated surfaces, and reptil-

ian scales, hair, feathers and other horny growths all may be considered as modifications or products of epithelium.

A special variety of epithelium is that of the taste buds, the rods and cones of the retina, the neuromast organs of the lateral line and inner ear. These **neuro-epithelial** cells usually are columnar or spindle-shaped and have processes which extend to, and make synapses with, the fibers of nerve cells, so that impulses set off by stimuli can be transmitted to the central nervous system.

2. **Neurons,** or nerve cells, are greatly modified to conduct impulses through the body as a communication system. These impulses, involving some chemical reactions, are most simply visualized as rapid waves of negative ionization passing along the plasma membrane of the neuron fibers, each impulse followed by a quick return of the membrane to the positive condition. Thus the rate of conduction is much less than that of an electric current, but is faster than would be expected of a chemical reaction alone in that situation; it is about 100 meters per second in most mammalian nerve fibers, but less in lower vertebrates.

A neuron, like other cells, has a nucleus and cytoplasm, but the **body** containing these is relatively small, while the **fibers** may be enormously long and complicated (Fig. 309). Any fibers which conduct impulses in the direction of the cell body are **dendrites;** those conducting away from the cell body are **axons.** This distinction has nothing to do with relative length or complexity of branching. It commonly happens that the dendrites of sensory neurons are much longer than their axons, while the reverse is true of motor neurons (those going to muscles or glands).

Evidently, to judge from their embryonic history and the condition of the nervous system in Hemichorda, neurons of chordates are derived from a specialized type of sensory epithelium, like that seen in the neuromast organs of vertebrates. The **ependymal cells** lining the cavities of brain and spinal cord are essentially of this form still, and of course they lie upon that surface of the neural tube which was, in the early embryo, the outer surface of the neural plate.

3. **Muscle** cells exaggerate the property of contractility found in many animal cells. As a part of this specialization they have an elongate form, contraction taking place in a single plane, and so are called **fibers.** In their protoplasm are exceedingly fine **myofibrils,** which we may think of as chainlike protein molecules capable of altering the angles at which their links cling together, so that the chain shortens without losing mass. The simplest muscle cells are spindle-shaped, relatively slow in contraction, and are called **smooth.** They are activated by autonomic nerves, which send fibers among them, and their action is nearly always "invol-

untary." (Note that this term is not useful if taken literally, since all muscles carry on a large part of their work without involving any actual volition or even consciousness.)

Cardiac muscle, found in the heart walls, is not only "involuntary" but is independent of nerve impulses for its contraction. The beat of the heart originates in the muscle cells, but it can be accelerated or inhibited by impulses from sympathetic and parasympathetic nerves, respectively. The cells branch and run together in such a way as to lose their individuality; that is, their myofibrils extend through conjoined fibers, and nuclei occur here and there without cell membranes intervening. Such an aggregation of cells, without membranes separating nucleated parts, is a *syncytium.* The fibers also show a cross-banded or *striated* appearance, which is due to alternating light and dark zones in the fibrils.

Skeletal muscle, which makes up by far the greater part of the muscular system and is organized into discrete units, the *muscles,* likewise has striated fibers which are syncytia, and much larger than ordinary single cells. But skeletal muscle fibers differ from cardiac in being simple bands or ribbons, unbranched, and in requiring motor nerve impulses in order to contract. Contractions may take place at irregular intervals, long enough to allow relaxation before another impulse arrives, or a contraction may be sustained for some time because impulses reach the fiber several hundred times in a second and relaxation cannot take place until such a volley stops. In a muscle, many fibers, a few, or most of them may be relaxed while the others are in contraction, so that the force exerted by the muscle will vary according to the proportion in use at the time.

4. *Connective* tissue is the most diverse of all these categories. It originates from *mesenchyme,* for the most part; this is an undifferentiated sort of mesodermal cell, not in distinct layers, loosely joined together by fibers, with intercellular spaces occupied by tissue fluid. Mesenchyme is present in the early embryo, of course, but may also occur much later, as for example in the limb buds of a tadpole about to metamorphose into a frog. If connective tissue lacks fibers, but the cells fill with fat and become swollen, it is called *adipose.* If the cells become flat and make a membrane lining the coelomic cavities (peritoneum, pleura, pericardium, and mesenteries), it is called *mesothelium;* this differs from epithelium in retaining an ability to differentiate into fibrous connective tissue or even blood cells. The membrane lining blood vessels, lymph vessels, and the chambers of the heart is *endothelium.*

Most connective tissue is fibrous; that is, the cells have elongate, branching processes, and among them may be intercellular spaces containing tissue fluid. Here is a point of possible confusion: Among the cells, but not in them, occur great quantities of *fibers* of three types, *collagenous* (composed of a gelatinous protein, collagen), *yellow elastic* (composed of a highly stretchable substance, elastin), *argyrophil* (fine network visible when stained with silver). These fibers are produced in the tissue spaces by action of the connective tissue cells called *fibroblasts.* Tendons and ligaments contain relatively few cells but a large proportion of densely packed collagenous and elastic fibers.

In *cartilage* the cells are at first like fibroblasts (called *chondroblasts*) but as they begin to secrete the intercellular matrix they lose their processes, become round or oval *chondrocytes,* and occupy spaces called *lacunae* (Fig. 128, 129). The matrix is either of translucent chondrin (as in *hyaline cartilage*), or may contain many collagenous fibers (*fibrous cartilage*), yellow elastic fibers (*elastic cartilage,* as in the external ear), or deposits of calcium salts (*calcified cartilage,* as in shark vertebrae).

Bone is still another tissue, whose cells, originally *osteoblasts,* are branched like fibroblasts, and remain in contact by the tips of their extended processes, while the intercellular spaces become filled with a hard matrix of calcium salts deposited on a framework of collagenous fibers. When embedded in their lacunae the bone cells are called *osteocytes;* communication for the sake of osmosis is through fine *canaliculi* in the matrix, occupied by processes of the cells (Fig. 131).

Finally, if lymph and blood be regarded as special circulating tissue fluids, it is permissible to consider the detached cells that live in these media as varieties of connective tissue. In fact *leucocytes* are closely related to fibroblasts, and some of them, at least, can become fibroblasts after leaving the vessels and entering connective tissue. All leucocytes (white cells) have nuclei and a more or less plastic form (round or amoeboid). One class, *agranulocytes,* includes those whose cytoplasm does not show granules; originating in lymph nodes and spleen as small round *lymphocytes,* these may transform into large *monocytes,* which feed on cell fragments or bacteria (as *phagocytes*). A second class, the *granulocytes,* contains cells with cytoplasmic granules which can be shown by various chemical stains; these, too, are largely phagocytic. Since the leucocytes can creep in an amoeboid fashion and squeeze between the endothelial cells of capillaries and lymph vessels, they are free to enter blood, lymph, or tissue fluid alike.

Erythrocytes begin their existence with nuclei and an appearance much like leucocytes; they are then *erythroblasts.* But they are not released into the blood plasma until they acquire a substantial amount of the respiratory pigment, hemoglobin. In mammals (but not other vertebrates) the erythrocytes also lose the nucleus. They vary in diameter from 2.5 micra in the musk deer to about 50 micra in the salamander *Amphiuma*. Those of man average about 7.5 micra. Erythrocytes develop first from mesenchyme, later from various sites in the body, but finally, in mammals, from bone marrow.

Blood platelets are cell fragments found in mammals, believed to originate in bone marrow from the disconnected pseudopodia of giant cells (megakaryocytes). The platelets are a source of thrombokinase, an enzyme used in blood clotting. *Thrombocytes* are cells serving the same function in lower vertebrates.

CHAPTER III

Integument

General Nature of Integument

Integument is the covering of animals—the skin and associated organs and structures. Meeting the environment directly, it repels a part of what it meets, helps maintain constant conditions inside the body, reacts in highly specialized ways to certain influences in the environment, and so (speaking loosely) makes the animal aware of important matters outside. We might then include sense organs as a part of the integument, but it is customary to treat them in relation to the nervous system because they translate stimuli into nervous impulses. Teeth are integumentary structures, often studied as part of the digestive system, or in connection with the skull, but it expresses more clearly their morphological meaning to put them here.

The unadorned skin is a complex sheet of tissues many cells in thickness (Fig. 91). The outer part, *epidermis,* develops from ectoderm in the embryo, but the inner layer, *dermis* (or *corium*), arises from mesoderm. The epidermis is an essentially uniform epithelial tissue, modified here and there as it contributes to scales, hair, feathers, sweat glands, and the like, but in no case is it a mixture of diverse tissues. The human epidermis grows continually, new cells being added by division of those in its *germinative* or *Malpighian* layer, which is the one nearest the underlying dermis. As successive strata of cells appear they are pushed towards the outside by those beneath them, and go through a sequence of changes of shape and appearance, recognized by the names *granulosum, lucidum,* and **corneum.** In the last of these the cells are thin, flat, horny, and dead, but instead of accumulating they drop off in small flakes, and their place is taken by others coming from below. So it is with mammals in general. The other vertebrates seldom show more than two distinct strata, germinativum and corneum. Reptiles and Amphibia shed their stratum

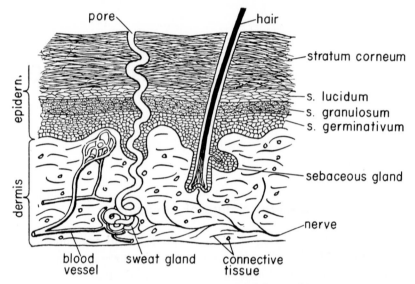

Fig. 91. Diagram of section through human skin.

corneum as a whole, periodically. This is called *ecdysis.* The **molting** term applies to the seasonal change of feathers in a bird, or of fur in many mammals. Fishes do not usually have a horny epidermal layer because their skins are protected by scales, mucous glands, or both.

The *dermis* is complicated, with a network of connective tissue into which penetrate small blood vessels and nerves. Smooth muscles are found here, and small end organs for the senses of touch and temperature. The dermis hurts when a hornet stings us; the dermis bleeds when we scratch ourselves. Leather, made of tanned skins, gets its toughness from the fibrous connective tissue of the dermis.

Color

Color occurs either in the skin itself or in scales, plates, beaks, feathers, hair, and other products of the skin. Usually it is not evenly distributed over the body but forms a pattern characteristic of a species. In a very great number of cases, but not all, this color and pattern have some adaptive relationship with the surroundings, such as to make the animal difficult to see (tree frog), or, less often, to make it exceedingly conspicuous (skunk). The most thorough treatment of this subject is by Hugh B. Cott (1940).

In the epidermis and structures derived from it, color results from pigment (either diffused or in granules), from diffraction (physical color, iridescence), or from a combination of the two. Human skin is colored by pigment in the epidermal cells, as is that of many mammals. Hair gets its color from pigment deposited during its growth, sometimes uniformly, sometimes in alternating light and dark zones, as in many rodents. Bird feathers receive their pigment in the same way, but often with the addition of structural color; that is, diffraction of light takes place in the horny surface layer of the feather, breaking it into many colors according to their wave lengths, as in the throats of male hummingbirds. The beaks of birds and the shells of turtles often contain a variety of pigments.

In contrast with these epidermal colors, those of the dermis usually are produced by pigment within specialized cells, the **chromatophores.** This is true of the lower vertebrates, whose epidermis is transparent enough to allow color to show through. Thus when a toad pulls off his stratum corneum, this is dull and colorless, but the body appears fresher and brighter than before. Chromatophores branch irregularly, and as a rule the distribution of pigment in them changes slowly or not at all, but there are many fishes, frogs, and lizards capable of rapid adjustment to match a change in their surroundings. Pigment flows out from the center of a cell along all its branches, thus causing intensification of that color, or it withdraws to the center, allowing a different color to show from adjoining cells (Fig. 92). **Neurohumors** (substances released from nerve endings) cause these changes, which are reflexes initiated by visual stimulation, temperature, humidity, and other factors; they are also induced (not as reflexes) by a hormone from the intermediate lobe of the pituitary gland. The kinds of chromatophores are the **melanophores,** with brown or black melanin pigment; **xanthophores,** with red or yellow pigment; and **guanophores,** which are white owing to reflection of light by guanin crystals. Chromatophores often occur in deep

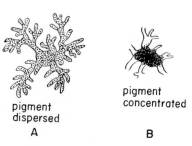

pigment dispersed

A

pigment concentrated

B

Fig. 92. A melanophore in frog skin.

connective tissue, as the peritoneum or the myosepta; they are sometimes able to migrate from one part to another.

Glands

The skin glands of primitive vertebrates are single cells which secrete mucus on the surface of the skin. They are characteristic of fishes and the young (or aquatic) stages of Amphibia. It is likely that the mucous glands of mouth and cloaca in higher vertebrates represent a local persistence of this same type where it is necessary to maintain a moist surface, and of course in the broad view digestive glands are themselves special modifications of primordial mucous glands.

The most common skin glands of fishes are simple mucous cells, but with them occur granular gland cells and beaker cells. In elasmobranchs enlarged cells arise from the Malpighian layer, move to the surface, and pour out their secretion. Some teleosts have developed multicellular poison glands, as in catfishes at the base of the pectoral spines (*Noturus*, *Schilbeodes*), or in some scorpaenids on the dorsal spines. The African lungfish, *Protopterus*, has both uni- and multicellular mucous glands, the latter pushing in from the surface like sweat glands (Fig. 93).

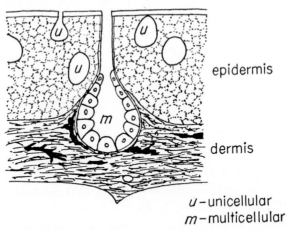

Fig. 93. Mucous glands in skin of lungfish, *Protopterus*. (After Kingsley, *Outlines of Comparative Anatomy of Vertebrates*, 3rd ed., Blakiston.)

The egg capsule of some embryonic frogs and salamanders is thought to be digested by a secretion from unicellular glands. At metamorphosis to the terrestrial (adult) stage the mucous glands in Amphibia become multicellular and alveolar (branched, with pockets). One type of these, the granular glands, pour out a thick, frequently poisonous secretion when violently stimulated; the ordinary mucus is also poisonous in a few kinds of frogs (*Dendrobates*, etc.). It is common for either granular or mucous glands to produce an odor.

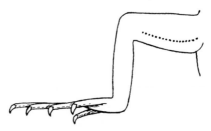

In tree-climbing frogs and salamanders the toes may have adhesive swollen tips.

Reptiles, being terrestrial primarily, have almost given up any skin glands whatever, for it is necessary to conserve water in the body. Therefore reptiles are not slimy; their skin is dry. Even those which returned

Fig. 94. Femoral pores on ventral side of thigh of a lizard, *Crotaphytus collaris*.

secondarily to aquatic life (most turtles, crocodiles, etc.) have not regained a mucous secretion. The musk glands of Crocodilia (a pair on the under side of the lower jaw and another pair in the cloaca, in both sexes) and the cloacal stink glands of some turtles and snakes are virtually all that is left of integumentary glands among reptiles. Regarding the femoral pores (Fig. 94) found on the legs of most lizards, Smith (1946, p. 13) says, "The pores are really integumental glands formed of the epidermis infolded near the middle of a scale. The glands are particularly active during the mating season, secreting a corneous substance that may project fingerlike a considerable distance from the glands. . . . Apparently the organs have the sole function of stimulation of the female in courtship and mating activities. Therefore in females they are vestigial."

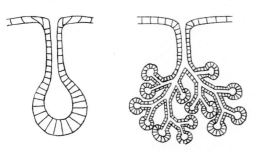

Fig. 95. Simple and compound alveolar glands, diagrammatic.

So likewise in birds the skin glands are few and of little consequence. The only ones commonly met are the uropygial glands just above the tail in ducks, geese, chickens, pigeons, and some other rather primitive types. They provide oil which is used in preening the feathers.

Mammals have either **tubular** or **alveolar** (**acinous**) (Fig. 95) skin glands. Wax glands in the ear canal are tubular. Sweat glands (Fig. 91) are also tubular, much coiled at the inner end, and not branched; evaporation of water through perspiration is an important device to regulate body temperature, but the loss of urea and carbon dioxide in sweat is so slight as to have no value in excretion. The distribution of sweat glands on the body is limited, especially in hairy mammals; in man they are most abundant on the palms and soles. Sirenia and Cetacea, being completely aquatic, have none, nor do the scaly pangolin, the spiny anteater (*Tachyglossus*), the golden mole (*Chrysochloris*, of South Africa), or the European mole, *Talpa*.

The third important type of tubular skin gland is the **mammary** or milk gland (Fig. 96), present in all mammals but with its functioning limited almost entirely to the female after birth of young. In monotremes the nipples are lacking, but the glands consist of two clusters of follicles whose ducts open on the ventral

Fig. 96. Section through human mammary gland.

side of the body near the middle; they are said to function in both sexes. A pair of mammary pouches develops at the breeding season, and they deepen to form a pocket for the young in *Tachyglossus*. Marsupials, excepting some of the opossums, have such a pouch or marsupium in which the young are carried after a very brief period of gestation in the uterus. The pouch contains nipples, varying in number according to the usual size of the litter in different species. The maximum number is probably thirteen (six pairs and one extra) in one species of opossum. Newly born marsupials, extremely small and unfinished, creep among the hair of the mother until they enter the pouch, then take hold of a nipple by swallowing it, and remain attached through what amounts to a second embryonic phase of development, before they are ready to escape from the pouch (Fig. 97).

Fig. 97. Young kangaroo in pouch, diagrammatic.

Among placental mammals the number and location of mammary glands is correlated with the size of litter and with accessibility to the young. For example, carnivores, rats, and pigs, which lie on their sides when feeding their offspring, have nipples in two series along the abdomen (the primitive arrangement), while elephants, sea cows, bats, and primates have a pair in the pectoral position, and in whales and ruminants the glands are beneath the pelvis. Lactation (milk secretion) in the great majority of mammals is seasonal, because reproduction, on which it depends, is also seasonal. The mammary gland originates as an epidermal thickening which pushes in, and gives rise to one or more milk ducts. As these grow they branch inwardly. The outer portion of the skin surrounding the ducts then protrudes as the nipple (Fig. 98).

Sebaceous or **oil** glands are alveolar instead of tubular, and generally associated with hair in the follicles or pits from which hairs grow, al-

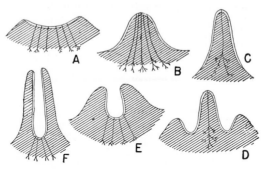

Fig. 98. Types of nipples. (From Kingsley, *Outlines of Comparative Anatomy of Vertebrates*, 3rd ed., Blakiston.) A, *Tachyglossus*; B, human; C, *Didelphis*, before lactation; D, *Didelphis*, at lactation; E, cow, embryonic; F, cow, adult.

though some oil glands occur where hair does not (edges of lips, rim of eyelids, genitalia). Oil glands are present in those mammals that have sweat glands and absent in those that do not; this rule has only one or two exceptions.

As a special modification of skin glands, many deep-sea fishes have light-producing organs called **photophores.** The property of luminescence

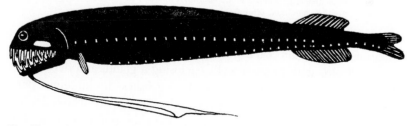

Fig. 99. A deep-sea fish, showing light organs (photophores). (Redrawn from Hegner, American Museum of Natural History photo.)

is common among invertebrates from Protozoa to insects, and especially in those swarms of marine animals that live beyond the reach of sunlight in the sea, or that come to the surface only at night. Among fishes we meet photophores in several unrelated groups, nearly all in the deep sea; they include a few small sharks, most members of the primitive teleost suborder Iniomi (lantern fishes, Fig. 99), many of the suborder Stomatioidei, and others. The light organ usually consists of a modified gland producing a luminous secretion, a concave reflector of dark pigment behind this, and outwardly a cluster of translucent cells acting as a lens. In *Spinax*, a shark, the photophore develops "as a modification of cells in the germinative or basal layer of the epidermis. These cells enlarge and, as a cup, sink slightly into the corium. . . ." (Daniel, 1934). Other enlarged cells nearer the surface meanwhile form a transparent lens which emits the light.

There is, however, one shallow-water fish, the midshipman (*Porichthys*), related to toadfishes, in which shiny white, buttonlike spots occur

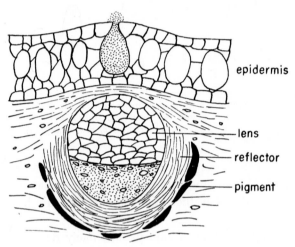

Fig. 100. Section through photophore of *Porichthys*. (Redrawn from Kingsley, *Outlines of Comparative Anatomy of Vertebrates*, 3rd ed., Blakiston, after Greene.)

in rows on the skin and have been shown to produce light under strong stimulation. Here again, each photophore (Fig. 100) is made of a deep, concave reflector with pigment cells enclosing a gland, and over this is a quite effective lens. In most light-producing fishes the luminous part is thought to be derived from skin glands which originally secreted a luminous slime; in some, luminous bacteria in the photophore accomplish the same result.

Usually the luminescence in fishes is intracellular, and is caused by oxidation of luciferin (containing phosphorus), with the help of an enzyme, luciferase. This takes place externally, however, in one of the rat-tailed fishes (*Malacocephalus*), and possibly in others with diffuse luminosity. Probably the primary function of light organs is for recognition among individuals of a species, for the patterns are different in various species but quite constant in any one. There appear to be special adaptations of the photophores for warning, defense, and luring prey in various families.

Epidermal Structures

HORNY TEETH, BEAKS

The teeth found in the oral funnel and on the tongue of lampreys (Fig. 101) and hagfishes are horny epidermal spikes, not true teeth. They can be removed as hollow cones. In most tadpoles (Fig. 102), before the jaws

Fig. 101. Buccal funnel and horny teeth of lamprey, *Entosphenus lamottenii.*

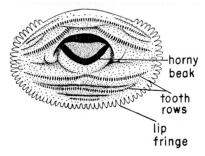

Fig. 102. Horny beak and tooth rows of tadpole, *Pseudacris clarki.*

have assumed the adult form, the lips bear several rows of minute horny teeth on folds of the skin, for nibbling plant food. They are shed at metamorphosis and have nothing to do with true teeth.

Beaks are horny epidermal sheaths enclosing the bones of the upper and lower jaws (Fig. 103). Usually beaks do not keep company with

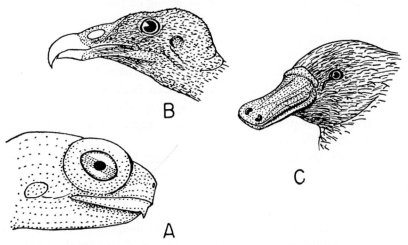

Fig. 103. Types of beaks. A, painted turtle, young; B, buzzard (after Chapman); C, duckbill (after Parker and Haswell).

teeth (turtles and modern birds, for example), but sometimes, as in ceratopsian dinosaurs, the two seem to have gone together. In monotreme
mammals a beak has almost but not quite displaced teeth, which appear
only temporarily in the duckbill. It is among birds that we see the greatest diversity of beaks, from the simple, straight cone of a flycatcher to the
stout, short, seed-cracking type found in sparrows or grosbeaks, the
hooked predatory weapon of hawks and owls, the delicate tube of nectar-
drinking hummingbirds, the powerful chisel of an ivory-billed wood-
pecker, or such monstrosities as the banana beak of a toucan or the
spatula-and-pouch combination of a pelican.

CLAWS, HOOFS, NAILS, SPURS

Claws are horny points produced on the ends of the digits by the epidermis, not only to protect the tip from abrasion but for many special
functions which the digit alone could not perform. They appear first,
sporadically, in Amphibia, where they may be found in a few mountain-
brook salamanders (*Onychodactylus*) and certain primitive frogs (Pipidae). But among reptiles claws are standard equipment, being useful for
clinging to rough surfaces, digging holes, or merely for running. Typically
a claw grows continuously from the germinative layer of the epidermis,
and by the curvature and convexity given to it as it forms, the distal part
continues out and down beyond the tip of the toe. A zone of softer material, the **subunguis,** lies beneath the claw where it leaves the toe. (See
Fig. 104.)

Birds use plain straight claws for scratching on the ground (chickens),
slender curved ones for grasping twigs (almost any songbird), sharp
hooks for seizing prey (falcons, eagles), and a variety of others, including what amount to hoofs on the two toes of the ostrich, for heavy
running. Wings, which are modified forelegs, have lost most external
evidence of digits, but the South American hoatzin has two movable
clawed fingers on the wing in its nestling stage; these aid in climbing. A
claw (first digit) is present in the screamers, and from one to three claws
in the ostrichlike birds.

In mammals the history of claws is of great interest. Upon a heritage
of simple, sharp claws, persisting through the majority of mammals
(marsupials, insectivores, rodents, carnivores, etc.), a few groups made
fundamental innovations. The various "ungulate" orders, independently
of one another, developed these claws into **hoofs,** on which a heavy
grazing or running animal could bear its weight. Generally this happened
after the digitigrade (toe-walking) habit was established, for otherwise

a claw would not be in the right position to support weight; enlarging laterally around the margin of each toe, and becoming either a deep crescent (horse) or a wedge (deer, pig), the claw thickened into a hoof, with its subunguis for a pad, to perform the double function of supporting weight and resisting wear and tear against the ground. At least two extinct ungulates (*Homalodotherium,* a South American notoungulate,

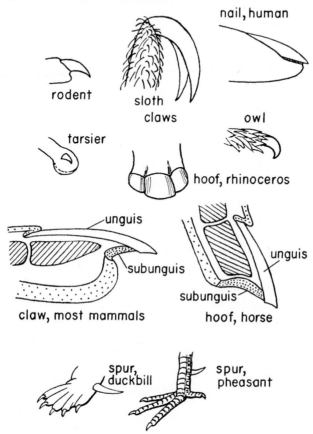

Fig. 104. Claws, hoofs, nails, and spurs.

and *Moropus,* a North American chalicothere) remade their hoofs into claws, apparently as an adaptation for digging, although the animals were very large. The order Primates is distinguished by the flattening of claws into **nails,** a process which began but was not completed in the lemurs. Apparently nails are better instruments for holding small objects, as they do not get in the way and the ball of the finger is free to feel the thing it grasps.

   Spurs are another matter. Roosters, but not hens, develop a horny spur on the back of each leg, used for fighting. It is not a modified claw.

Males of the tropical jacanas and screamers (Fig. 105) bear a spur on the front of each wing. The male duckbill (monotreme) has a spur on the inner side of each hind foot, hollow and provided with a poison gland.

Fig. 105. Crested screamer, showing wing spurs. (After Evans.)

EPIDERMAL SCALES

Scales make the exoskeleton of most reptiles, and they occur in particular parts of the body in birds and many mammals. They are rigid pieces of the stratum corneum, and it is only the presence of a narrow zone of thin epidermis between one scale and the next that makes a scaly armor flexible (Fig. 106). In snakes and lizards the stratum corneum is shed as a whole, periodically, because otherwise the animal would be unable to grow beyond the limits set by its exoskeleton. There is no morphological relationship between the epidermal reptilian scales and the dermal scales of fishes.

Frequently dermal bone develops in the skin immediately below each scale, as in the alligator lizards (*Gerrhonotus*) and "glass snakes" (*Ophisaurus*). The plates of the carapace (above) and plastron (below) of

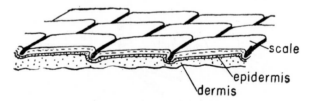

Fig. 106. Reptilian type of scales.

turtles are horny and correspond in their development to scales, but beneath them is a layer of bony plates whose edges do not match those of the horny plates. In Crocodilia the skin of back and tail is also provided with bony plates (Fig. 36).

FEATHERS

The earliest known bird, the Jurassic fossil *Archeopteryx*, had feathers like those of modern birds. From the study of development of individual feathers we infer that they are derived from the horny scales of reptiles, but a feather is infinitely more complicated, and adapted to the two functions of flight and temperature control. By specially developed flight feathers (*remiges*) on the margins of the wings the flying surface is made great enough to be effective. Layers of air, a poor conductor of heat, between the overlapping feathers prevent too rapid radiation of heat from the body. The "tail" of all modern birds consists of feathers (*rectrices*) extending out from the small movable stump of the true tail, the *uropygium.* Feathers also contribute to a streamlining of the body, without which flight, considering a bird's shape, would be awkward or impossible; such are the *contour* feathers. The arrangement of feathers on the skin is in certain distinct zones, the *pterylae* or *feather tracts,* between which lie areas without feathers, the *apteria* (Fig. 107). These allow groups of feathers to slip past one another in the movements of wings, legs, or neck, with a minimum of friction.

We should take a moment to look at the structure of the contour and flight feathers, known collectively as *quill feathers* (Fig. 108). Any of these has a median *shaft,* at the base of which is the hollow *quill.* We find at the lower tip of the quill, where it

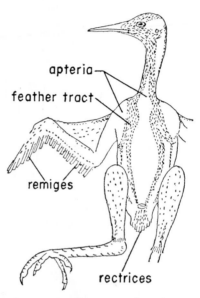

Fig. 107. Feather tracts of roadrunner, Geococcyx, ventral side. (After Kingsley, Outlines of Comparative Anatomy of Vertebrates, 3rd ed., Blakiston.)

inserted in the skin, a hole, the *inferior umbilicus.* A similar hole, often difficult to see, marks the upper end of the hollow (quill) part, and is called *superior umbilicus.* Beyond this the central shaft continues as a flexible but not hollow axis (the *rhachis*) for the wide part of the feather, the *vane.* This consists of numerous fine *barbs* emerging on each side. On trying to handle these, we find that they cling to one another with considerable tenacity, and a lens shows that each barb has smaller *barbules* branching from it; the barbules carry hooks which interlock with barbules of the next series. Thus the vane, without being a solid surface, is so tightly knit that it accomplishes the same effect. (Compare Fig. 109.)

Besides the familiar quill feathers, a bird has *down* feathers, consisting mainly of fine soft barbs arising directly from a short quill, with no shaft and no vane. The barbs are not linked together but form a loose fluff. *Nestling down* is the feathering of newly hatched young birds, while *powder down* persists in adults as an extra cushion or padding under the contour feathers. There are also *filoplumes* or *hair feathers,* in which few

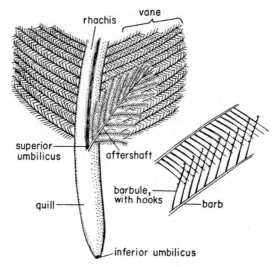

Fig. 108. Diagram of quill feather, with detail showing interlocking barbules.

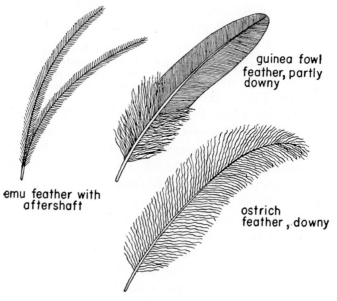

Fig. 109. Feather types.

barbs or none remain, but only the shaft, and such a feather often performs the function of a hair or bristle.

Birds regularly go through a *molt,* or change of plumage, according to age or season. Starting with a downy *nestling* plumage, quill feathers gradually replace the down, so that the bird can fly, but this *juvenal* plumage is not that of the adult. *Nuptial* plumage, put on as the breeding season approaches, will in most birds show a marked contrast between the sexes, the male being far more conspicuous, but the pattern of the female remaining similar to that of the immature bird. *Postnuptial*

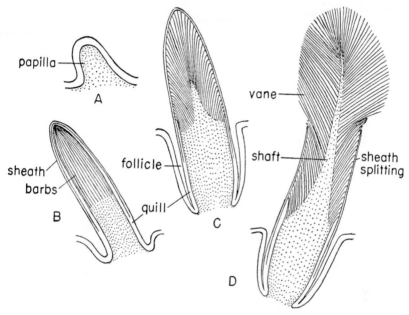

Fig. 110. Development of a feather.

plumage is seen in many birds in the fall and winter after breeding, and they may repeat the nuptial pattern as many years as they live to reproduce. Not all these statements would be correct for all birds.

We can better understand the relationships between the types of feathers by watching their development (Fig. 110). The earliest stage in a feather resembles the corresponding stage in a reptilian scale; that is, a cap of ectoderm overlies a dermal papilla containing a blood supply. The *papilla,* with its cap, lengthens into a cylindrical cone, and the pit surrounding its base deepens into a *follicle,* so that any suggestion of a scale is promptly lost. Now the basal portion of the prospective feather grows as a cylinder of ectoderm, producing a layer of horn (keratin) around itself and enclosing a *pulp cavity* within; this region is to be the *quill.*

The surface layer of keratin splits away from the deeper, making a *sheath.* The deeper layer, while still covered by the sheath, begins to produce distally a series of hairlike ridges, at first still clinging together in a bundle; these are the future *barbs.* If the feather is to be a *down* feather, little more development is necessary except the breaking of the sheath and release of the barbs, which split apart distally but remain attached to the top of the hollow quill. The pulp cavity of the latter dries up. But if a *quill* feather develops, its *shaft,* beyond the quill, arises by the exaggerated growth of one ridge, among the prospective barbs, while still in the sheath; others then are drawn out, as it were, along both sides of this shaft, until few or none are left attached to the quill directly. At the splitting of the sheath, the barbs separate only slightly, spread flat to make the *vane,* and the pulp cavity of the quill dries and makes it a hollow tube, open at its two ends, the *umbilici.*

HAIR

Hair is limited to mammals, in which it performs at least two of the functions served by feathers in birds, namely insulation against temperature change, and coloration. Overlapping hair, especially thick fur or wool, carries a blanket of trapped air, slow to transmit heat. Hair pigments are the basis for protective coloration, or, as with skunks, for display. Hair also occasionally becomes a defensive weapon, as in the porcupine (rodent), European hedgehog (insectivore), and spiny anteater (monotreme).

Essentially, then, hair is a specialized outgrowth of the stratum corneum (Fig. 91), possibly originating from reptilian scales, although there is disagreement about this. A single hair consists of a dense rod of cornified dead cells, in which one can distinguish a *medulla* (middle), surrounded by a *cortex,* and sometimes a *cuticle.* This hair is produced rapidly from a cluster of germinative cells in the bottom of a pit, the *hair follicle.* In order to meet the special needs of a growing hair (speaking unscientifically) the epidermal germinative layer sinks into the dermis (Fig. 111), but at the bottom of the pit it makes a cap over a papilla of dermal cells, and then starts to proliferate a column of horny material. Meanwhile the dermal papilla usually receives a special blood supply and a sensory nerve ending, while against the side of the follicle a minute smooth muscle (*arrector pili*) takes its place, so that the hair can be moved. This is helpful in allowing air to enter the spaces among hairs, or for display of anger or fright.

The hair of most mammals is of *definitive* growth; that is, it reaches a certain length and then drops out. This happens at least twice a year in many mammals of temperate or polar climate, often with a change of color and density. The pubic and axillary hair of man is definitive, but that of the head is not. During late embryonic stages (human) there is a nearly complete coat of fine hair, the *lanugo,* on the head and body, but it is usually shed before birth.

There are many local specializations of hair, as the short screening hairs of nostrils and ear openings, to discourage entry of insects and dirt; the eyebrows and eyelashes, which help keep rain and sweat out of the

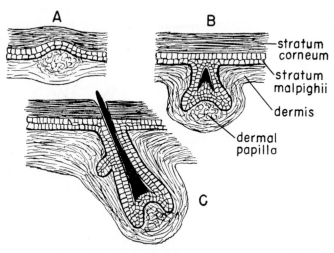

Fig. 111. Development of a hair.

eyes; the whiskers or vibrissae of a cat, which are delicate organs of touch; the tail switch used by nearly all grazing animals to drive away annoying insects; the broad winter fringe on the feet of snowshoe hares; the sex-limited mane of the lion.

Special Armor

HORNS AND ANTLERS

Under this heading we place, for convenience, structures of altogether different origins and quite unrelated composition. *Antlers* (Figs. 72, 112) of deer, elk, and moose are of bone, formed beneath the "velvet," connected with the frontal bone, and naturally cannot continue to grow except while they are supplied with blood vessels; therefore during the "velvet" stage they are covered with skin and short hair, but this rubs off when the antlers are full-sized. After the fighting and mating season antlers break off at a zone of weakness close to the skull, and then the following spring, under the influence of the sex hormone, a new and usually larger set grows. Usually these weapons are limited to the males, but reindeer have them in both sexes. A great number of other mammals, mostly extinct, also possess bony horns. Those of the giraffe and okapi (Africa) are short, unbranched, and permanently covered with skin. Extinct relatives of deer had two, three or four "horns."

The "hollow-horned ruminants" are those in which an outer epidermal shell grows as a cap over an inner core of bone, as in cattle, sheep, goats and antelope (Fig. 112). In all these the horn is permanent and unbranched, continuing to grow from the germinative layer between it and

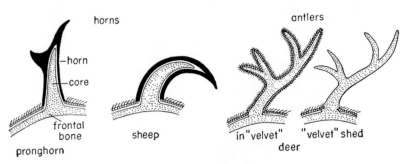

Fig. 112. Horns and antlers.

the bony core. Again, types with two, three, and four horns are known. But the pronghorn and Saiga antelope (not true antelopes) shed their branched horns annually, although they do not lose the core. Sexual differences in size and shape of horns are the rule, notably in sheep and cattle.

The extinct uintatheres and titanotheres had bony horns, the former as many as six. Curiously enough, there have been horned gophers and horned armadillos. The rhinoceroses belong in a different category, for their nose horns are integumental entirely, consisting of closely fused horny fibers; whether these fibers are modified hairs is a disputed question.

SCALES AND PLATES IN MAMMALS

Reptilelike scales are not uncommon in mammals, mingled with hairs, as on the tails of rats and their relatives, or the feet of kangaroos. But a more extreme sort of armor develops in the scaly anteater or pangolin (*Manis*, of Africa and Asia), encasing it, like a pine cone, in large overlapping plates. On the other hand, armadillos (Fig. 113) and the extinct glyptodonts have a mosaic of bony plates or knobs embedded in the dermis; these have nothing to do with hairs or with the stratum corneum, nor have they any relationship to bony plates in reptiles.

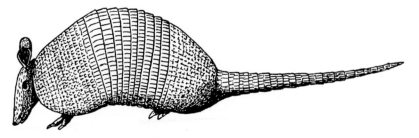

Fig. 113. Nine-banded armadillo, showing bony plates in skin.

Dermal Armor

SCALES, PLATES, AND DENTICLES

A dermal armor characterized the oldest known groups of fossil fishes, including ostracoderms, placoderms, paleoniscids, and Choanichthyes. Only in some secondarily modified descendants of these is there reduction to a naked or unarmored skin. The armor we are considering here is *dermal,* in contrast to epidermal, for it develops in the dermis of the skin and has, so far as known, no epidermal components, even though the scales may push through the epidermis and be exposed to the outside.

Among ostracoderms both scales and bony plates are found, and since they are alike in details of structure there is no doubt that dermal bone goes back in its history to the Ordovician period. The absence of bone in a peculiar form, *Jamoytius,* of the Silurian, is quite possibly due to its being immature rather than an unarmored ancestral type. The placoderms likewise exhibit both scales and bony plates, and since they include the oldest vertebrates with jaws and teeth, it is likely that the origin of teeth from scales took place in early (Silurian) members of this class. Scales of primitive placoderms were complex, essentially like the *cosmoid* scales described below, but in others were *ganoid.*

Chondrichthyes, the sharks and their relatives, undoubtedly arose in the Devonian from placoderms but are not on a line leading to any other group. Therefore the incomplete armor of fine broad-based *denticles,* commonly called *placoid scales* (Fig. 114), present in sharks and rays, must have been derived from a much heavier covering of scales. The cap covering their tips is a hard form of dentine, and is produced, like the deeper dentine, by the dermis. *Dentine* is much like bone, and is provided in these scales as in teeth with a *pulp cavity* and *dentine canals.* A relationship clearly exists between teeth and dermal scales, although we may not be sure in which early group the transition took place.

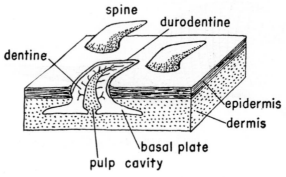

Fig. 114. Placoid scales or dermal denticles of shark, diagrammatic.

Among Osteichthyes, supposedly derived from placoderms along a different line, the ancestral type of scale is a *cosmoid* scale, a flat and rather elaborate structure. The deep layer is of bone. Over this is a middle layer of porous bone through which capillaries run. Outwardly there is a cover of cosmine (dentine, with many pulp cavities and a hard surface). These scales project through the skin and overlap one another.

The cosmoid scales of lungfishes and lobefins show progressive reduction until the modern representatives are left with thin, *cycloid* scales.

Ganoid scales, found in acanthodians and the primitive ray-finned fishes (Actinopteri) have little or no spongy bone between the basal layer and the superficial one. This outer layer has few or no pulp cavities, but is of hard, shiny ganoin. The scales are usually rhomboid, without overlap.

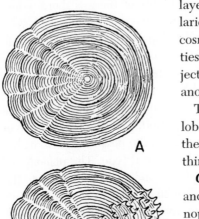

Fig. 115. Fish scales. A, cycloid; B, ctenoid.

But more advanced Actinopteri, beginning with *Amia*, the bowfin, have thinner, round, overlapping scales (Fig. 115). These are *cycloid* (*Amia,* herring, carp, minnows, etc.) or *ctenoid* (perch, bass, flounder, and most advanced teleost fishes). The latter differ from cycloid in having toothed outer margins. During the life of a fish the scale grows around its edges, and since its rate of increment differs seasonally, concentric rings of growth show on the scale, by which it is possible to tell the age of the fish.

Among many families of fishes the scales are reduced, concealed, or entirely lost, as in lampreys and hagfishes, chimaeras, most eels, catfishes,

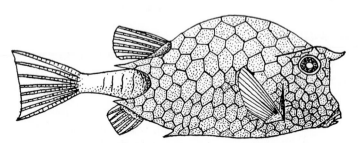

Fig. 116. Cowfish, showing plates of bones (not scales) in skin.

the ocean sunfish, etc. Sometimes the body becomes encased in a secondary armor of bone, as in trunkfishes (Fig. 116); or in spiked bony plates, as the porcupine fishes. Bony plates of many shapes and sizes occur in sturgeons, the extinct placoderms, and ostracoderms. A few show small denticles, surprisingly similar to placoid scales, as in some South American catfishes.

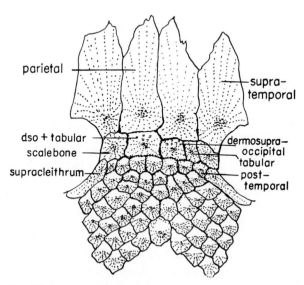

Fig. 117. Occipital region of gar, *Lepisosteus,* showing transition from ganoid scales to skull bones.

We need only add here that there is a direct, close relationship between dermal scales, as found in primitive fishes, and dermal bone of the skull and superficial parts of the pectoral girdle (Fig. 117). This will be discussed more fully in the chapter on the skeleton. Bony scales, presumably derived from those of crossopterygians, were present in the skin of some labyrinthodont Amphibia, and persist today as vestiges, called *osteoderms,* in the caecilians.

DERMAL SPINES AND FIN RAYS

Fin rays are the rods supporting the fins of fishes; they may be cartilaginous (lampreys and hagfishes), bony, horny, or fibrous. Those of most fishes are formed from two different structures which occur together or separately in various groups. These structures are: (1) paired rods called *ceratotrichia,* which are either horny, fibrous, or bony, and in the latter case jointed; (2) *scale rows,* which tend during development to align themselves with the paired rods, and often to fuse with them or replace them entirely.

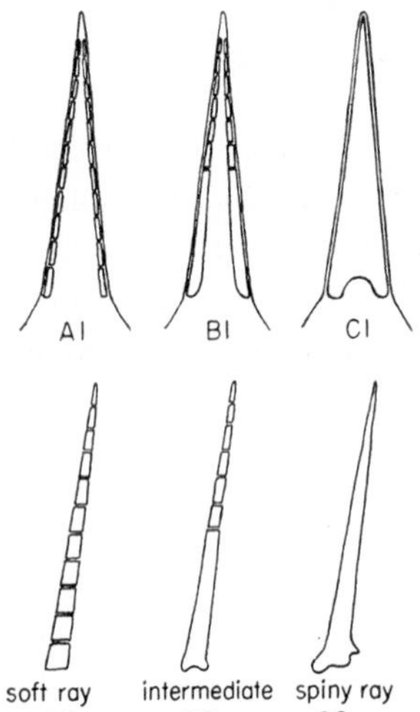

Chondrichthyes have fin rays composed of horny nonjointed ceratotrichia only. These may be supplemented by stiff spines at the anterior margins of dorsal and anal fins.

In bony fishes the paired rods, either horny or fibrous, are usually replaced by scale-rows forming jointed soft rays called *lepidotrichia* (Fig. 118). In lungfishes, lobefins, and some of the primitive Actinopteri the paired rods were often bony and jointed, with scale rows only partially fused with them.

Dermal spines are found commonly at the anterior edges of various fins in fishes, where they serve as a mechanical support and cutwater for the fin, and often as an organ of defense. They have certainly originated in several groups independently of one another (e.g., sharks and catfishes), and probably in different ways. In some primitive bony "ganoids" a few median dorsal scales on the body, known as *fulcra,* were enlarged and formed effective fin spines. In addition to these miscellaneous examples, a vast number of progressive teleosts, the spiny-rayed fishes, show a series of anterior *spiny rays* supporting the dorsal fin, besides the more posterior soft rays, and

soft ray   intermediate   spiny ray
A2   B2   C2

Fig. 118. Diagrams of soft and spiny rays in Actinopteri. 1, transverse sections; 2, lateral views.

the anal fin has one, two, three or more of these spiny rays. Apparently this type can be traced back to certain Cretaceous teleosts (*Ctenothrissa*) in which the anterior dorsal fin rays were spinelike at the base and retained joints distally (Fig. 118A). The movement of spiny rays is restricted to a raising and lowering, but the soft rays will move laterally as well, so that a soft-rayed fin can undulate.

Teeth

There is a relationship between teeth and dermal scales, as shown by their development and by their form in primitive fishes. When vertebrates began to use jaws in the capture of prey, presumably the scales at

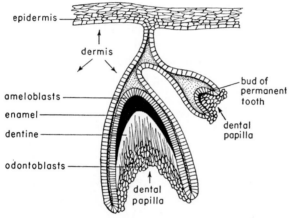

Fig. 119. Development of mammal teeth; a milk tooth preceding a permanent tooth.

the margins of the mouth became modified to hold, cut, or tear, and an infinite variety of special uses followed thereafter. Teeth do not, in most lower vertebrates, occupy sockets in the jaw bones but rest their bases on the surface of bone or cartilage. Also it is the rule that such teeth, being lost easily, are replaced by new ones developing in series.

In the development of a tooth (Fig. 119), the germinative layer of the epidermis sinks down into the dermis, and there it spreads over a papilla of dermal cells. The inner, dentine layer of the tooth is then secreted by this **dental papilla,** while the enamel capping it is produced by the **enamel organ** from the epidermis. As the tooth enlarges, the dental papilla becomes the pulp, which contains **odontoblasts** (dentine-secreting cells), a blood vessel, and a nerve. As long as the tooth remains below the surface, ameloblasts (cells of the enamel organ) add to the enamel, but presently it erupts through the epidermis, and at the same time becomes attached to the bone or cartilage of the jaw. If this attachment is on the rim only, as in most fishes and amphibians, the dentition is **acrodont**

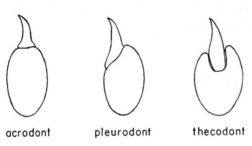

acrodont   pleurodont   thecodont

Fig. 120. Types of tooth attachment.

(Fig. 120); if on the inner margin of the bone, as in most lizards, it is **pleurodont;** if in sockets, as with crocodiles, dinosaurs, toothed birds, and mammals, it is **thecodont.** In the latter case the tooth does not push down into the bone, but the bone grows up around the root of the tooth, and at the zone of contact **cement** is deposited by dermal cells, to anchor the roots against the periosteum of the jaw.

When teeth may be replaced several times, the succession is **polyphyodont.** Beneath the integument just behind or below the functioning tooth rows there is a series of developing buds, those most nearly complete being nearest the functional teeth, so that when one of the latter drops out the new tooth next behind replaces it; this occurs in many fishes, amphibians, and some reptiles (lizards and snakes). Mammals are generally **diphyodont,** having only two sets of teeth, the **deciduous** or "milk" teeth and the **permanent** teeth (Fig. 121). A few are **monophyodont** (moles, some rodents, and the toothed whales).

The comparative anatomy of teeth is of great interest. Sharks, which are predatory, have sharp conical teeth, with

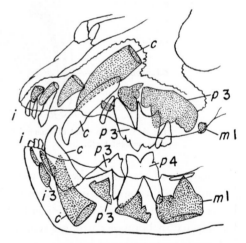

Fig. 121. Jaws of six-month lion, showing tooth replacement.

c, canine; i, incisor; m, molar; p, premolar. (From Kingsley, after Weber.)

from one to five or more prongs (Fig. 122). A typical shark tooth, sectioned, shows in its center **osteodentine** (bonelike material, with vascular canals), then **orthodentine** (with fine tubes but not vascular), and finally an outer layer of **enamel.** There is a pulp cavity, and the tooth is fundamentally like a placoid scale. Since the teeth rest, without sockets, on the cartilage of the jaws, frequent replacement is necessary, and they arise in a long succession from behind, the incomplete teeth being hidden in the integument. Each functional tooth therefore has behind it a "family" coming forward slowly, in line. The line cannot readily be accommodated except by curling around the jaw itself; therefore coils or spiral whorls of tooth "families" are commonly present around the jaws of sharks. The most primitive sharks usually have 3 to 7 or more cusps on a tooth. In advanced forms there is often a single cusp (mackerel shark), or the teeth may be flattened (*Heterodontus*), or minute (*Rhineodon*, the whale shark).

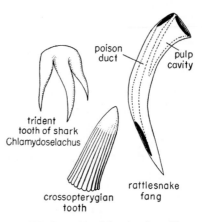

Fig. 122. Examples of functional modifications of teeth.

Rays have pavementlike grinders with flat or rounded surfaces, for crushing molluscs. *Rhina* (guitar-fish) is a shark with much-flattened body, transitional toward rays, but its teeth are pointed. Eagle rays have a distinctive median series of broad, bricklike teeth in longitudinal rows. *Manta*, the giant ray, is a plankton-feeder, and has numerous but minute teeth in the young. In sawfishes (*Pristis*) the flat rostrum carries on each margin a series of enlarged denticles, socketed in the cartilage. The chimaeras (Holocephali), instead of separate teeth, bear either two or three pairs of crushing and cutting plates in the upper jaw, one pair in the lower. In correlation with this, the palatoquadrate cartilage (upper jaw) is fused solidly with the cranium. These conditions can be traced to the extinct sharks of the family Cochliodontidae (Carboniferous to Triassic), ancestors of the chimaeras.

Most bony fishes have simple conical teeth in single or multiple rows or in patches. Succession commonly occurs but is not as conspicuous as in sharks. The teeth at the edges of the jaws are mounted on, or set in grooves or sockets of, the dermal jaw bones (premaxillary, maxillary, dentary). Also they may be clustered on other bones in the mouth and pharynx (vomer, palatines, parasphenoid, the roof and floor of pharynx, and "tongue"). Since the oral and pharyngeal cavities are lined with ectoderm, at least anteriorly, they have the same capacity for tooth development as the edges of the jaws. In some groups (sturgeons, suckers, sea horses, etc.) teeth fail to develop. In others they may fuse into beaks or cutting edges (parrot fish, porcupine fish, ocean sunfish), or be extraordinarily modified (for instance in the armored catfishes, *Plecostomus*, true teeth are replaced by stacks of scythe-shaped horny denticles, coming in succession out of trenches in the jaws).

Lungfishes show crushing dental plates analogous with those of chimaeras, and the palatoquadrates are similarly fused with the cranium. In primitive species of the Devonian genus *Dipterus* we can see radiating rows of cusps on the dental plates, representing rows of teeth whose bases have fused together. In a microscopic section of one of these teeth we find an outer cosmine layer, with very fine canals, and an inner vascular layer, quite comparable to the layers in cosmoid scales of the same fish.

In the lobefinned crossopterygians the tooth arrangement characteristic of early tetrapods is established; that is, in the upper jaw two rows, and in the lower, one row of simple, conical teeth, set in shallow sockets. The inner row above, located on the prevomers, palatines, and pterygoids, contains fewer but larger teeth than the outer row, on premaxillary and maxillary. A cross section of a tooth reveals complex inward folds of enamel and of the accompanying inner vascular layer, which, being passed on to the early Amphibia, were responsible for the name "labyrinthodont" for the latter. The far-reaching changes which accompanied the conquest of land by vertebrates had, then, virtually no effect on the teeth and jaws. Essentially the same pattern is seen in primitive reptiles and some of the modern Amphibia, although without the labyrinthine folds inside a tooth.

Apoda, the limbless tropical amphibians, retain two rows above and one below. With minor changes these are also seen in salamanders, especially the primitive families and the larvae, although the inner row is reduced or lost in more advanced terrestrial adults. Most frogs have a single row of small teeth in the upper jaw, none in the lower, while toads are toothless. Tadpoles lack true teeth, their function being performed by rows of horny nibbling "teeth" on the skin outside the mouth.

Like most other features of reptiles, the teeth are highly diversified according to the special adaptations of various groups. We may take it that the ancestral condition was like that of Amphibia, a single row in the dentary bone of the lower jaw, and two rows in the upper, and that the teeth were set into the bones. Cotylosauria and other primitive groups commonly show palatal as well as marginal teeth above, and these are still found, with modifications, in Rhynchocephalia (*Sphenodon*) and Squamata. Teeth in *Sphenodon* are **acrodont** (set on the edge of the jaw bones), while those of Squamata are generally **pleurodont** (against the inner face); see Fig. 120.

The development of poison glands in several families of snakes independently of one another has been accompanied by various types of fangs, and just as venomous snakes do not form a single natural group, so the modification of teeth to conduct venom has occurred more than once, in different ways. Crotalidae (rattlers, etc.) and the Old World vipers have fangs in front, movable, with a closed duct like a hypodermic needle, apparently originating by closure of a groove on the anterior face of the tooth. Not directly related to these are the Elapidae (cobras and coral snakes) and Hydrophidae (sea snakes) in which the fangs are immovable, yet with a closed duct, and in front. Unrelated to either of the above and comprising more than one group amongst themselves are the rear-fanged snakes, in which an open groove conducts the venom either on the anterior or on the lateral surfaces of the fangs.

Turtles (Chelonia) are toothless, except that the early genus *Triassochelys* had a few teeth in the roof of the mouth.

The subclass Archosauria, possessing only marginal teeth in upper and lower jaws, is **thecodont;** that is, with sockets for the teeth, and the same is true of the early toothed birds, descended from Archosaurs.

The mammal-like reptiles, Therapsida, were also thecodont, as are the mammals. More important, the Therapsida "invented" the distinction of different adaptive forms of teeth in the same series (incisors, canines, and molars) but did not carry this **heterodont** condition to the high degree of specialization seen later in mammals.

We should now look at the teeth of mammals, and in so doing pass over the practically toothless monotremes (only the duckbill has temporary rudiments of teeth).

In marsupials the primitive number of teeth is about 50, as shown in the opossum (Fig. 123), although most other marsupials have reduced this number considerably. In each half of the upper jaw, counting from the front, the opossum has 5 short incisors, each with one root, then 1 canine with one root, 3 premolars each with two roots, and 4 molars with three roots each. In the lower jaw are 4 incisors, 1 canine, 3 premolars and 4 molars. This arrangement can be expressed by a **dental formula:** $\frac{5\text{-}1\text{-}3\text{-}4}{4\text{-}1\text{-}3\text{-}4}$. Multiplying these numbers by 2 (for the two sides) gives 50.

Any particular tooth may now be designated by a letter and a superscript or subscript number; for example, the second upper premolar is P^2, the first lower molar is M_1. Unlike placental mammals, the marsupials have no extensive tooth replacement. The last premolar has a predecessor which is shed, and rudimentary buds of others appear but are not completed. Thus the teeth in general may be regarded as the permanent set.

Placental mammals seem to have started with 44: $\frac{3\text{-}1\text{-}4\text{-}3}{3\text{-}1\text{-}4\text{-}3}$. This number is found in tree shrews and other primitive Primates, early ungulates, and pigs, but again, it is reduced in more progressive types. The incisors, canines, and premolars come in two sets, the first being the lacteal or milk dentition, without complete roots, and this is deciduous, to be replaced by the permanent dentition. The molars come only once, in the permanent set (Fig. 121).

Something remains to be said of the adaptive specializations of teeth in mammals, and of the form of their molars and premolars, for these

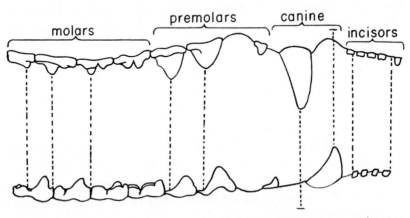

Fig. 123. Teeth of opossum, *Didelphis,* right lateral view, showing heterodonty and manner of occlusion.

present much important evidence on relationships and classification. In each large order of mammals the primitive members generally show the more complete series of teeth, while advanced forms progressively develop modifications fitted to special methods of feeding, and often reduce the number of teeth in doing so. Thus in Primates the dental formula, $\frac{3\text{-}1\text{-}4\text{-}3}{3\text{-}1\text{-}4\text{-}3}$, of tree shrews becomes $\frac{2\text{-}1\text{-}3\text{-}3}{2\text{-}1\text{-}3\text{-}3}$ in most lemurs and New World monkeys, but $\frac{2\text{-}1\text{-}2\text{-}3}{2\text{-}1\text{-}2\text{-}3}$ in Old World monkeys, apes, and man. Rodents have lost the more lateral incisors, the canines and more anterior premolars, leaving a wide gap called the **diastema** (Fig. 163) between the single enlarged pair of gnawing incisors and the cheek teeth. A typical rodent formula is that of the porcupine, $\frac{1\text{-}0\text{-}1\text{-}3}{1\text{-}0\text{-}1\text{-}3}$. From the earliest known Eocene elephant, with $\frac{3\text{-}1\text{-}3\text{-}3}{3\text{-}0\text{-}3\text{-}3}$, the recent elephants have come down to one huge pair of upper incisors (the tusks) and a single pair of elaborately ridged molars in each jaw; the three molars actually are present, but replace each other successively, so that normally one upper and one lower is in action at a time, on each side. Among carnivores the cheek teeth are sometimes reduced (cat: $\dfrac{3\text{-}1\text{-}3\text{-}1}{3\text{-}1\text{-}2\text{-}1}$, or see Fig. 165 for an

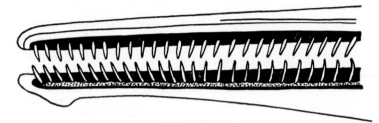

Fig. 124. Jaws of porpoise, *Lagenorhynchus*, showing homodont teeth. (After Parker and Haswell.)

extreme case); these animals commonly develop shearing edges on one or more premolars, called **carnassials**, for cutting meat.

In porpoises (Fig. 124) and toothed whales the teeth are secondarily increased in number and have lost their differentiation, becoming homodont.

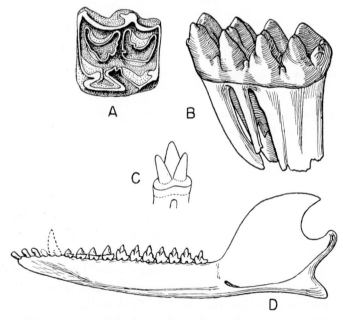

Fig. 125. (A) Molar tooth of horse, showing selenodont pattern. (B) Tooth of mastodon, bunodont type. (After Scott.) (C) Tritubercular tooth of *Spalacotherium*. (After Kingsley.) (D) Lower jaw, inner side, of *Amphitherium prevostii*, a Jurassic trituberculate mammal. (After Simpson.)

Regarding the cusp pattern of the molar teeth, it is thought that the source of that in modern mammals lies in the three-cusped teeth of certain Mesozoic types, symmetrodonts (Fig. 125C) and pantotheres (Fig. 125D). In generalized placentals (Fig. 126) these teeth are triangular, as seen in crown view, except that each lower molar bears a posterior extension, the *talonid*, at a lower level than the triangle, the *trigonid*. When fitted in normal occlusion, each upper molar rests between two trigonids of the lower series, but with its innermost cusp (*protocone*) resting in the talonid. Since the upper and lower three primary cusps obviously do not correspond (the triangles being reversed in position),

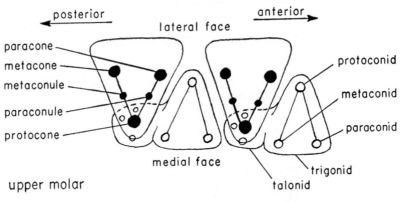

Fig. 126. Diagram of cusp patterns of upper (dark) molar teeth and lower molar teeth of primitive mammals, showing the manner in which they fit when in contact (occlusion).

the names (*protocone, protoconid; paracone, paraconid; metacone, metaconid*) should not be taken as indicating homology. It is thought that the (upper) paracone and the (lower) protoconid may represent the original reptilian cusps, to which the others have been added by expansion of the tooth surface and perhaps by splitting.

Omnivorous mammals, such as pigs, bears, and man, have *bunodont* molars; that is, with low, rounded, or blunt cusps. In many herbivores the cusps spread out and make enamel ridges shaped like the new moon; this type is *selenodont*. But in the still more specialized molars of horses (Fig. 125A), rhinoceroses, etc., the ridges unite, forming a *lophodont* pattern. Naturally no sharp demarcation can be made between these two. As a further specialization, the cheek teeth of modern horses (since the Miocene) have become *hypsodont*, having continuous growth at a rate which compensates for the wearing away of the grinding surface, and at the same time they have added *cement* in the grooves between ridges.

This is because grass, containing silica, abrades the teeth when chewed for many hours a day, and grass first became widespread in the Miocene. Previously horses browsed on softer vegetation, such as the leaves of forest trees; they were then **brachyodont** (with short-crowned molars) like most mammals.

CHAPTER IV

Skeleton

THE SKELETON is the framework of the body. But it is not a wholly inert frame. In the same sense that epithelium, muscle, and nerve are living tissues, so, in part, are bone and cartilage. They contain cells which perform special functions, primarily the secretion of a firm matrix around themselves.

The *endoskeleton* is the internal framework of bone and cartilage, while the term *exoskeleton* is used commonly to mean the covering of scales, plates, feathers, hairs, or other hard materials on the surfaces of most animals. This is an arbitrary distinction, for the scales of fishes are internal in origin, and one cannot, in many cases, draw the line between scales, plates, and the superficial bones of the skull, which are part of the "endoskeleton."

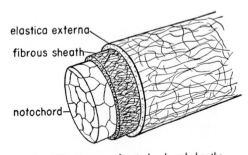

elastica externa

fibrous sheath

notochord

Fig. 127. Diagram of notochord and sheaths.

The earliest sign of a skeleton that appears in the development of man or any other chordate is a semistiff rod along the axis of the body, the *notochord* (Fig. 127). This is neither typical cartilage nor bone, for its cells secrete almost no matrix. Instead they grow to a large size, so

110

distended by watery vacuoles that the protoplasm is crowded against the cell membrane, while the notochordal epithelium produces around itself an elastic membrane, so that the turgor of the cells within keeps it rigid. Outside of this the mesoderm adds another, thicker sheath of fibrous connective tissue.

These layers are most obvious in fishes with a persistent notochord, and least evident in the higher tetrapods where the notochord is a transitory embryonic structure.

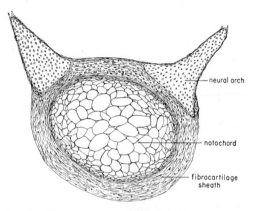

The notochord is no more rigid than a rubber tube filled with water under pressure. It bends readily, but springs back straight. In an embryo, therefore, such a simple axial rod gives partial support to the body and

Fig. 128. Transverse section of developing vertebra of *Ascaphus*, showing contrast between hyaline cartilage of neural arch, fibrocartilage of notochordal sheath, and expanded cells of notochord.

serves as a central spring against which the body muscles can pull, first on one side and then on the other, in fishlike swimming motions.

Cartilage or gristle is soft enough to cut with a knife, and contains a large amount of water so that it shrinks when dry. But it is firm enough to provide support for other tissues, attachment for muscles, or protective enclosure for delicate parts. Cells lie throughout cartilage in minute spaces called *lacunae* (Figs. 128, 129), singly or in pairs or fours, all secreting a protein (collagenous or albuminous) matrix. Usually this contains no hard calcium salts, although the cartilage skeletons of sharks and rays are partly calcified

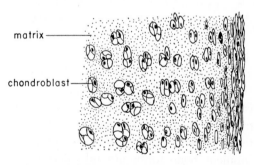

Fig. 129. Microscopic section through cartilage of human trachea, showing transition from perichondrium (right) to hyaline cartilage (left). Note change in shape and arrangement of cells, increase of matrix, and development of vacuoles.

(Fig. 130) and so are some cartilages in lizards and snakes. As a rule, the lacunae do not connect with one another by any kind of canals, nor do capillaries or nerve endings penetrate to them, so that as long as cartilage does not grow too thick these cells satisfy their physiological requirements through the water of the matrix.

Cartilage can grow from within, which bone cannot, and thus it has an advantage over bone in the early stages of development when the shape of the skeleton must change rapidly. The skeletons of embryos consist of cartilage, and bone is then added afterwards, either replacing the cartilage or appearing in new positions.

Precartilage is the name given to cartilage when its matrix first begins to form around young **chondroblasts** (cartilage cells). At this time the cells are closely packed, but as the matrix increases, they may be pushed farther apart and lose contact with one another (Fig. 129). *Hyaline* cartilage has a firm, translucent matrix; it occurs in the head as a forerunner of the bony skull, in growing limbs and the vertebral column, in the series of rings which keep the trachea and bronchial tubes from collapsing, and in many other parts of the skeleton. When this matrix becomes filled with white connective tissue fibers, as in the tough intervertebral discs, it is *fibrous* cartilage. *Elastic* cartilage is occupied by fibers of yellow elastic tissue, where flexibility is necessary, as with the external ear and the epiglottis.

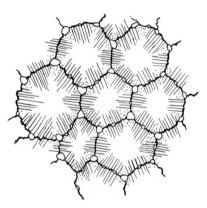

Fig. 130. Plates of calcified cartilage in surface of chondocranium of ray, much enlarged.

Although **bone** never comes as early in life as cartilage, it seems to be fully as old historically, for the most ancient known fishes were more bony than cartilaginous. But its matrix is much harder, has a higher specific gravity, and adjusts its shape less readily during developmental changes. Instead of protein, it is almost entirely lime. Therefore the bone cells cannot depend on the matrix for water, food, and gas exchange, but must all be reached by minute *canaliculi,* which in turn are supplied from capillaries. During development bone forms around microscopic blood vessels and nerves, and frequently encloses other kinds of tissue as well. The part of a bone which bears the most strain, which contains no visible cavities, is *compact* bone; other portions, as the deeper part of large bones, are full of small spaces called *cancellae;* this is *cancellous* bone.

Bone cells (*osteocytes*) lie in regular order, grouped concentrically around capillaries (Fig. 131). The capillary occupies a *Haversian canal.*

Radiating from this are countless extremely fine *canaliculi,* which pass through a narrow layer or *lamella* of bone and reach the lacunae occupied by the cells which secreted that lamella. By other canaliculi these cells connect with one another and with a further series beyond the next lamella, and so on for several such layers. But presently they overextend their communication lines, so to speak, and come under the influence of another Haversian canal, which has its own series of concentric lamellae and cells. Thus bone consists of innumerable *Haversian systems,* each built around a blood vessel.

Since the matrix is calcareous, the cells can never change their positions or secrete more bone than will fill up the spaces between them. Therefore bone does not grow from within, but only by addition on the

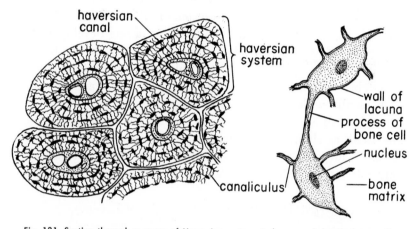

Fig. 131. Section through a group of Haversian systems in bone, and detail of two cells.

outside. It can, however, be absorbed on the surface, by *osteoclasts* or "bone-devouring" cells, and thus change its shape while developing.

Functions of the skeleton are largely based upon resistance to strain. Muscle attachment is perhaps the primary function, since movement and support of the body depend upon interrelations of bone (or cartilage) and muscle. Skeletal parts transmit movement, which begins as muscle contraction, by acting as levers. They often amplify this movement; the hand, for example, swings through a wider arc than the basal part of the forearm where the biceps muscle attaches. In order to do this the bones of the arm must resist the tendency to bend, which the weight of the hand would cause a softer material to do. The sound-transmitting bones of the middle ear are a special case of lever action, for they translate vibrations of the ear drum into vibrations of perilymph.

Sesamoid bones, forming as nodules in tendons, are a special example of resistance to strain, for they occur where tendons pass over a joint (kneecap or patella). The majority of bones replace, during development, cartilages which occupied corresponding positions in the younger stages (Fig. 132). Such are called *replacing* or *cartilage* bones. This does not imply that the cartilage becomes bone. Other bones, especially superficial parts of the skull and shoulder girdle, develop in membranes under the skin, or in the skin, without reference to any previous cartilage. These are *dermal* or *membrane* bones. In the detailed structure of these two categories of bone there is no distinction, but only in their topographic relation to cartilage during development.

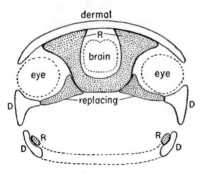

Fig. 132. Diagram of relationship between (D) dermal and (R) replacing bones in cross section of a generalized skull.

We customarily divide the skeleton into an *axial* portion (the skull and vertebral column with their accessory parts), and an *appendicular* portion (limbs, with pectoral girdle and pelvic girdle). This distinction does not hold in all vertebrate animals, but is convenient.

The skull, as shown by its development, is essentially a *cranium* or braincase, with which are incorporated the nasal capsules (cartilage enclosing pits for the olfactory organs) and otic capsules (cartilage sur-

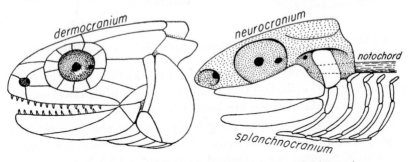

Fig. 133. Diagrams of dermocranium, neurocranium, and splanchnocranium.

rounding the inner ears). It is not correct to include "optic capsules," which form the sclerotic coats of the eyeballs, for there is no evidence that they were ever a part of the skull. Over this *neurocranium*, preformed in cartilage, there is added in most vertebrates a *dermocranium* consisting of dermal bone (Fig. 133). The jaws, hyoid arch, and cartilages found in the throat are the *splanchnocranium* or *visceral skeleton*, originally developed in association with gill support.

Comparative Anatomy of the Skull

THE AGNATHA (CYCLOSTOMES)

In its oldest stages, as in ostracoderm fishes, the skull formed a protective covering for the brain, sense organs, and most other soft parts of the head (Fig. 134). At the same time it was a strong base for attachment of the body muscles used in swimming, and into its floor, beneath the brain,

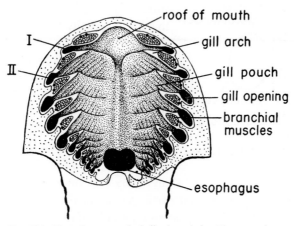

Fig. 134. Ventral aspect of skull of cephalaspid ostracoderm, showing oropharynx from below. I, mandibular cleft; II, hyoid cleft. (From Gregory, *Transactions of the American Philosophical Society,* Vol. 23, 1933, after Stensiö.)

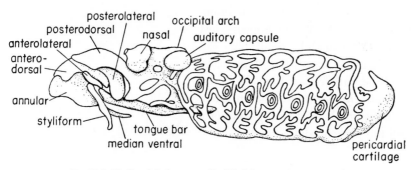

Fig. 135. Skull, adult lamprey. (Modified from various sources.)

extended the notochord. In the skull, too, were parts corresponding to the visceral arches and even the shoulder girdle of higher forms, but these were not jointed. Ten pairs of curved ridges formed the gill arches in the wall of the pharynx in cephalaspids, all much alike. A thin layer of dermal bone covered all external surfaces of the skull, while replacing bone lined the internal cavities and surrounded the cartilage portions.

The cartilaginous skull of a lamprey, *Petromyzon* (Fig. 135), is both reduced and specialized as compared with that of cephalaspids. Neither dermal nor replacing bone appear at all, and the braincase proper is little more than a small trough of cartilage forming a floor and lateral walls around the brain, but no roof except a narrow occipital arch (**synotic tectum**) bridging the gap between the otic capsules. A thin, elastic frame of cartilage surrounds the gill pouches *and the heart;* this lies externally to the branchial muscles. In connection with the parasitic method of feeding, a longitudinal tongue bar supports the rasping teeth, while the annular and other anterior cartilages stiffen the oral walls. A skull like this gives no clue to the derivation of gnathostome skulls (those with jaws).

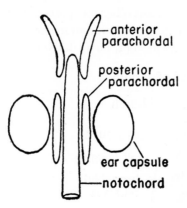

Fig. 136. Early larval skull of lamprey.

But the **larva** of *Petromyzon* (Fig. 136) has perhaps the simplest skull of any vertebrate. A pair of diverging rods, the **anterior parachordal** cartilages, lie at the sides of the forward end of the notochord; two **posterior parachordals** come a little farther back, next to the ear capsules. Soon these capsules and the four parachordals meet and fuse, making an incomplete floor and side walls for the brain. A single nasal capsule appears just in front. Meanwhile small bars develop between successive gill pouches, which lie farther back than the brain; these *visceral cartilages* unite to make a jointless gill basket, fusing anteriorly with the parachordals.

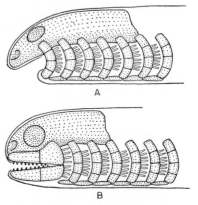

Fig. 137. Diagram of origin of jaws from first gill arch. A, arches all alike, no jaws, as in Agnatha; B, first arch converted into jaws, but still carrying gill, as in acanthodians.

EARLIEST GNATHOSTOMES

Probably the greatest advance ever to take place in the evolution of the skull was the formation of jaws from a gill arch (Fig. 137). This may have accompanied a change in feeding habits from mud-grubbing to capture of active prey. With this came a jointing of all the arches. The arch at the rim of the mouth appears to have bent forward both above and below the mouth, forming on each side an upper and a lower jaw (*palatoquadrate* and **mandible**). This condition we meet in acanthodians. The jaws now bore teeth, yet had not forsaken their gills, a full set of which remained along their posterior margins. When each upper jaw, as in this case, articulates movably in two places with the cranium but receives no hyoid support, it is said to have **auto-diastylic** suspension (De Beer and Moy-Thomas, 1935). The manner of jaw suspension is important in skull evolution, and the major types will be noted as we go along (Fig. 139).

Although little is known of the inner cranium of the oldest gnathostomes, they had a striking diversity of dermal armor. In antiarchs and arthrodires there were large headplates bearing lateral-line canals, and the anterior part of the trunk was armored like the head (Figs. 138, 190). In acanthodians the head, body, and fins were covered with small diamond-shaped scales. In all the eyes were far forward, usually well in ad-

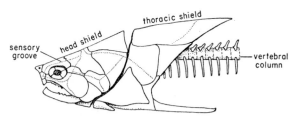

Fig. 138. Coccosteus decipiens, a Devonian Arthrodire. (After Jaekel.)

vance of the angle of the mouth, and the front part of the brain cavity was between the eye sockets; this type of cranium is **platybasic**, in contrast to the **tropibasic** type found later in teleost fishes, many reptiles, birds, and a few others, where the orbits practically meet each other in the middle of the head, and the brain lies behind them.

ELASMOBRANCH FISHES

The **chondrocranium** of elasmobranch skulls is simply the cartilage braincase, persisting without the addition of bone (Fig. 140A). In lacking bone the elasmobranch skull is specialized (degenerate, if you like). In most sharks and rays the upper jaw remains loosely articulated with the cranium at the basal process, just under the orbit. But the wide-open gill cleft which was present in acanthodians has closed from the bottom up, like a zipper pocket, leaving only a vestigial cleft, the **spiracle**, at the top, as if the zipper had jammed before it quite got there. Thus the angle of the jaw fits against, and is supported by, the upper piece of the hyoid arch (*hyomandibular*); recall that the palatoquadrate articulates also with the basal process of the cranium. This is the **hyostylic** type of jaw suspension (Fig. 139). Evidently the use of the hyomandibular in anchoring the upper jaw (and lower) makes it possible for the mouth to be larger and open more widely than it otherwise could; this extension of the jaws backward brought about the reduction of the first gill cleft to a spiracle. Primitive sharks, like *Heptanchus*, have two points of attachment of the palatoquadrate to the cranium, one at the basal process (as usual), and another behind this, at the postorbital process. The hyomandibular also participates in this kind of jaw suspension, called **amphistylic.** In Holocephali (ghost fishes) the spiracular cleft closes entirely without involving the hyoid arch in support of the jaw, for the upper jaw unites solidly with the cranium; we call this jaw **autostylic.**

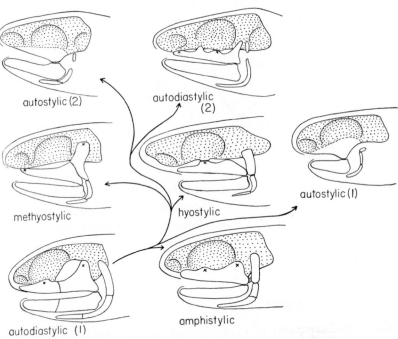

autostylic (2)

autodiastylic (2)

methyostylic

hyostylic

autostylic (1)

autodiastylic (1)

amphistylic

Fig. 139. Methods of jaw suspension in vertebrates. Most primitive, *autodiastylic* (1), is that of acanthodians: the palatoquadrate is attached at two points to the cranium but the hyoid provides no support. Note that a similar condition comes again, *autodiastylic* (2), in labyrinthodonts. *Amphistylic* occurs in some primitive sharks, and *hyostylic* in modern sharks and rays. Crossopterygians have a special primitive hyostylic type, not shown here, in which the hyomandibular is two-headed. The *methyostylic* condition is that of Actinopteri, where the hyomandibular meets the otic region above the lateral head vein instead of below it as in sharks. In Holocephali the method is that shown as *autostylic* (1), also called *holostylic.* Dipnoi are again, independently, autostylic (2), and this also occurs in modern Amphibia, some reptiles such as turtles and crocodiles, and in the Therapsida and mammals.

ACTINOPTERAN FISHES

The Actinopteri or ray-finned fishes are an immense class, containing all higher fishes except Dipnoi (lungfishes) and Crossopterygii (lobefins), with which, however, they share many characteristics. The pattern of dermal bones in the skull of all these is similar and suggests derivation from a coating of scales on the head, like that of acanthodians. The skull in most cases is bony, but a few kinds show reduction or loss of bone.

In the oldest Actinopteri, the paleoniscid fishes of the Devonian pe-

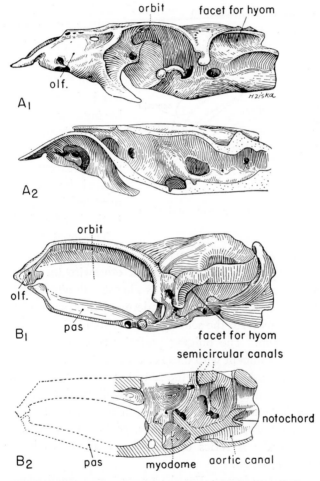

Fig. 140. Shark neurocranium (A₁) compared with paleoniscid neuro-cranium (B₁) in lateral view. A₂ and B₂ are sagittal sections of the same. (From Gregory, *Transactions of the American Philosophical Society*, Vol. 23, 1933, after Allis and Watson.)

hyom, hyomandibular; *olf*, olfactory capsule; *pas*, parasphenoid.

riod (Fig. 141), the eyes were well forward, and there was a bony operculum or gill cover like that in most recent fishes. Apparently hyostylic jaw suspension had been adopted. The spiracle was small. Dermal bones of the shoulder girdle articulated with the dorsolateral corners of the skull. The cranium was already tropybasic (Fig. 140B).

Three branches of this ancient group survive today. *Polypterus,* of African rivers, might be thought a long-headed paleoniscid, with certain changes in details but retaining the spiracle. The sturgeons and paddlefishes declined to a mud-grubbing, cartilaginous form, in which the bony armor is reduced, the rostrum enormously lengthened, and the mouth ventral. The third group, Holostei, we have today in the freshwater gars and bowfins of the southern United States. The first ones came in the Permian, and differed from paleoniscids in having a more extended snout, the mouth not reaching behind the eyes, and some correlated rearrangements of the dermal bones. The spiracle persisted in some; it is found in the bowfin, *Amia.*

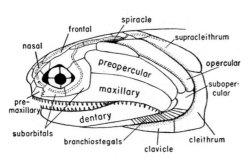

Fig. 141. Skull of paleoniscid, *Cheirolepis trailli.* (From Gregory, after Watson.)

The great superorder Teleostei, containing all higher fishes, was derived in the Jurassic from Holostei. They have no spiracle, but it is difficult otherwise to define the skull characters, for the diversity of form is almost unlimited. Ordinarily the cranium is overlain by numerous thin dermal bones, some of them carrying canals or grooves for the sensory canal system (Figs. 142, 143).

1. **Neurocranium.** The bulging posterior section contains the brain, and its cavity is confluent with those of the inner ears. Only a thin septum lies between the orbits, while the anterior section consists of a dorsal *ethmoid* and a ventral *vomer,* the latter usually with teeth.

2. **Dermal bones.** Roughly these are in four groups:
   a. Roof: *Nasals, frontals, parietals, posttemporals,* etc.
   b. Suborbitals: A series of small bones below each eye, bearing a sensory canal.
   c. Dermal jaw bones: For the upper jaw, a small *premaxillary* on each side, followed by a larger *maxillary.* In advanced kinds the maxillaries recede from the margin of the mouth, and their places are taken by the enlarged, toothed premaxillaries, which become

protrusible. In the lower jaw the *dentaries* form the tooth-bearing rim.

    d. Opercular series: Just behind the jaws come the bones of the gill cover, diminishing from the large *opercular* above to the slender *branchiostegal rays* beneath.

  3. **Primary jaws and suspensorium.** The primary upper jaw, preformed in cartilage, usually ossifies in four or five pieces. The term *suspensorium* refers to these bones plus the upper pieces of the hyoid arch, all of which work as a mechanical unit in supporting the lower jaw. The primary lower jaw is represented in teleosts by (1) the *articular* bone, which replaces the base of *Meckel's cartilage,* and (2) the unossified distal part of Meckel's cartilage, hidden and enclosed by the dentary. The *hyomandibular* is large and important; it articulates dorsally on the side of the cranium, and supports the upper jaw (*methyostylic* condition, Fig. 139) and the opercular bones. Five pairs of branchial arches succeed the hyoid in the wall of the pharynx, but only the first four bear gills. (Since the term "hyostylic" was used for the type of jaw suspension in most sharks and in rays, a minor difference may be noted: In the Chondrichthyes the

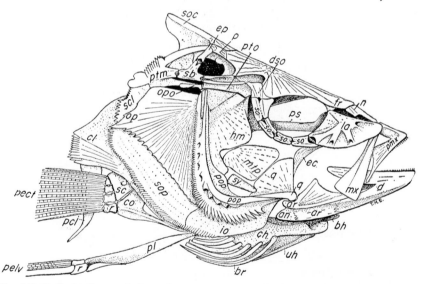

Fig. 142. Skull of yellow perch, *Perca flavescens.*

  an, angular; *ar,* articular; *bh,* basihyal; *br,* branchiostegal ray; *cl,* cleithrum; *co,* coracoid; *d,* dentary; *dso,* dermosphenotic; *ec,* ectopterygoid; *ep,* dermal epiotic; *fr,* frontal; *hm,* hyomandibular; *io,* interopercular; *la,* lacrimal; *mtp,* metapterygoid; *mx,* maxillary; *n,* nasal; *op,* opercular; *opo,* opisthotic; *p,* parietal; *pcl,* postcleithrum; *pect,* pectoral fin; *pl,* pelvis; *pop,* preopercular; *ps,* parasphenoid; *ptm,* posttemporal; *pto,* pterotic; *q,* quadrate; *r,* radial; *sb,* scale bone; *sc,* scapula; *scl,* supracleithrum; *so,* suborbital; *soc,* supraoccipital; *sop,* subopercular; *sy,* symplectic; *uh,* urohyal.

hyomandibular cartilage articulates with the lower part of the otic capsule allowing the anterior cardinal vein (or vena capitis lateralis) to pass above it; some authors refer to this as the *euhyostylic* condition. In Actinopteri, however, the hyomandibular articulates with the skull at a higher level, so that the corresponding vein, often called internal jugular, passes beneath the joint; the term *methyostylic* applies to this. In all

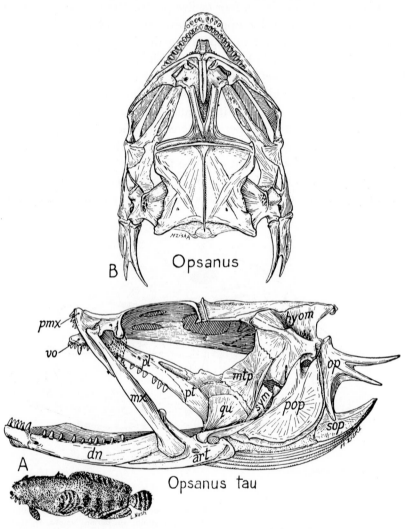

Fig. 143. Skull of toadfish, *Opsanus tau*. A, lateral; B, dorsal. (From Gregory, *Transactions of the American Philosophical Society*, Vol. 23, 1933.)

art, articular; dn, dentary; hyom, hyomandibular; mtp, metapterygoid; mx, maxillary; op, opercular; pl, palatine; pmx, premaxillary; pop, preopercular; pt, pterygoid; qu, quadrate; sop, subopercular; sym, symplectic; vo, vomer.

probability the vein passed, originally, between an upper and a lower head of the hyomandibular, somewhat as in early crossopterygians.)

DIPNOI (LUNGFISHES)

The dermal skull bones of higher fishes are so much like scales as to suggest that they originated in an ancestor whose head was covered with small scales. In Westoll's (1943) review of the origin of tetrapods he showed that such an ancestor must have had something like 90 dermal bones (scales) in the roof of its skull alone, and that the lines of descent leading to Actinopteri, lungfishes, and lobefins consolidated these units according to different plans. Consequently it is almost impossible to give

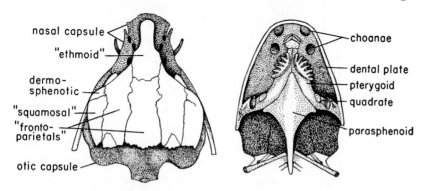

Fig. 144. Skull of lungfish, Neoceratodus; dorsal and palatal views. The names given to dermal bones on left do not necessarily indicate homology with bones so named in other groups. (After Parker and Haswell.)

equivalent names to the roofing bones in these three groups, but there is every reason to believe that the roofing bones of a lobefin can be compared directly with those of tetrapods.

In the Australian lungfish, *Neoceratodus* (Fig. 144), the skull and shoulder girdle are still connected laterally, above the gill chamber. The palatoquadrate (primary upper jaw) fuses with the cranium, another example of *autostylic* suspension; this releases the hyoid from any share in jaw support. Autostyly here seems to be correlated with development of fanlike crushing dental plates instead of teeth, much as in Holocephali.

CROSSOPTERYGIAN FISHES, AND THE CHANGE TO TETRAPODS

Of the lobefinned fishes the only ones we shall consider are the Rhipidistia, which lived from the Devonian to the Permian period, for it is among them that the stem leading to Amphibia may be found (Fig. 145). During the change to land life the *opercular series* in the fish was lost (since gills were no longer useful to a terrestrial animal), the *shoulder girdle* was detached from the skull (allowing the head to bend freely), the *nostrils* rose above the rim of the mouth and became holes rather than notches, the whole *nasal region* lengthened out considerably, and the parts behind the eye became much shorter. In the notch at the posterior corners of the skull there was probably an *eardrum,* where formerly had been the spiracle.

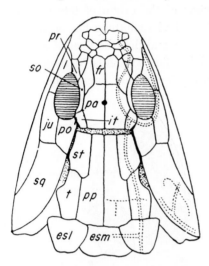

Fig. 145. Dermocranium of primitive lobe-fin, Osteolepis. (From Gregory, *Transactions of the American Philosophical Society,* Vol. 23, 1933, after Watson.)

esl, lateral extrascapular; esm, median extrascapular; fr, frontal; it, intertemporal; ju, jugal; l, lacrimal; pa, parietal; po, postorbital; pp, postparietal; pr, prefrontal; so, supraorbital; sq, squamosal; st, supratemporal; t, tabular.

But the old pattern of sensory canal grooves still appears in the early amphibians, suggesting that many of these were aquatic during a large part of their lives. The bones of the primary upper jaws, now forming most of the roof of the mouth, are surprisingly similar in the lobefin and early amphibian. Apparently only the quadrate, which articulates with the lower jaw, and the epipterygoid, articulating with the cranium, actually replace the palatoquadrate cartilage, but other palatal bones (vomers, palatines, ectopterygoids and pterygoids) are dermal in origin (see Fig. 149C).

This brings us to the important question of the fate of the hyomandibular bone. In Rhipidistia the rather weak hyomandibular attached to the angle of the upper jaw, and no doubt gave it some support. As in no other known fishes, this hyomandibular had two points of articulation with the cranium, one above and one below the jugular vein on the side of the ear region (Figs. 146, 147). It also had a connection with the operculum, and with the lower part of the hyoid arch (five in all).

In Amphibia it seems as if the hyomandibular, discouraged by loss of the operculum (its chief responsibility), started to degenerate, but the long arm of coincidence reached out to save it, and gave it a wholly different function, to transmit sound waves from the air to the inner ear. Thus the hyomandibular of fishes evolved into the *stapes,* a middle ear bone, in tetrapods (Fig. 147). But all five of the original articulations can still be recognized in a number of higher groups.

One more item should be noticed in Rhipidistia. The cranium was very long and consisted of two blocks, a sphenethmoid and an oticooccipital (the latter having a large canal for the notochord); between these was a movable joint, so that the head could be tilted slightly up and down. But it need not be thought that this peculiarity excludes them from possible

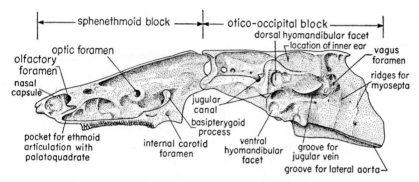

Fig. 146. Braincase of a crossopterygian, *Megalichthys* (*Ectosteorhachis*). (After Romer.)

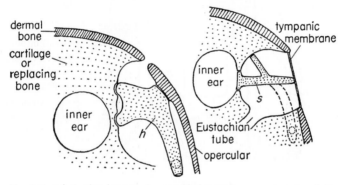

Fig. 147. Relationship between hyomandibular (h) in crossopterygian (left) and stapes (s) in tetrapod (right), diagrammatic.

ancestry to the Amphibia, as all other features point that way, and a fusion of the two blocks during development is all that is necessary. In the oldest known Amphibia, the Ichthyostegids, a distinct suture shows where this union took place.

AMPHIBIANS

The skull in primitive labyrinthodont Amphibia bore the characters we have just traced from lobefinned fishes (Fig. 148). One tendency is conspicuous in labyrinthodonts from Lower Carboniferous to Triassic times; this is to enlarge and flatten the skull to an almost unbelievable degree. Culminating in the huge Stereospondyli, these skulls were three or four feet long, about two feet wide, practically flat all over the upper surface, and completely decked with dermal bone except where nostrils, eyes, and pineal foramen opened upward. The braincase was ridiculously small, and cartilaginous. These animals died without further issue.

We show as an example the more conservative *Edops*, found in the Permo-Carboniferous of Texas (Romer and Witter, 1942) (Fig. 149).

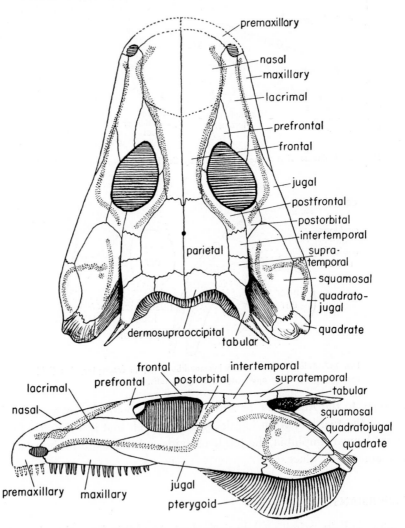

Fig. 148. Skull of *Paleogyrinus decorus*, a primitive labyrinthodont amphibian, in dorsal and lateral views. (After Watson.)

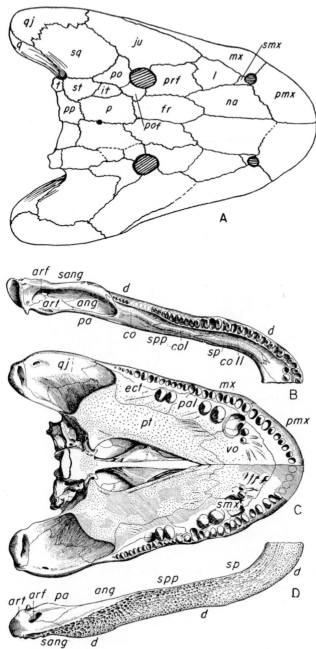

Fig. 149. Skull of Edops craigi, a labyrinthodont. A, dorsal view; B and D, upper and lower views of mandible. (From Romer and Witter.) ang, angular; arf, articular foramen; art, articular; co, coi, coll, coronoids; d, dentary; ect, ectopterygoid; fr, frontal; it, intertemporal; ju, jugal; l, lacrimal; mx, maxillary; na, nasal; p, parietal; pa, prearticular; pal, palatine; pmx, premaxillary; po, postorbital; pof, postfrontal; pp, postparietal; prf, prefrontal; pt, pterygoid; q, quadrate; qj, quadratojugal; sang, surangular; smx, septomaxillary; sp, splenial; spp, postsplenial; sq, squamosal; st, supratemporal; t, tabular; vo, vomer.

The similar but slightly later *Eryops* is better known (Sawin, 1941). The skull of primitive labyrinthodonts articulated with the first vertebra by a **single condyle** just as in reptiles, which are descended from them; but among the later labyrinthodonts and modern Amphibia the condyle is double. A condyle implies free mobility of the joint, which had not been possible until the shoulder girdle detached from the skull; such condyles therefore occur in tetrapods but not in fishes.

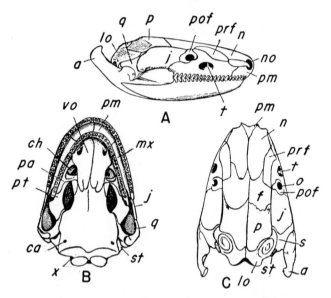

Fig. 150. Skull of caecilian, *Ichthyophis glutinosa*. A, lateral; B, palatal; C, dorsal. (From Parker and Haswell.)

a, articular; ca, carotid foramen; ch, inner nasal opening; f, frontal; j, jugal; lo, exoccipital; mx, maxillary; n, nasal; no, nostril; p, parietal; pa, palatine; pm, premaxillary; pof, postfrontal; prf, prefrontal; pt, pterygoid; q, quadrate; s, squamosal; st, stapes; t, tentacular groove; x, vagus foramen.

Modern Amphibia represent three lines of descent from labyrinthodonts:

1. The limbless, burrowing Apoda of the tropics show a partial fusion of cranial bones (Fig. 150), as well as a fairly complete deck. The eyes, being reduced, have very small orbits. The teeth suggest the labyrinthodont arrangement.

2. Caudata or salamanders have usually a narrow cranium with large orbital spaces laterally (Fig. 151). Most of the superficial deck of dermal bones has disappeared, thus giving the jaw muscles a larger area for attachment.

3. Salientia (frogs, toads, Fig. 152) have gone still further in loss of the skull roof, and in forming an immense orbital space for the eye and jaw muscles.

These trends characterize the recent groups of Amphibia: reduction of the number of skull bones; firm union of primary upper jaws with the cranium (*autostyly*); shortening of the posterior part of the cranium so that the last two pairs of cranial nerves (of the 12 pairs found in laby-rinthodonts) now emerge from the spinal cord, behind the skull, leaving

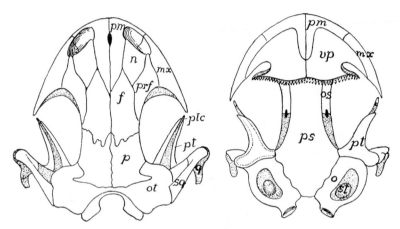

Fig. 151. Skull of salamander, *Ambystoma punctatum;* dorsal on left, ventral on right. (From Kingsley.)

f, frontal; mx, maxillary; n, nasal; o, ot, exoccipital; os, sphenethmoid; pm, pre-maxillary; prf, prefrontal; ps, parasphenoid; pt, pterygoid; ptc, pterygoid cartilage; q, quadrate; sq, squamosal; st, stapes; vo, vomer.

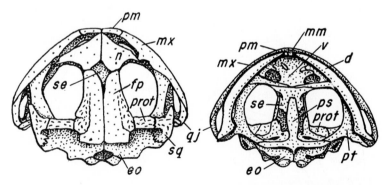

Fig. 152. Skull of a toad, *Bufo americanus:* dorsal on left, ventral on right. (Re-drawn from Kingsley, *Outlines of Comparative Anatomy of Vertebrates,* 3rd ed., Blakiston.)

d, dentary; eo, exoccipital; fp, frontal, mm, mentomeckelian; mx, maxillary, pl, palatine; prot, prootic; ps, parasphenoid; pt, pterygoid; qj, quadratojugal; se, sphenethmoid; sq, squamosal; v, vomer.

only 10 pairs of actual cranial nerves. The gill arches are usually reduced because of loss of the gills in most adult Amphibia (Fig. 153).

REPTILES

Living reptiles are but a scanty vestige of the far richer population of Mesozoic times. It is important in discussing the origin of birds and mam-

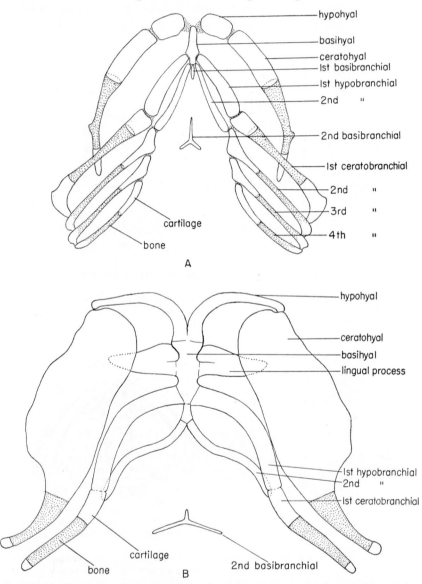

Fig. 153. Hyoid and branchial arches of a salamander. A, larva, and B, adult *Dicamptodon ensatus*; ventral view; bone stippled, cartilage clear.

mals, as well as in understanding the scope of this remarkable class, to mention skull characters of some of the orders.

Most reptiles have a single occipital condyle, received from early amphibians. The condyle is ordinarily formed by the basioccipital, as one would expect, but in turtles (Fig. 154) it may involve the exoccipitals. In the mammal-like reptiles (Therapsida) of the Triassic the single condyle becomes double and remains so in mammals.

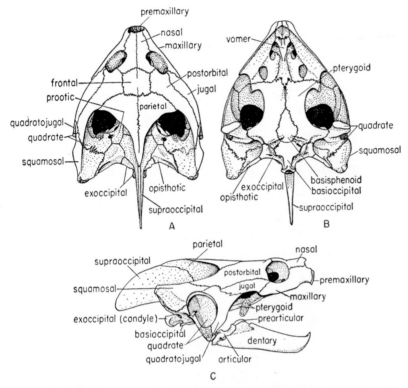

Fig. 154. Skull of snapping turtle, *Chelydra serpentina*. A, dorsal; B, ventral; C, lateral.

The primitive reptilian stem, among Cotylosauria (Fig. 155), retained the movable articulation of the palatal bones with the braincase (*autodiastylic* condition), and this seems to be transmitted directly to the subclass Lepidosauria (Eosuchia, Rhynchocephalia, Squamata—in which it is variously reduced or exaggerated), to the subclass Archosauria, and to birds. Although such mobility is lost through solid union of these bones with the cranium in many reptiles independently of one another (e.g., Chelonia, Crocodilia, Pterosauria, Therapsida, Fig. 156) which thus become *autostylic*, certain others take full advantage of the loose structure and improve on it. The anterior part of the cranium in lizards, snakes, and some dinosaurs, as well as birds, is capable of slight up-and-down movement against the posterior. An extreme case of this **kineticism** of the skull is seen in snakes, in correlation with their ability to swallow prey larger in diameter than themselves (Fig. 157). In pit vipers the maxillaries are hinged against the prefrontals and these against the frontals, while a sliding beam composed of palatine, ectopterygoid, and pterygoid either thrusts the maxillaries forward or drags them back, allowing the fangs to stand erect or recline, respectively. This beam in turn is supported by the quadrate, jointed at both ends and capable of swinging forward or back. The double-jointed quadrate mechanism, called **streptostyly,** also occurs in birds (Fig. 160).

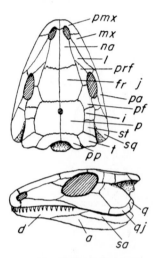

Fig. 155. Skull of *Seymouria,* dorsal and lateral, to illustrate cotylosaur type. (Modified from Watson.)

a, angular; *d,* dentary; *fr,* frontal; *i,* intertemporal; *j,* jugal; *l,* lacrimal; *mx,* maxillary; *na,* nasal; *p,* parietal; *pf,* postfrontal; *pmx,* premaxillary; *po,* postorbital; *pp,* postparietal; *prf,* prefrontal; *q,* quadrate; *qj,* quadratojugal; *sa,* surangular; *sq,* squamosal; *st,* supratemporal; *t,* tabular.

The primitive "upper deck" of dermal bones in the posterior part of the skull becomes reduced in various ways, either by recession of the edge or by development of one or two pairs of windowlike temporal openings, and the manner of this reduction is of great importance in understanding relationships among reptiles. Since the muscles used in elevating the lower jaw had their origins on the cranium and the lower surface of the deck bones in labyrinthodont amphibians, the only way in which more space could be secured for expansion of these muscles in reptiles was to remove part or all of the deck and allow the areas of origin to spread up and outward. In Cotylosauria none of this had yet taken place; in Chelonia there is a recession of the deck at the posterior edge, either slightly (sea turtles) or extensively, but without the formation of windowlike openings. These two orders are grouped together as the subclass Anapsida, and the lack of temporal openings is called the **anapsid** condition. In more advanced reptiles temporal openings are in the following different patterns, on each side of the skull: (1) A single opening bounded laterally by an arch composed mostly of the jugal (zygomatic) bone; this arrangement, clearly the same as in mammals, is called the **synapsid** type, and occurs in pelycosaurs and therapsids, which are therefore placed in a subclass Synapsida. (2) A single opening more dorsally located, so that it is bounded laterally by the postorbital and either the squamosal or

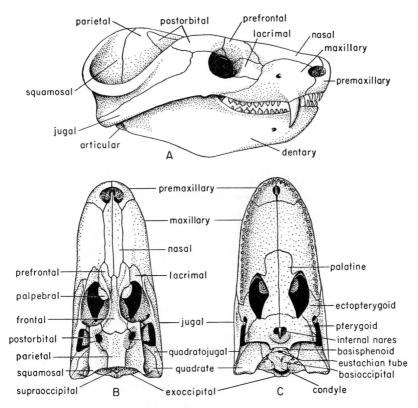

Fig. 156. Skulls of (A) mammal-like reptile, *Cynognathus* (modified from Watson); (B, C) *Alligator*, dorsal and ventral.

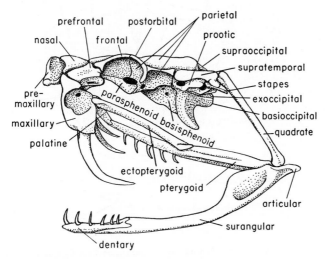

Fig. 157. Skull of rattlesnake, *Crotalus*, showing streptostylic mechanism of jaws.

some other bones; this is the *parapsid* pattern, which may have originated more than once in different groups; it is found in ichthyosaurs, plesiosaurs, and some other extinct reptiles. (3) Two temporal openings, one above (dorsal and medial to) the other; this *diapsid* condition (Fig. 158) is the basic one in two subclasses, Lepidosauria and Archosauria, but in both it may be secondarily modified. For example, lizards (Fig. 159) reduce the marginal bones of the lower temporal opening so that it is no longer en-

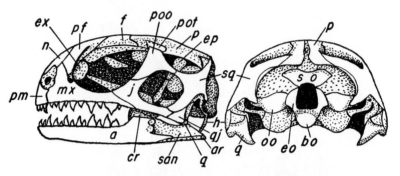

Fig. 158. Skull of young *Sphenodon*, side and posterior. (Redrawn from Kingsley, *Outlines of Comparative Anatomy of Vertebrates*, 3rd ed., Blakiston.)

a, dentary; ar, articular; bo, basioccipital; cr, coronoid; eo, exoccipital; ep, epipterygoid; ex, "extranasal"; f, frontal; h, hyoid; j, jugal; mx, maxillary; n, nasal; oo, opisthotic; p, parietal; pf, prefrontal; pm, premaxillary; poo, postorbital; pot, postfrontal; q, quadrate; qj, quadratojugal; san, surangular; sq, squamosal; so, supraoccipital.

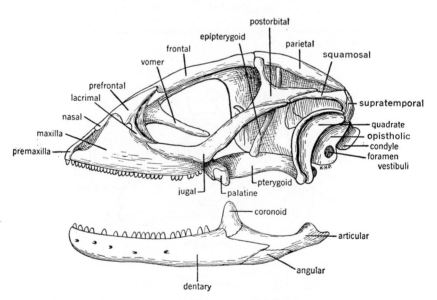

Fig. 159. Skull of lizard, *Sceloporus*. (Reproduced by permission from *Comparative Anatomy* by L. A. Adams and S. Eddy, published by John Wiley & Sons, Inc., 1949.)

closed, and the skull therefore does not appear diapsid; snakes go even farther, losing the margin of the upper opening as well. These reductions are correlated with the release of the quadrate bone and development of streptostyly.

The palate of reptiles usually differs but little from that of Amphibia. but in two groups there is formed a second roof to the mouth, the hard palate, by which the nasal passages become separate from the mouth cavity. Crocodilia are one such group (Fig. 156C). The device here makes it possible to breathe by putting the nostrils just out of water, while the mouth is wide open under water, perhaps holding and drowning the prey. The hard palate of Therapsida originated quite independently of this, and indeed is incomplete in most of the known kinds; it anticipates the mammalian condition, presumably being a device to aid breathing while chewing, for the teeth suggest that these reptiles had more refined table manners than their grab-and-gulp contemporaries.

BIRDS

In sharp contrast with the variety of important characters in reptile skulls, those of birds show little fundamental variation (Fig. 160). The

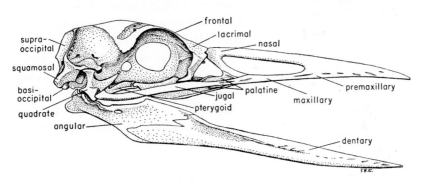

Fig. 160. Skull of loon, *Gavia immer.*

more uniform traits are expanded and rounded cranium (brain large), with a thinning of bones (flying calls for reduced weight); extension of premaxillaries, and often maxillaries and nasals, into a beak, toothless in all modern birds; movable quadrate, hinged dorsally on the squamosal but ventrally on (1) mandible, (2) pterygoid, and (3) a lateral rod consisting of quadratojugal and jugal, which forms the lower margin of the temporal fossa; frequently but not always some up-and-down hinge movement of the anterior parts of the skull upon the posterior, aided by the quadrate and attending muscles; single occipital condyle; extensive fusion of skull bones with one another except at movable articulations.

Comparing the palatal view of a bird skull (Fig. 161) with that of a reptile (e.g., lizard), the differences at first appear great, but they are mostly differences of proportions, for the bird skull is much longer in front of the internal nares, on account of the beak. The originally separate vomers become one, this in many cases forming a thin internarial septum, or disappearing. The illusion of an elongated hard palate is furthered by the greatly lengthened premaxillaries in most birds, so that the nasal region is left far behind, yet it represents approximately the front of the skull in a reptile.

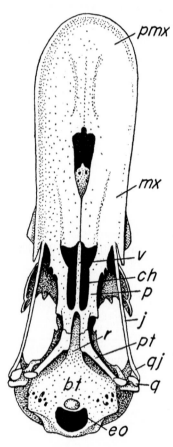

Fig. 161. Palatal view of duck skull. (Redrawn after Kingsley, *Outlines of Comparative Anatomy of Vertebrates*, 3rd ed., Blakiston.)

bt, basisphenoid; *ch*, choana; *eo*, exoccipital; *j*, jugal; *mx*, maxillary; *p*, palatine; *pmx*, premaxillary; *pt*, pterygoid; *q*, quadrate; *qj*, quadratojugal; *r*, parasphenoid; *v*, vomer.

The basisphenoid (floor of the braincase) and parasphenoid, just anterior to it, have fused, and the latter makes a so-called "rostrum" against which the bones of the palate fit, usually with a loose contact which permits them to slide. Since the work of T. H. Huxley (1867) the several ways in which the details of the palate differ in various groups have counted heavily in classifying birds. Only two major divisions need be noted here: In *paleognathous* birds, as the Ratitae, tinamous and the extinct *Hesperornis*, the palate is comparable with that of reptiles in having a long beam formed of pterygoid and palatine on each side not articulated directly with the cranium, and relatively large vomers; in *neognathous* birds, which are virtually all others (Fig. 161), the vomers are reduced and narrowed, the palatines articulate by a movable joint with the pterygoids and also are in firm contact with the cranium.

The hyoid apparatus of birds is much modified in the service of the tongue. Besides some slender median rods, it has a pair of delicate "horns" which are actually the first branchial bars, and which extend posterolaterally, serving for attachment of the muscles that thrust out the tongue. In

long-tongued birds, like woodpeckers and hummingbirds, these horns
become so extraordinarily long that they must curve up over the back
of the head (under the skin) and come down in front of the eyes, and
they may even (in the flicker) go forward through the right nostril into
the cavity of the beak.

MAMMAL-LIKE REPTILES AND MAMMALS

Returning briefly to the Triassic mammal-like reptiles, we shall follow
some of the changes in skull structure which led to mammals. This is one
of the two or three greatest transitions in vertebrate history. Already
showing in therapsid reptiles are the following:

1. Double occipital condyle, which remains in mammals.

2. Heterodont teeth (distinguishable as incisors, canines, molars).

3. Single pair of temporal openings, as in mammals.

4. Hard or secondary palate in various stages of completion, by the
extension inward of palatal processes of the premaxillaries and maxillaries, so that a sheet of bone forms the roof of the mouth and at the
same time a floor for the nasal passages. The small paired vomers, commonly called prevomers, fuse together in some mammal-like reptiles and
support the palate, between the two nasal cavities, just as the single
vomer does in mammals; the "prevomers" in all vertebrates from the
lobefinned fishes up are evidently vomers. (The theory prevalent for
many years was that the mamma-
lian vomer was the reptilian parasphenoid, and that the reptilian vomers disappeared.)

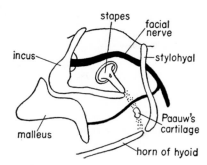

Fig. 162. Developing ear ossicles in young
opossum, *Didelphis*. (After De Beer, *Development of the Vertebrate Skull*, Oxford
University Press.)

5. In advanced Therapsida the
glenoid fossa, where the lower jaw
articulates, is composed of two bones,
internally the quadrate (which was
the only one in that position before),
and externally the squamosal. Immediately behind this fossa is the
cavity of the middle ear. In the course
of the change to mammals the quadrate leaves the glenoid fossa, becomes
connected with the stapes in the ear, and thus makes a sound-transmitting
bone, known as the *incus* (Figs. 162, 301). (The quadrate and stapes
are, of course, connected by ligament embryonically, so that this is not
fundamentally a new arrangement.)

6. At the same time the articular facet on the lower jaw, in some Therapsida, is composed of both dentary and articular bones. When the quadrate becomes an ear bone the articular does also, in this way keeping its contact with the former, and thus making a third sound-transmitting bone, the mammalian *malleus.*

7. The angular, another small lower-jaw bone of reptiles, becomes the *tympanic,* a crescent-shaped bone supporting the eardrum or tympanum in mammals (usually fused with the squamosal, however). With these changes, and the disappearance of other lower-jaw units, we have left only the dentary as the lower jaw of mammals, and it articulates only with the squamosal. The latter term, however, is not extensively used in mammals, because the reptilian squamosal fuses with the tympanic, and frequently too with the periotic (combined prootic and opisthotic of reptiles) to make the mammalian *temporal.*

8. The transition from mammal-like reptile to mammal includes a radical change in the form and location of the jaw articulation. In a typical reptile the *quadrate* has a convex articular surface fitting into a concavity

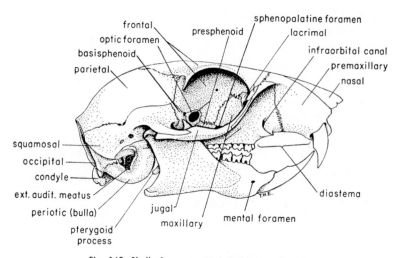

Fig. 163. Skull of gray squirrel, *Sciurus carolinensis.*

in the *articular* of the lower jaw. In a mammal these two bones no longer take any part in the joint, having become the incus and malleus respectively. The joint is now made by a *convex* surface of the *dentary* (lower jaw) fitting into a *concavity* of the *squamosal* (= part of *temporal*). This joint is anatomically anterior to that in reptiles, and strictly speaking is not homologous with it; also the convexity and concavity are reversed

138   COMPARATIVE ANATOMY OF THE VERTEBRATES

in position. Thus in order for a functional joint to have existed during the brief interval of transition it is likely that the squamosal-dentary articulation was already present and working before the quadrate-articular joint had been abandoned. There is evidence that this double articulation did exist.

Thus evolved the skull of mammals, by reduction, fusion, and translocation of certain bones. We see here, as in the change to birds, the

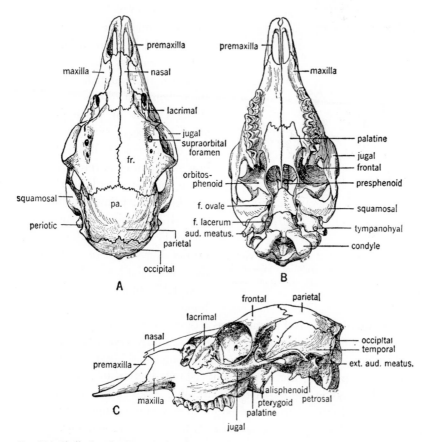

Fig. 164. Skull of mule deer. A, dorsal; B, ventral; C, lateral. (Reproduced by permission from *Comparative Anatomy* by L. A. Adams and S. Eddy, published by John Wiley & Sons, Inc., 1949.)

operation of Williston's law that the number of separate elements in the skull tends to decrease during evolution.

Usually the braincase is conspicuously larger in mammals than in reptiles, because of the larger brain (Fig. 163). The dentary bone develops a high *coronoid process* in most mammals, for insertion of the temporal and masseter muscles. Ordinarily the jaws and snout extend far forward of the eyes. Several thin scroll-like **turbinal** bones are present in the nasal passages on the sphenoid and ethmoid bones (Fig. 294), and the olfactory epithelium is thus greatly increased in area. The **hyoid** connects with the ear capsule by a ligament to the **styloid process**, while its middle portion, plus some vestiges of the branchial arches, takes part in forming the **larynx.**

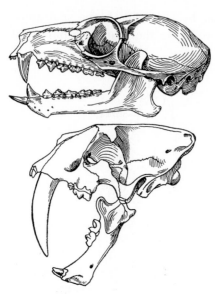

Fig. 165. Above, skull of *Lemur* (from Parker and Haswell). Below, skull of sabertooth, *Smilodon californicus* (redrawn from Scott, after Matthew).

Beyond these general features we find an endless variety of skull structure in mammals (Figs. 164, 165). Some of the more striking changes seen in particular cases are: (1) Loss of some or all teeth. (2) Increase in bulk of skull, the bones becoming extremely massive; this is correlated with bearing great weight or providing attachment for powerful muscles. In such skulls the brain cavity and other passages do not increase in proportion with the whole skull. (3) Formation of a variable number of **air sinuses,** lined with mucous membrane and connected with the nasal passages, as a device for reducing the weight of bones without sacrificing their strength; similarly **cancellae** (numerous small cavities) may develop between the inner and outer layers of thick bones, accomplishing the same result. (4) Reduction to much less than average bulk, as in the paper-thin skull of a shrew. Here the orbits, ear capsules, and brain cavity are of larger than average proportions, and the bones do not develop conspicuous crests for muscle attachment.

CHAPTER V

Skeleton (Continued)

Notochord

THE *notochord* is the one distinctive feature of the skeleton of all chordates, and therefore of all vertebrates. Among most of the latter it is succeeded in development by a series of *vertebrae,* which partly or wholly replace it. They are not formed by the notochord, but develop, as a rule, out of small cartilages adjacent to it; these in turn are usually replaced by bone in the complete vertebrae. In or around the sheaths of the notochord cartilage or bone may be deposited to produce the centrum. Among several of the most primitive groups of vertebrates no actual vertebrae exist, but only separate cartilages or blocks of bone in various degrees of elaboration, lying against the notochord. Vertebrae (as structures which take the place of the notochord) originated several times in the course of evolution, and by means of different patterns of development.

The notochord typically has two sheaths, an outer *elastica externa,* and an inner *fibrous sheath.* The somites, or body segments of the embryo which are to form longitudinal muscles, lie in series along each side. Between each somite and the next one there forms a connective tissue *myoseptum,* which reaches inward to the surface of the elastica externa. Along the inner face of each somite in early stages, against the notochordal sheaths, appears a cluster of cells called a *sclerotome* (Fig. 166), one of these on each side of the notochord, per segment. Sclerotomes are therefore *segmental* in position, and septa *intersegmental.*

141

Each sclerotome gives rise to embryonic cartilage blocks, which may be called *arcualia*, or *arch-elements*, on account of their relationship to the neural and hemal arches of the vertebra-to-be. Commonly there are two, three, or four of these arcualia; if a full set occurs, their names and positions, *in relation to the original sclerotome*, are (Fig. 166):

Basidorsal—posterior, dorsal
Basiventral—posterior, ventral
Interdorsal—anterior, dorsal
Interventral—anterior, ventral

Now a process of **resegmentation** takes place, by which the finished vertebra incorporates the more posterior arcualia of one sclerotome with

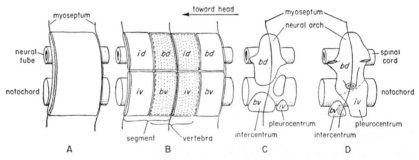

Fig. 166. Stages in development of vertebrae, diagrammatic. A, sclerotome; B, four procartilage arcualia formed by each sclerotome, and the basidorsal (*bd*) and basiventral (*bv*) of one segment combine with interdorsal (*id*) and interventral (*iv*) of next following segment to make a vertebra (stippled); C, a rhachitomous vertebra (*Chelidosaurus*, a labyrinthodont) in which the intercentrum is larger than the pleurocentrum; D, a vertebra of the *Seymouria* type (early reptile) in which the pleurocentrum is larger. (D after Romer.)

the more anterior ones of the next succeeding. This means that a complete vertebra is intersegmental, with the corresponding myoseptum meeting its lateral surface, while the muscle segments themselves alternate with the vertebrae, as they must do to produce movement of the column.

Such, for many years, has been the common, simplified scheme used to describe vertebral development in, presumably, the generalized lower vertebrates. Where it is possible to recognize four units in a vertebra (as in Fig. 166C) we may perhaps associate them with the above-named embryonic arcualia, remembering, however, that no one has seen the embryonic stages of labyrinthodont vertebrae. In the diagrams given here labels are used which indicate a possible association of the parts of vertebrae with arcualia. But there are no tetrapods and few fishes living today which give even an approximation to the scheme outlined above. Resegmentation does occur, but the cartilaginous or bony elements involved will not, as a rule, fall into the positions designated, and their number is seldom more than two, even at an early stage. Therefore it is not helpful to lean too heavily upon the pattern of arcualia as an explanation of the way vertebrae develop in different groups of animals. We must take each group on its own merits.

CYCLOSTOMES

In modern cyclostomes the notochord is present throughout life. In lampreys each segment has two small arch-cartilages on each side, of which the more anterior may be the interdorsal, and the more posterior the basidorsal. Hagfishes have none. From the notochordal canal seen in the floor of the cranium of ostracoderms it is known that they also had a fully developed notochord, but arcualia are not indicated by the fossils.

In early gnathostomes the notochord must, likewise, have persisted throughout life. Its anterior end occupied a canal in the floor of the skull, as far forward as the pituitary gland.

ELASMOBRANCH FISHES

In elasmobranch fishes we meet true vertebrae with centra, neural arches, and hemal arches, and an accompanying reduction of the notochord (Fig. 167). But the oldest sharks (*Cladoselache* and the pleura-

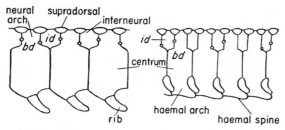

Fig. 167. Vertebrae of shark, *Scyllium*. Left, trunk; right, tail. (After Bridge.)
bd, basidorsal; *id*, interdorsal.

canths, Devonian period) retained an unconstricted notochord and had no centra. A few Paleozoic sharks, however, had centra, and at least one (Romer, 1942) shows bone as well as cartilage in the centrum.

Among modern sharks and rays the notochord becomes largely replaced by cartilage which is formed by mesoblast cells migrating in from outside the sheaths. The fibrous sheath, occupied by these, thickens greatly, and the cartilage partly calcifies. The centrum is of the *chordal* type; it is concave or funnel shaped at each end (*amphicoelous,* Fig. 169). If, as in *Squalus,* a cross section of the centrum shows a single ring of calcification surrounding the pinched notochord, the vertebra is *cyclospondylous,* but there are other patterns of calcification as well.

Turning now to the arcualia, the two basidorsals, resting on the centrum outside the notochordal sheaths, develop into a *neural arch* by meeting and fusing above the neural canal. Just behind, fitting over the joint between two centra, the interdorsals do likewise, making an *interneural* arch. On the lower side of the centrum each basiventral forms a lateral flange or *parapophysis,* to which, in the trunk, ribs attach. But in the tail the two basiventrals of each vertebra unite beneath the dorsal aorta and caudal vein to make a *hemal arch,* practically an inverted image of the neural arch above. The tail vertebrae are double; that is, for each segment there are two centra. This is *diplospondyly.* It occurs in some other fishes, as we shall see, evidently increasing the flexibility of the tail.

ACTINOPTERI

Among Actinopteri, the ray-finned fishes, the earliest retained a complete notochord with no centra, but above the notochord lay a series of neural arches, usually prolonged into high neural spines, and in cor-

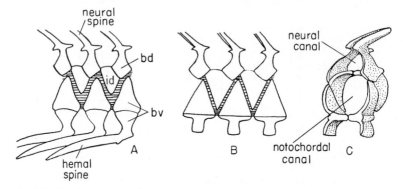

Fig. 168. Vertebra of an early holostean fish, *Caturus furcatus.* A, caudal; B, C, trunk. (After Zittel.)
    bd, basidorsal; *id,* interdorsal; *bv,* basiventral.

responding positions below were subnotochordal pieces (no doubt basiventrals) which in the tail became hemal arches with hemal spines (Fig. 168).

Polypterus, which we have mentioned before as a modern side-line descendant of the paleoniscids, has complete bony amphicoelous centra, with neural arches leading into sloping neural spines dorsally, and prominent parapophyses for the ribs, in the trunk, while in the tail hemal arches and spines replace these by a gradual transition. The superficial resemblance of these vertebrae to those of higher fishes is no doubt secondary, since evidence from the skull and elsewhere indicates that the latter arose along an independent line.

Chondrostei (sturgeons, etc.) retain a complete notochord, and may be regarded as either primitive or, possibly, neotenic (keeping immature traits in maturity), in having all four pairs of arcualia distinct in the adult. They are cartilaginous.

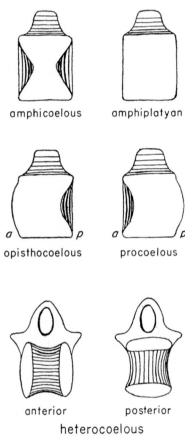

Holostei show through their history a gradual increase of completeness of vertebrae and replacement of the notochord. The centrum is *perichordal* (Fig. 168), and remains so in teleosts; this means there is no penetration of the notochordal sheaths by cartilage-forming or bone-forming cells, but the skeletogenous layer outside deposits bone on the surface of the outer sheath in a layer which grows deeper and heavier until the notochord is replaced. Typically the vertebrae are *amphicoelous*, but those of *Lepisosteus* (gar) are *opisthocoelous* (centra concave posteriorly, convex anteriorly, Fig. 169), unlike those of any other fish.

Amia shows, in early development, the four pairs of arcualia, but the interventrals soon disappear by fusion with basiventrals, and the centrum is formed by the latter uniting with the interdorsals. Curiously, the relationship of the neural arches

Fig. 169. Shapes of centra.

(basidorsals) is with the interdorsals *in front* of them, and that of the basiventrals is with the interventrals in front; this contrasts with the method of development in elasmobranchs and tetrapods, and is another indication that vertebrae have appeared independently in these groups. *Amia* is diplospondylous in the tail.

Vertebrae of teleosts develop in fundamentally the same manner as in *Amia* (Figs. 170, 171). The growing centrum, cylindrical in form, tends to engulf the arcualia. Anterior and posterior processes develop from the

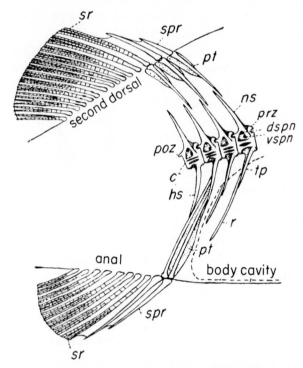

Fig. 170. Portion of vertebrae and fin skeleton of yellow perch, *Perca flavescens*.

c, centrum; dspn, dorsal foramina for spinal nerves; hs, haemal spine; poz, postzygapophysis; prz, prezygapophysis; pt, pterygiophore; r, rib; spr, spiny ray; sr, soft ray; tp, parapophysis; vspn, ventral foramina for spinal nerves.

upper corner of each centrum, interlocking with those of the preceding and following centra to strengthen the whole column. These are *zyga-pophyses*, comparable to but not homologous with those in tetrapods.

DIPNOI

Modern lungfishes have a large, unconstricted notochord with incomplete vertebrae (Fig. 172). Standing on the basidorsals of each segment is a neural arch and spine; the basiventrals of the tail support hemal arches and spines, while those in the trunk connect with ribs. Probably the size of the notochord in recent kinds is a result of delay or "regression" in vertebral development, for early Devonian lungfishes are known to have had amphicoelous bony centra, some with and some without a canal for the notochord.

CROSSOPTERYGII

The crossopterygian notochord was also large, but anteriorly ringlike centra constricted it somewhat (Fig. 173). Farther back in the trunk the centra separated into right and left crescents and became thin; finally in the tail none were represented, unless they were of cartilage. This is the situation in *Eusthenopteron* according to Gregory and Raven (1941); the vertebral column is not adequately known in other kinds. Jarvik (1952) found that short ribs were present in *Eusthenopteron* from about the second vertebra to the posterior part of the trunk (Fig. 173).

TETRAPODS

With the coming of tetrapods we shall see the beginning of certain more familiar trends of vertebral structure, not very obvious at first. One is to develop complete bony centra. Another is to brace each vertebra against the next by overlapping *pre-* and *postzygapophyses;* both of these features we found independently evolved in the teleost fishes. A third, not so apparent among fishes, is to differentiate the column according to functional differences in its regions. This is carried out impressively in birds and mammals. All three of these trends are strongest in terrestrial animals because of the more complex mechanism needed to carry and move the body out of water. In secondarily

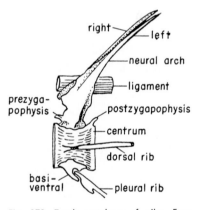

Fig. 171. Trunk vertebrae of pike, Esox lucius. (After Goodrich.)

aquatic groups of long standing, as whales and ichthyosaurs, there is a return to a less differentiated column.

Some of the early labyrinthodont Amphibia, as *Archeria* (Fig. 174), had vertebrae with a double centrum, against both parts of which the neural arch fitted. This type of vertebra is called *embolomerous,* and was long considered to be ancestral in tetrapods. The neural arch bore zygapophyses and laterally a transverse process to meet the tuberculum (upper head) of the rib. There was a small facet on each side of the centrum for the lower head (capitulum) of the same rib; this facet involved both the anterior section (*intercentrum*) and posterior section (*pleurocen-*

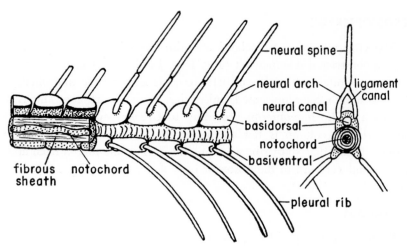

Fig. 172. Vertebrae of lungfish, *Neoceratodus*. (After Goodrich.)

trum). In addition both inter- and pleurocentrum were almost complete, leaving only a minute passage for the notochord.

Many other labyrinthodonts, which are now known to include the ancestral stock, had a *rhachitomous* vertebra (Fig. 166C). The notochord was constricted only slightly, if at all; and the units corresponding to inter- and pleurocentra were distinctly separate, the former usually larger. (Presumably, as indicated in the figure, the intercentrum represents the embryonic basiventral cartilage, the pleurocentrum being the interventral.)

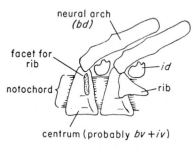

Fig. 173. Trunk vertebrae and rib of early Crossopterygian, *Eusthenopteron*. (After Jarvik.)

bd, basidorsal; *bv,* basiventral; *id,* inter-dorsal; *iv,* interventral.

Last and largest of the labyrinthodonts were those of the Triassic, with *stereospondylous* vertebrae, in which the intercentrum had enlarged at the expense of the pleurocentrum, the latter disappearing; the intercentrum then almost or wholly replaced the notochord, and bore a strong neural arch evidently formed from the basidorsal arcualia. These animals were not, of course, ancestors of reptiles, which first appeared in the

Pennsylvanian. Their vertebrae, in contrast, emphasized the pleurocentrum while reducing the intercentrum (Fig. 166D).

Practically all modern Amphibia have, in the adult, vertebrae of a single piece each, but their development is diverse. The more primitive, aquatic kinds of salamanders (Caudata) have a continuous notochord around which the centra ossify as cylinders, bearing dorsally neural arches and ventrally, in the tail, hemal arches. Between any two centra is an intervertebral ring of cartilage. The notochord is more constricted by the intervertebral cartilage in terrestrial kinds (Salamandridae, Plethodontidae), and the joints are opisthocoelous (ball and socket, the socket being on the posterior face of each centrum). The *sacrum* in Caudata, Salientia, and labyrinthodonts (Apoda have none) consists of one or two scarcely modified trunk vertebrae from which short sacral ribs extend laterad to meet the ilium on each side.

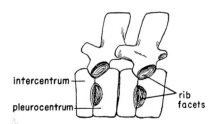

Fig. 174. Embolomerous vertebrae of *Archeria* (*Cricotus*). (Modified after Noble.)

Frogs and toads (Salientia) show a great variety and high specialization of vertebrae. The number is nine or less, in two cases being only six; this is the least known in any vertebrate animal. Reduction is partly by loss and partly by fusion of formerly separate vertebrae, as in the rodlike *urostyle* at the posterior end. The joint between vertebrae is formed by a ball that fastens to either the anterior end of a centrum, making it opisthocoelous, or the posterior end, making it procoelous (concave in front); the latter condition exists in our native frogs and toads. A tadpole has no vertebrae in its tail. Those of the trunk ossify at the time of transformation.

REPTILES

Vertebrae of reptiles are as various as their other characters. Generally the centrum is a pleurocentrum; there may in some primitive kinds be a small intercentrum in front of it. This is contrary to the arrangement in Amphibia, where the intercentrum is primary, or may be the only part. In the tail there frequently occur hemal arches distinct from the centrum, and serially homologous with the intercentra of the trunk (if any); these are familiarly called *chevron bones.*

The first two vertebrae of the column, the atlas and axis, begin in early reptiles to show changes of shape in connection with increasing mobility of the head (Fig. 175). From Evans (1939) we may summarize some of these changes, which are not completely realized until we reach mammals: "the atlas spinous process is lost and the opposite halves of the neural arch fuse with each other and with the atlas intercentrum to form a ring; with the rise of the reptiles the anterior facets on the atlas become markedly concave for the reception of the ball-like occipital condyle; the atlas centrum becomes separated from its neural arches . . . and finally fuses with the axis centrum to form the odontoid; and prominent lateral processes grow out from the sides of the atlas." The odontoid process of the axis (second vertebra) acts in a sense as a pivot around which the ringlike atlas can rotate; up-and-down movements of the skull take place at the joint where

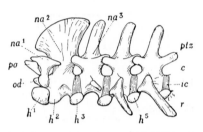

Fig. 175. Anterior vertebrae of *Sphenodon*, left side, showing proatlas (*pa*), atlas (*na¹*, *h¹*), axis (*na²*, *h²*). (From Goodrich, *Studies on the Structure and Development of the Vertebrates*, The Macmillan Company.)

c, pleurocentrum; h, hypo- or intercentrum; ic, intervertebral disc; na, neural arch; od, odontoid process (first pleurocentrum); pa, proatlas; ptz, postzygapophysis; r, rib.

the condyles fit against the atlas. The development in mammals of the transverse processes of the atlas, to which Evans refers, is related directly to the appearance of strong muscles which reach from them to the skull. *Sphenodon* and a few primitive extinct reptiles have a proatlas, which is evidently a partial neural arch formed by a pair of basidorsals anterior to the atlas. Other points of general interest in the vertebrae of reptiles are these:

1. Most reptiles have ribs all the way from the third vertebra of the neck to the sacrum (Fig. 176). They attach by a double articulation: the lower head (capitulum) of the rib meets either a simple facet or a process, the *parapophysis;* the upper articulation of the rib (tuberculum) is to a more prominent process, the *diapophysis;* sometimes para- and diapophysis are on one common transverse process. In several orders the cervical (neck) ribs have been reduced to short spines, either articulated or fused with their vertebrae; the small canal which was present between the upper and lower articulations still remains as the *vertebrarterial canal,* and distinguishes these reduced ribs from actual transverse processes belonging to the vertebrae alone.

2. In the *sacrum* two vertebrae usually take part. Each bears a pair of sacral ribs, short peglike bones extending from the centrum to the adjacent ilium. But reptiles which have no hind limbs and therefore no pelvis also lack a sacral region. Contrasted with this is the great enlargement of the sacrum in certain dinosaurs. For example it included eight or nine

vertebrae among the trachodonts or duckbills, and seven to ten in the quite different Ceratopsia. The neural canal was so much enlarged in the sacrum of the sauropod dinosaurs that it must have housed a ganglion several times the size of the brain. This has inspired a much-quoted poem

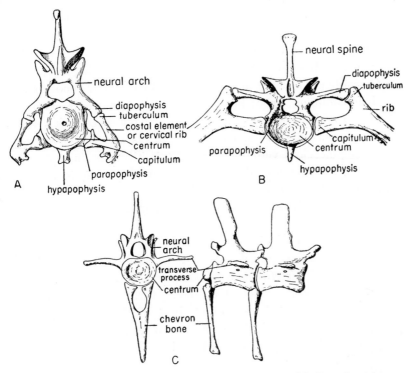

Fig. 176. Vertebrae of crocodile. A, cervical; B, thoracic; C, caudal. (Reproduced by permission from *Comparative Anatomy* by L. A. Adams and S. Eddy, published by John Wiley & Sons, Inc., 1949.)

about the dinosaur's displaced intellect: "If something slipped the forward mind, 'twas rescued by the one behind," and so on. Among flying reptiles, Pterosauria, the sacral vertebrae numbered four to seven, and in such advanced types as *Pteranodon* of the Cretaceous period there was also a fusion of thoracic vertebrae with a bony shield overlying them, forming a *notarium*, to the sides of which the scapulae articulated. This extraordinary arrangement, reminiscent of that in rays, doubtless strengthened the delicately built skeleton, for supporting the bases of the wings.

3. The carapace of turtles holds all the trunk vertebrae in a solid grip, so that they make little more than a narrow ridge along its inner face. The neural spines fuse with (but do not themselves form) the flat neural

plates which lie in series along the center of the carapace. Short transverse processes from the centra and neural arches meet the bases of the ribs internally, and the latter then join the flat costal plates, laterad of the neural plates.

4. The centrum is amphicoelous in the oldest reptiles, Cotylosauria, and so it remains in some Therapsida, in geckos and Uropeltidae among lizards, in some Rhynchocephalia, and a few more. The centra become *amphiplatyan* (flat on anterior and posterior faces) in a few aquatic reptiles, as the plesiosaurs, one family of Rhynchocephalia, and some extinct Crocodilia. They are amphiplatyan also in a few dinosaurs. The procoelous condition comes in turtles, most lizards, mosasaurs, snakes, modern Crocodilia, and pterosaurs. There are opisthocoelous vertebrae in some dinosaurs and turtles. This may be less bewildering if we suggest that the amphicoelous vertebrae are the primitive type in reptiles, and that from them arose, according to functional adaptations in various orders, the other kinds of centra. Hence the presence of any one type does not necessarily imply direct relationship among those animals that have it.

5. In Pelycosauria, which were early relatives of the mammal-like reptiles, occurred a strange modification. The neural spines of *Dimetrodon* rose like the masts of a ship far above the dorsal surface of the body; there is evidence that they supported an upright sheet of skin. In *Edaphosaurus* (Fig. 177) these spines also bore numerous horizontal bars, suggesting yardarms!

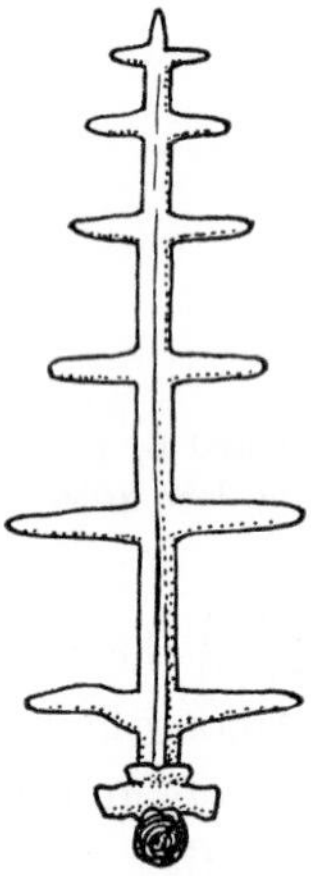

Fig. 177. Dorsal vertebra of a pelycosaur, *Edaphosaurus*, showing high neural spine. (After Goodrich.)

BIRDS

In correlation with the great expansion of the pelvis in birds, from twelve to sixteen or more vertebrae and their ribs commonly fuse to form a *synsacrum* (Fig. 178); this means that not only are the two primitive reptilian sacral vertebrae included, but also some that would be (if they lacked ribs) lumbar vertebrae, one rib-bearing thoracic vertebra, and some of the caudals. The thoracic region is short, with a maximum of eleven or twelve vertebrae bearing fully developed ribs in *Archeopteryx*, the earliest known bird, to five or six in the more advanced kinds. Often several thoracics fuse in the shoulder region. The neck contains a variable number. The cervical ribs articulated by two heads in *Archeopteryx* but fuse with the vertebrae in modern birds. The tail, finally, was long, with freely movable vertebrae, in *Archeopteryx,* but in Neornithes (modern) is reduced to a few free units followed by a block, the *pygostyle,* containing several fused caudals.

The ends of the neck vertebrae are saddle shaped (*heterocoelous,* Fig.

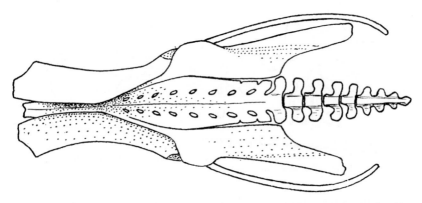

Fig. 178. Synsacrum and caudal vertebrae of flamingo. (Drawn from photo in Beebe, *The Bird,* Henry Holt and Co.)

169). This combines a strong joint with great flexibility. If you sat in the saddle on the front of a centrum you would face left or right; if you sat in the posterior saddle you would face dorsally or ventrally. Only the atlas vertebra is procoelous, to fit the condyle of the skull. But in *Archeopteryx* and in *Ichthyornis,* a toothed bird of the Cretaceous period, the vertebrae were amphicoelous, a heritage from the reptiles.

MAMMALS

Most mammals (Fig. 179) have five regions in the vertebral column: cervical, thoracic, lumbar, sacral, and caudal. The neural arch and spine develop from basidorsal arcualia, and the centrum from interdorsals and perhaps also interventrals. It is a pleurocentrum, as with birds and most reptiles, while the intercentrum is here seldom present except as the *chevron bones* (*hemal arches*) of the tail in several of the older orders. The articular surfaces of the centra are slightly concave, or may be flat (*amphiplatyan*) as in whales. They carry throughout their growth a disc, the *epiphysis,* between which and the body of the centrum growth mainly takes place, until at maturity the epiphysial joints close and the vertebra is complete.

The cervicals bear ribs which fuse with the centra and are recognizable only by the persistent *vertebrarterial canal* which they enclose. The number is nearly always seven (exceptions: six in manatees and two-toed sloth; nine in three-toed sloth).

The thoracics, most often thirteen in number, carry transverse processes for the tubercula of the ribs, while the capitulum usually meets a facet

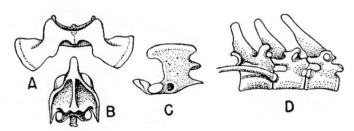

Fig. 179. Vertebrae of hare, Lepus. A, atlas, ventral; B, axis, ventral; C, axis, lateral; D, thoracic, lateral. (After Parker and Haswell, Textbook of Zoology, 6th ed., The Macmillan Company.)

on two adjoining centra. Neural spines develop in proportion to the bulk of dorsal muscles; therefore in those animals, as the larger ruminants or the elephants, which bear a heavy head, they are particularly long and powerful. In the lumbar vertebrae of most mammals the neural spines and transverse processes are long and project obliquely forward. The sacrum is usually small, containing three or four fused vertebrae, but in whales and Sirenia, which have no hind limbs, a sacrum cannot be distinguished.

Ribs and Sternum

Ribs are by no means universal among vertebrates, nor are the kinds of ribs in various groups all derived from a single ancestry. Those of sharks and rays are short rods of cartilage attached to the centra of corresponding vertebrae in the trunk and extending laterally for a short distance in the horizontal septum between epaxial and hypaxial muscles. They develop in continuity with the basiventral arcualia, at least in the procartilage stage. This type of rib may be called *dorsal.*

In actinopterous fishes there are sometimes *dorsal* ribs and *ventral,* or *pleural,* ribs (Fig. 180); both occur in *Polypterus.* The dorsals project out from the centra in the horizontal septum; the pleurals lie along the inner surface of the body muscles. The pleurals extend ventrally as the tail is approached and finally unite, behind the abdominal cavity, thus becoming the hemal arches. Clearly the pleural and dorsal ribs are not homologous, since they can occur separately on the same vertebra.

154 COMPARATIVE ANATOMY OF THE VERTEBRATES

Pleural ribs characterize Chondrostei, Holostei, and many teleosts, but the latter may also have one, two, or three sets of riblike *intermuscular bones* which ossify in the myosepta and are not preceded by cartilage. A

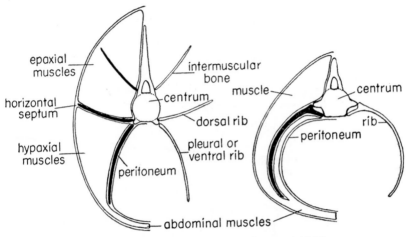

Fig. 180. Types of ribs in fish (left) and tetrapod (right).

sardine is well equipped with these, but among higher teleosts they appear less often, and in several groups even the pleural ribs are lost.

Lungfishes have bony pleural ribs, articulated with the basiventral cartilages. We can probably say that this type goes back to the common ancestry of lungfishes and Actinopteri. Ribs in crossopterygians, recently described by Jarvik (1952), are short and of the dorsal type found in tetrapods (Fig. 180). Evidently such ribs could have originated independently of those found in other bony fishes. In the earliest known Amphibia (ichthyostegids, likewise described by Jarvik) some of the ribs were apparently already two-headed. In this condition, usual among tetrapods, the dorsal head or *tuberculum* anchors the rib in its extended position and the ventral one (*capitulum*) acts as a brace against the centrum. Typically a short *parapophysis* receives the capitulum and a longer *diapophysis* the tuberculum (Fig. 176). One or both may be borne on a more extensive *transverse process.* The ribs may become single-headed, as in a number of reptiles, while frogs and toads have (except for certain primitive species) lost them, and much lengthened transverse processes take their place.

Among modern Amphibia ribs do not reach the sternum but in other ribbed tetrapods some, at least, do. The attachment usually is by a flexible band of cartilage or a separately ossified part of the rib, called the *sternal rib.* The remaining part, associated with the vertebra, is the *vertebral rib.*

Any which do not meet the sternum are *floating ribs.* Rhynchocephalia, Crocodilia, and many kinds of birds carry an *uncinate process* on the posterior margin of each rib, which overlaps the rib behind. We have noted already in connection with vertebrae the differences between cervical, thoracic, and sacral ribs.

Abdominal ribs or *gastralia* are slender dermal bones not related to true ribs, set in two or three series in the ventral wall of the abdomen. They seem to have originated in the early labyrinthodont Amphibia as

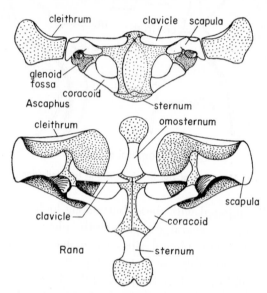

Fig. 181. Arciferous (overlapping) pectoral girdle of primitive frog, *Ascaphus* (after Noble), and firmisternal (fixed) girdle of advanced type, *Rana* (modified from Parker and Haswell).

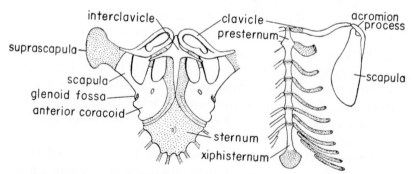

Fig. 182. Pectoral girdle and sternum in lizard, *Xantusia* (on left, after Kingsley), and marsupial, *Didelphis* (on right, after Romer.)

oblique rows of scales or scutes. They did not persist in higher Amphibia but were inherited by a number of orders of reptiles. *Archeopteryx,* the earliest known bird, had twelve or thirteen pairs of abdominal ribs, but they do not appear in any later birds, or in mammals.

The *sternum* is a plate or rod of cartilage or bone between the ventral ends of the thoracic ribs. It occurs in tetrapods but not fishes, is much reduced in modern Amphibia and absent in Apoda, amphisbaenids, snakes, plesiosaurs, and ichthyosaurs. It develops in reptiles, birds, and mammals from a pair of separate longitudinal cartilage bars which attach to the lower ends of the ribs and later fuse medially with each other. But it is likely that even in its beginning the adult sternum was single and served primarily for origin of the pectoral muscles, and that the paired embryonic cartilages are a modification.

In several families of more advanced frogs and toads the sternum fuses with the median portion of the shoulder girdle and a more anterior *omosternum* to make a fixed median rod, as we find in *Rana.* Probably this *firmisternal* condition arose more than once in Salientia (Fig. 181).

In reptiles the sternum comes to take the place of the original breast-plates of the dermal shoulder girdle (clavicles and interclavicle, Fig. 182). Among mammals it usually becomes a row of several small median bones, *sternebrae.* In flying reptiles (Pterosauria), bats, and birds it is much broadened because of the increase in area of origin of the pectoral muscles. Flying birds and some others like penguins which have well-developed wings, though flightless, bear a prominent keel on the sternum, which adds still more to the pectoral muscle area. The Ratitae (ostriches, etc.) lack such a keel, perhaps through loss.

Tail and Median Fins

The *tail* is that part of an animal, posterior to the body cavity, borne primarily by the vertebral column; this means in most cases that it starts behind the anus and the pelvic limbs, but there are exceptions. In fishes, again with exceptions, the tail is the primary locomotor organ, because in the flexing of the body the most effective action is at the posterior end. As a rule, then, a flattened surface, the *caudal fin,* develops there in any group of tail-swimming animals, whether fish, salamander, sea snake, ichthyosaur, or whale; in the latter, of course, the flattening is horizontal, making flukes.

Among terrestrial vertebrates and the few fishes that do not swim with their tails, other functions appear: a counterbalance used while running, as in bipedal reptiles, or leaping, as in kangaroos; a base to support tail feathers of birds; a prehensile organ, as in sea horses, chameleons, and several kinds of New World monkeys; a defensive weapon, as in stingrays and porcupines; a reservoir of food or water, as in Gila monsters; or, finally, to swish away insects, as in most grazing animals. If none of these functions exist, the tail may disappear; so it has done in frogs, sloths, bears, apes, and man.

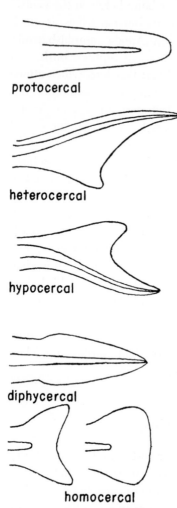

protocercal

heterocercal

hypocercal

diphycercal

homocercal

Fig. 183. Shapes of fish tails and caudal fins.

As to the *caudal fin,* there are several kinds, whose relationships we may show (Fig. 183):

1. *Protocercal.* Possibly ancestral type of fin, with notochord (or vertebral column) ending straight and with fin equally extended above and below; present in many young larval fishes but in no adults, so far as known; those of lampreys and hagfishes undoubtedly diphycercal (see below).

2. *Heterocercal.* Many fishes of the older groups have this, in which the vertebral column ends in the elongated upper lobe. Some ostracoderms and nearly all the older gnathostome groups were heterocercal.

3. *Hypocercal,* or "reversed heterocercal." Vertebral column ends in lower lobe of caudal fin; occurred in Anaspida and some other ostracoderms, and in ichthyosaurs, where a tail fin evolved with a down-swept vertebral column upon their return to marine life.

4. *Diphycercal.* Vertebral column goes to end of fin, and dorsal and ventral parts are equally developed; but the term applies to fins which are secondarily, not primitively, thus. Modern cyclostomes, Holocephali, living lungfishes, and the later crossopterygians all have (or had) diphycercal tails; when dorsal and anal fins unite with the caudal to make a continuous median fin, the tail is *gephyrocercal.*

5. *Homocercal.* In teleost fishes the heterocercal condition shows temporarily in larval stages, and is succeeded by a fully symmetrical caudal fin beyond the end of the vertebral column; this appears to be the lower lobe of the ancestral heterocercal fin, for it grows up and out behind the upturned end of the notochord as the latter degenerates. Upon this successful plan has evolved a great variety of homocercal fins.

The Fin-Fold Theory

Since this theory concerns the fundamental subject of the origin of limbs, we must examine it carefully. It is that the separate fins, median and paired, originated in some early ancestor from one continuous median and two ventrolateral folds along the body (Fig. 184). Usually the following evidence is given:

1. Muscles which move the fins are derived from many segments of the

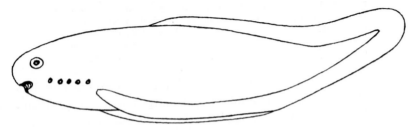

Fig. 184. Imaginary primitive fin folds.

body (Fig. 185), often converging towards the developing limb bud from before and behind; and the spinal nerves going to these muscles also come from more segments of the body than the adult fin or limb covers at its base; the inference would be that originally fins were more extensive than now, and at some time were continuous.

2. In the very ancient acanthodian fishes (Fig. 186A) there were up to seven pairs of ventrolateral fins, which suggests breakup of two folds.

3. In the Devonian shark *Cladoselache* (Fig. 187) the paired fins were broader at the base than distally; their skeletal supports ran out parallel and quite uniformly from the base; this again might imply departure from a once continuous fold on each side.

4. Even *Branchiostoma* (Amphioxus) is often brought into the picture because its metapleural folds seem to match the hypothetical plan (Fig. 186C, D).

Here, however, are some contrary arguments: In the study of living and fossil fishes one does not find any truly primitive group in which the fins are continuous (Fig. 188). They fuse and make continuous median folds in a number of cases, including lampreys and the very ancient pleuracanth sharks; but fossil evidence reveals that these are specialized

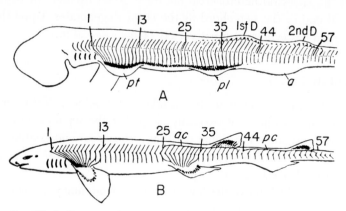

Fig. 185. *Scyllium canicula.* A, embryo, showing somites, muscle buds, and limb buds; B, adult, showing relationship of spinal nerves to fins. (From Eaton, 1945, *J. Morphology,* Vol. 76 (3): 209, after Goodrich.)

a, anal fin; *ac,* anterior commissural nerve; *pc,* posterior commissural nerve; *pl,* pelvic fin; *pt,* pectoral fin; numerals indicate body segments.

and came from still earlier kinds in which the fins were separate. Indeed in the oldest of all known vertebrates, the ostracoderms, the median and paired fins were short-based and often no more than spines. In acantho-

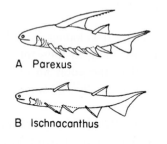

A Parexus

B Ischnacanthus

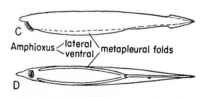

C
Amphioxus $\Big\langle$ lateral
$\Big\langle$ ventral $\Big\rangle$ metapleural folds

D

Fig. 186. Two acanthodians. A, *Parexus* with five pairs of ventral fins; B, *Ischnacan-thus* with two pairs; C, D, lateral and ventral views of Amphioxus, showing meta-pleural folds.

dians the author cannot see that the several paired "fins" represent anything but a special multiplication of defensive spines, which sometimes but not always support fin membranes. Gregory and Raven (1941) give reasons to believe that the broad-based fins of *Cladoselache* were not primitive but specialized, and analogous to those of rays. Amphioxus would seem to be irrelevant, since its metapleural folds develop in correlation with, and on the outside of, the atrium; several writers now incline to the view that Amphioxus is not at all an ancestral chordate.

As to the argument that segmental muscles and nerves converge towards the growing limb from points before and behind its base, it is not difficult to show that this "convergence" is an illusion. When a limb bud first appears, it is, like some other embryonic organs, relatively large (Fig. 185). The body segments from which it receives muscles are those

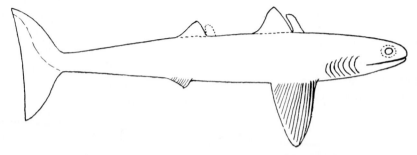

Fig. 187. Primitive shark, *Cladoselache*. (Based on Romer.)

that lie adjacent to it. After the muscle buds and their accompanying nerves enter the limb bud they adjust their rate and direction of growth to the limb, rather than the body. But the body grows faster antero-posteriorly than does the limb, which is concerned with lateral growth. Therefore the body segments from which muscles and nerves of the limb originated will cover, in the adult, a greater distance forward and back

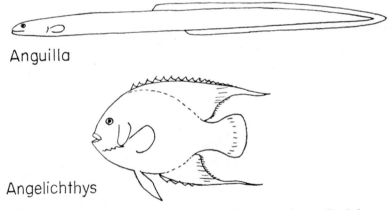

Anguilla

Angelichthys

Fig. 188. Specialized bodies and fins in teleosts. Above, an eel, *Anguilla;* below, a coral-reef fish, *Angelichthys.*

than does the base of the limb. This is true of median, as well as paired, fins, in, for example, a shark. There has been no convergence towards the limb base, but a divergence of nerves and muscle segments within the body.

Thus the balance of evidence at present seems to weigh more heavily against than for the fin-fold theory. The indications seem to be that fins arose in connection with median and paired spines, already established in ostracoderms (Figs. 12, 13). Perhaps the defensive function of such spines was at first more important than the locomotor. The pectoral spines were in a position to act as props, keeping the body upright when resting on the bottom. It would seem natural that a membrane or fold of skin should extend out between the spine and the adjacent wall of the body, as in many cases it did, but not until we reach the placoderms, apparently, did such a fold begin to contain an internal structure of rays. Without such rays, and deeper pieces for their support, no effective loco-

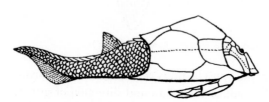

Fig. 189. An antiarch, *Pterichthyodes milleri*. (After Moy-Thomas.)

motor action could be produced by the fins, since fin muscles need places for insertion. The evolution of fins for locomotion (except the tail) seems to have been slow, haphazard, and with curious experiments on the way (see, for instance, arthrodires and antiarchs, Fig. 189), until a successful "basic patent" was finally attained in fishes above the placoderms.

Dermal Fin Rays

Whether median or paired, fins are nearly always supported by parallel rods just beneath the epidermis. Such dermal rays may be jointed or not. To their deep ends attach the muscles that move the fins, or sometimes

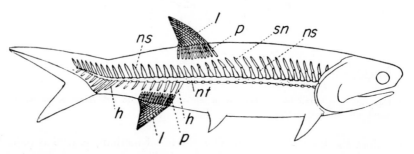

Fig. 190. Diagram of axial skeleton and fin supports in a primitive actinopteran. (From Eaton, 1945, J. Morphology, Vol. 76 (3): 202.)
  h, hemal arches; *l*, lepidotrichia; *ns*, neural spines; *nt*, notochord; *p*, pterygiophores; *sn*, supraneurals.

to bones or cartilages that in turn hold the dermal rays. In elasmobranch fins the dermal rays are nonjointed flexible rods called *ceratotrichia.* In Actinopteri, the ray-finned fishes, jointed rays derived from rows of scales replace ceratotrichia; they are called *lepidotrichia* (Figs. 118, 190). Other groups of fishes show one or both of these types in differing combinations.

Pterygiophores

These are the deeper bones or cartilages on which dermal rays rest (Fig. 190); the word means "fin bearers." Each consists of a single piece, or two or three; the single ones are in more advanced fishes and are the result of fusion. The separate elements, if present, are called *radials;* if, as in sharks, some are much larger than others, they are called *basals.*

Paired Limbs and Girdles

PAIRED LIMBS

There is no clear evidence that the paired fins of fishes were primitively continuous, and there is excellent evidence that the two girdles had very different beginnings. Nevertheless, the pectoral and pelvic fins, or limbs, usually resemble each other in surprising detail.

The *pectorals* lie close behind the head. Their girdle consists of (1) a paired *scapulocoracoid* portion of cartilage or of replacing bone, with which the fins or limbs articulate, and (2) a superficial, usually more elaborate series of *dermal bones* primitively connected with the skull.

The *pelvic* appendages in most cases lie next to the anus and the posterior end of the body cavity. Their girdle consists of paired cartilages or replacing bones, often joined medially, and in most tetrapods attaining a dorsal connection with the vertebral column by way of the sacral ribs.

Although no trace of paired fins remains in lampreys and hagfishes, most ostracoderms had pectorals, either in the form of flaps preceded by spines (Fig. 12), or spines alone. In either case these are not necessarily homologous with those of Gnathostomes. Some Anaspida (Fig. 13) had paired rows of spines along the abdomen; these, with the frequent addition of fin membranes behind them, we see again in acanthodians (Fig. 14, 186A, B). Most placoderms had spines rather than fins, either movably or (at first) immovably fixed on the sides of the thoracic armor. These facts seem to indicate (1) that a dermal spine acted as the first skeletal support of a fin, (2) that such spines may have occurred before any fins, (3) that movement of fins in swimming was a later development, and (4) that pectoral fins appeared earlier than pelvics.

An internal fin skeleton of **radials** extending towards the margin made undulatory movement of the fins possible (Fig. 192A), for radial muscles could raise and depress them. This mechanism came in acanthodians, if not earlier. Still more effective action resulted from enlargement or fusion of some inner radials, now called **basals.** Gregory and Raven (1941) suggest that the scapulocoracoids, and also the pelvis, are simply further enlarged and fused basals.

Apart from the girdle, the basal elements of the fin proper in elasmobranchs are usually three, **propterygium, mesopterygium,** and **metapterygium** (Figs. 191, 192A). A similar, although doubtless independent, structure is found in *Polypterus* (Fig. 192B). Beyond these large pieces extend radials, usually many-jointed and sometimes, as in rays, forked at the tips. Among Actinopteri it is usual for the internal skeleton of the

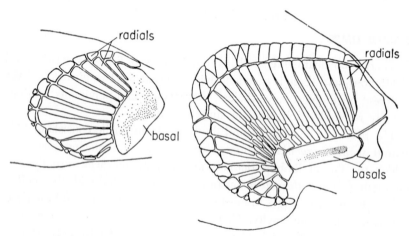

Fig. 191. Skeleton of pelvic (left) and pectoral (right) fins of Chimaera.

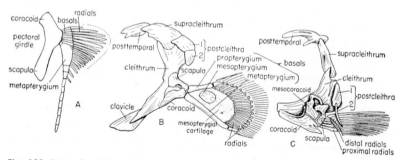

Fig. 192. Pectoral girdles and fin skeletons of (A) primitive shark, *Cladodus* (after Goodrich); (B) *Polypterus* (after Goodrich); (C) *Salmo fario* (after Bridge).

paired fins to be much reduced, for dermal rays bear the brunt of fin support and movement. Usually not more than two rows (salmon) or one row (most other teleosts) are left, articulating with the scapulocoracoid or the pelvis.

PECTORAL GIRDLE

Deferring the paired fins of lungfishes and lobefins to a later paragraph, we may look more carefully at the *pectoral girdle* of fishes. Its dermal bones (Fig. 192B, C) can be traced to the dermal plates covering the trunk in ostracoderms and placoderms. As this armor was associated with the head, so the dermal bones of the girdle in bony fishes nearly always retain a connection with the dermal roof of the skull on either side.

Counting downward from the skull, these dermal bones are the *supracleithrum* (attached to the posttemporal of the skull), *cleithrum, postcleithrum* (often present in teleosts), *clavicle* (absent in teleosts and other advanced Actinopteri, but present in lungfishes and lobefins). As elasmobranchs have no bones they lack a connection between the skull and girdle; the rays, however, have a peculiar dorsal plate developed from the neural spines of several anterior dorsal vertebrae, to articulate laterally with the upper end of each scapulocoracoid. The connection between the posttemporal and supracleithrum in crossopts was apparently lost even in the early Amphibia; both of these bones promptly disappeared so that the head became more readily movable on the neck.

To trace the origin of the endoskeletal (cartilage or replacing bone) part of the girdle, namely the scapulocoracoid, is more difficult, since we cannot easily choose between two alternatives. In the ostracoderms Stensiö (1927) found a large internal wall at the back of the skull, which he called postcranial because it lay behind the gill region and must have provided part of the base for attachment of the pectoral fins. This wall might, by detaching from the skull and reducing, become the scapulocoracoids. The other alternative is (Gregory and Raven, 1941) that, like the pelvis, the scapulocoracoids originated from enlarged basal elements of the fin, and secondarily took up relationships with the dermal bones of the shoulder girdle. In most fishes, but not elasmobranchs, these pieces remain paired and separate, except that they may be linked indirectly by union of cleithra or clavicles beneath.

PELVIS

The *pelvis,* which has not the shape of a girdle in fishes, seems to have originated by enlargement or fusion of basal pieces, which served for origin of radial muscles of the pelvic fins. The pelvis is therefore paired in primitive fishes (early sharks, Holocephali, crossopterygians, *Amia*, etc., Fig. 193).

In the modern sharks and rays the two pieces fuse to make a single

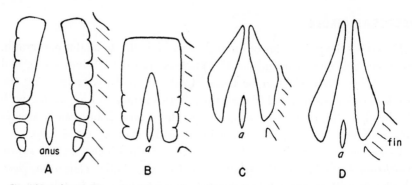

Fig. 193. Pelvis of fishes, showing its presumed origin from deep basal cartilages, diagrammatic. A, primitive shark; B, modern shark; C, primitive actinopteran, lobefin, etc.; D, teleost.

crossbar in front of the anus. Likewise the halves fuse, although differently, in modern lungfishes, and again, still differently, in teleosts. Thus the pelvis, at first paired, has become a single structure not less than four times among vertebrates, if we add the tetrapods to those already mentioned.

Among many higher teleost fishes the pelvic girdle and fins forsake their traditional place near the anus (Fig. 194) and become *thoracic;* in doing so, the anterior end of the pelvis attaches to the ventral tip of the united cleithra. A few groups carry the process even further; codfishes and blennies have *jugular* pelvics, that is, beneath the throat. Not uncommonly they may be lost altogether (eels), or modified in peculiar ways, as the circular sucking disc of the lumpsuckers (Fig. 210).

PAIRED FINS

The nature of dipnoan and crossopterygian paired fins, and derivation of tetrapod limbs from the latter, is the most important part of our study of paired appendages. In early days of comparative anatomy lungfishes (Dipnoi) were held to be the probable ancestors of Amphibia. Their paired fins, called *archipterygia,* have a central axis of numerous bones, and towards both margins diverge corresponding sets of smaller radials (Fig. 195). The anterior edge of the pectoral is held higher than the posterior, but both pairs trail in the water. The attempt to imagine this structure changed into that of a salamander's leg and foot met insurmountable difficulties, for nothing intermediate could be found.

With better understanding of crossopterygians and of the early Amphibia (labyrinthodonts) the claim of lungfishes to tetrapod ancestry collapsed. Lungfish skulls and teeth, as well as fins, are far too highly specialized, but those of crossopts meet the requirements much better. The view given here is accepted in essentials by those who have worked on the problem recently, but in some particulars it may be criticized.

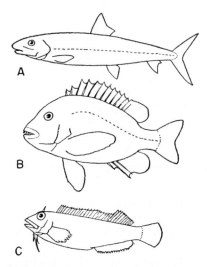

Early crossopts had broad paddle-shaped paired fins (Fig. 196). The pectorals were carried with the anterior edge lower than the posterior. A row of diminishing pieces ran out from the base, forming an axis. From the anterior (preaxial) side there diverged a set of more slender radials, but not from the posterior. Beyond the radials and axials the fin mem-

Fig. 194. Positions of pelvic fins in teleosts. A, abdominal, in *Albula;* B, thoracic, in *Archosargus;* C, jugular, in *Clinus.*

brane was supported by dermal fin rays, but these, along with the thin margins of the fins, were lost during the transformation to amphibian limbs. We may take it that in the most generalized crossopterygian fins each *axial* piece was attended by a *primary radial* and beyond these lay

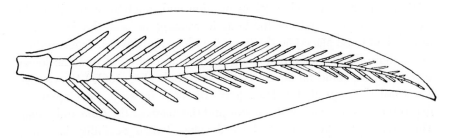

Fig. 195. Skeleton of archipterygial fin of lungfish, *Neoceratodus.* (After Parker and Haswell.)

one or two *secondary radials.* Westoll (1943) suggested that such a series corresponds with one body segment. Thus in the entire fin five or six segments are indicated, each presumably with its own set of levator and depressor muscles, and its own spinal nerve.

In the limb of *Eryops,* an early amphibian (Fig. 196C), the general pattern is similar. The first axial piece has become the **humerus,** while its radial has made the **radius** of the forearm, and the second axial, by lengthening, is recognizable as the **ulna.** The small **carpal** bones of the foot (wrist) make a succession of diagonal rows slanting towards the pre-

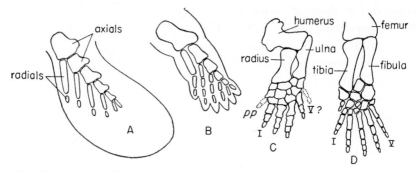

Fig. 196. Diagram of (A) crossopterygian fin skeleton; (B) possible transition to tetrapod limb; (C) the forelimb of *Eryops;* and (D) hind limb of *Trematops.*
pp, prepollex, I, V, numbered digits.

axial edge, just as their counterparts did in the fin, but the bones of the *digits* are new; they were not represented at all in the fin. According to this scheme, the primary and secondary radials of the fish fin, plus a few more elements in series with them (tertiary and quaternary radials, if you like), can account for essentially the whole foot, and also for the oblique-ness of the rows of carpal bones. This is consistent with Westoll's seg-mental idea, and fits, with relatively little adjustment, the plan of foot muscles in Amphibia.

We must notice the changes in position and function of the limb. In order to bear the weight of the body in walking on land, the flat ventral surface had to be placed on the ground with its tip forward. This required (1) a more flexible shoulder joint, and (2) an elbow, so that the lower arm and hand could be flexed. In the hind limb (Fig. 196D) the change was similar except that a knee joint, directed forward, developed be-tween the rounded end of the **femur** and the heads of the **tibia** and **fibula.** The wrist and ankle seem to have developed their flexibility later and more gradually.

TETRAPOD LIMB

The tetrapod limb to begin with (labyrinthodont Amphibia and cotylo-saurian reptiles) was short, stout, and typically with five digits (Fig. 197).

There is evidence of a very short sixth digit in some labyrinthodonts, the **prepollex** (mediad of the thumb) or **prehallux** (mediad of the first toe in the hind foot). No modern amphibians have more than four digits in the front foot (**manus**), but nearly all have five in the hind foot (**pes**). The famous two-toed "fossil footprint" named *Thinopus antiquus*, supposed

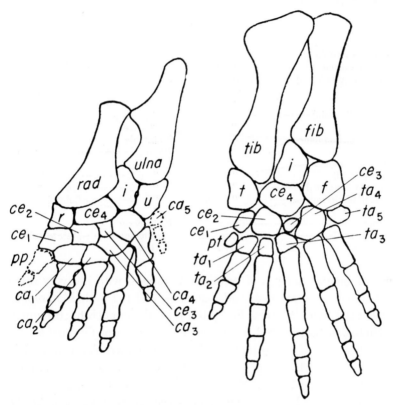

Fig. 197. A primitive manus (Eryops, left, after Gregory and Raven), and primitive pes (Trematops, right, after Schaeffer). Legend for manus: ca, carpale; ce, centrale; i, intermedium; pp, prepollex; r, radiale; u, ulnare.
Legend for pes: ce, centrale; i, intermedium; f, fibulare; pt, pretarsale; t, tibiale; ta, tarsale.

to be that of an Upper Devonian amphibian, is figured in many books and discussed widely, but unless its validity is confirmed, it can have no weight in the problem of tetrapod origin; it is perhaps a coprolite (impression of feces).

The oblique pattern of the small foot bones, which we have traced from the crossopterygian fin, was already somewhat obscured in labyrinthodonts by the close and many-sided articulation of these pieces with one another, for the foot now had to be firm enough to support the animal's weight on land. Eventually the oblique pattern disappeared as new methods of jointing developed, or as individual bones atrophied or consolidated with others. The following table shows the names applied to

NAMES OF HAND AND FOOT BONES

Hand (manus) Mammalian names	Primitive Tetrapod names		Foot (pes) Mammalian names
Navicular (scaphoid)——Radiale		Tibiale——Talus (astragalus)	
Lunate (semilunar)——Intermedium		Intermedium——Talus (astragalus)	
Triquetral (cuneiform)——Ulnare		Fibulare——Calcaneus	
	Centrale 1	Centrale 1——Navicular	
	" 2	" 2	
Centrale (in mole)—— " 3		" 3	
	" 4	" 4	
Greater multangular (trapezium)——Precarpale		Pretarsale	
——Carpale 1		Tarsale 1——1st Cuneiform	
Lesser multangular (trapezoid)			
	" 2	" 2——2nd "	
Capitate (magnum)—— " 3		" 3——3rd "	
Hamate (unciform)—— " 4		" 4——Cuboid	
	" 5	" 5	
Pisiform——Pisiform		Postminimus	
Metacarpal 1–5——Metacarpal 1–5		Metatarsal 1–5——Metatarsal 1–5	

bones of manus and pes of primitive tetrapods, with the very different set of names used for man and mammals, and the probable homologies between the two sets. Schaeffer (1941) has done much to straighten out the confusion that existed regarding the evolution of the tarsus.

Modifications of the primitive plan are innumerable. Tetrapod limbs display a wonderful range of structural differences. The fact most obvious in surveying them is that each adaptive type appeared more than once, in unrelated groups (e.g., *cursorial* or running, *graviportal* or weight bearing, *leaping, climbing, gliding, flying, burrowing, swimming*). This often results in a surprising similarity of body or limbs in animals of diverse ancestry, that is, convergent evolution (Figs. 198, 199).

In Amphibia the limbs are lost in certain eel-like ancient amphibians, in the burrowing wormlike Apoda, and nearly lost in *Siren* and *Amphiuma,* which are eel-shaped Caudata. Otherwise, salamanders have four toes in front, and five or rarely four on the hind feet, with carpal and tarsal bones varying from six to twelve. The Salientia, adapted usually for leaping, have the radius and ulna fused, with four toes in front, plus sometimes a prepollex. In the hind leg the tibia and fibula are fused, the tibiale and fibulare elongated and often partly fused (increasing the effective length of the foot), while the digits (five) are webbed.

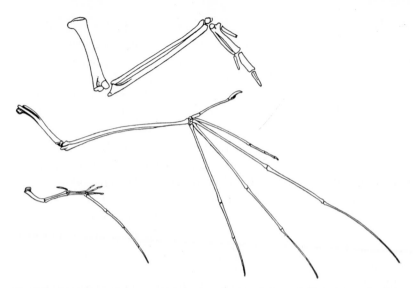

Fig. 198. Comparison of three unrelated types of wing skeleton. A bird, the condor (top, redrawn from Beebe); a fruit bat, *Pteropus* (redrawn from Parker and Haswell); a flying reptile, *Pterodactylus* (bottom, after Parker and Haswell).

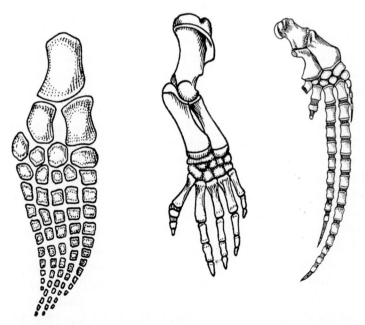

Fig. 199. Three unrelated types of flipper (forelimb) in aquatic animals: a porpoise, *Globicephalus* (right, after Parker and Haswell); a marine reptile, *Ichthyosaurus* (left); a dugong (middle, after Parker and Haswell). All are external aspects of right flippers.

In the tarsus of most reptiles the astragalus (tibiale) and calcaneus (fibulare) form a proximal row, followed by a transverse joint, and then the tarsalia plus perhaps one or two centralia; also the limbs are generally held laterally, as with Amphibia, so that the body is on the ground when at rest and may even drag along during locomotion. The Therapsida (mammal-like) held their limbs more nearly beneath, and the astragalus and calcaneus were mammalian in form, with the main joint of the hind foot proximal to them. In the flipperlike limbs of ichthyosaurs and other marine reptiles the humerus and femur were short and heavy, the more distal bones being small and often greatly increased in number, arranged in parallel rows. Dinosaurs, as we noted before, were primitively bipedal but in more advanced kinds often quadrupedal. The carpals and tarsals were much reduced, while the metacarpals and metatarsals were heavily built and supported the weight of the body; they and the digits in ornithischian dinosaurs were sometimes reduced to three in the hind feet, making enormous birdlike footprints in the Mesozoic mud.

The pterosaurs we have described briefly, but may add that the long bones, like those of birds, were hollow, apparently with air sacs in them, while the radius and ulna were fused, metacarpals fused and lengthened, and of course the phalanges of the fourth finger extraordinarily lengthened; in the hind leg the tibia and fibula were fused, the tarsals much reduced. All these features go with making a light, strong skeleton.

Crocodilia have reduced carpals and tarsals, five digits in the manus and four in the pes. In Chelonia the feet are quite primitive, but webbed (especially the pes) in many freshwater turtles, clublike in the heavy land tortoises (*Testudo*), and powerful flippers in the sea turtles. The astragalus and calcaneus in *Sphenodon* are fused and the tarsals reduced, but otherwise its limbs are generalized; those of lizards are similar but often with elongated digits. The burrowing, generally limbless group Amphisbaenia, Zangerl (1944) says, may not be lizards, as usually held, but a separate order. Loss of limbs in snakes may be associated with a burrowing habit in ancestral snakes; a few kinds burrow today.

In speaking of birds in the first chapter we mentioned some of the limb characters, but a few special points remain. The long bones are hollow, with air sacs extending into them; the tarsals and carpals are largely lost as discrete elements. Of course the manus (wing) has been reduced by fusion and loss of carpals and metacarpals, and of phalanges, leaving only vestiges of digits 1, 2, and 3 (Fig. 198A). In the legs (Fig. 200) the fibula is vestigial, and, most important, the tibia fuses with the proximal tarsal bones making a *tibiotarsus* (the lower leg bone), while the distal tarsals fuse with the metatarsals making a *tarsometatarsus* (the ankle bone). The digits are usually four, sometimes three (first and fifth lost); there are only two (third and fourth) in the ostrich.

The appendages in Mesozoic mammals are not known. Those of monotremes are somewhat specialized for digging or swimming. For the most primitive mammalian type we must therefore look to the generalized marsupials and insectivores. The fore feet of marsupials have five simple digits, but on the basis of hind foot structure there are two groups: Didactyla (including opossums) in which the hind foot also is simple and five-toed, and Syndactyla (the majority of marsupials) in which the first digit of the hind foot is thumblike or lacking, second and third small and not separated from each other, while the fourth and fifth are normal or enlarged. The latter situation may have resulted from an early arboreal adaptation in which the foot was used for grasping, as it still is in many marsupials, followed by a return of some types to the ground, when the fourth and fifth digits enlarged still further (as in kangaroos) but the useless thumb became vestigial.

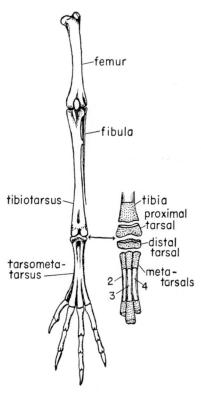

Fig. 200. Leg and foot bones of pigeon, *Columba*. Adult, left; embryo, right. (After Parker and Haswell, *Textbook of Zoology*, 6th ed., The Macmillan Company.)

Shrews, especially tree shrews, have the most primitive, plantigrade (walking on the soles), five-toed feet that we can find among placental mammals. In the burrowing insectivores (moles) the bones of the forelimb and hand are heavy and broad, and movement is lateral. The arboreal, gliding Indo-Malayan Dermoptera (the so-called "flying lemurs," which are not lemurs and do not fly), are related to both insectivores and primates; their feet are of a primitive sort, but a broad fold of skin extends between fore and hind legs, as in the flying squirrels. We have dealt in the first chapter with the hands and feet of Primates, noting that a grasping thumb and big toe are characteristic; in a few cases the fingers of the hand act together as a hook in seizing branches of trees while the animal travels rapidly through the forest; thus the gibbons have reduced, and spider monkeys completely lost, the thumb. It is an example of sacrificing a primitive character in favor of a high specialization.

We need not review the limb characters of carnivores, whales, and sea cows, for they were mentioned before. We showed also that the various orders of ungulates (hoofed animals) arose along different lines from ancestors with four and five toes, tending in most of those lines to em-

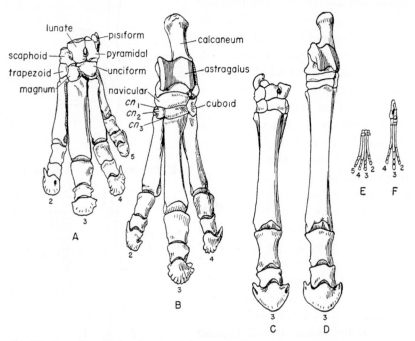

Fig. 201. Feet of perissodactyls. A, B, left manus and pes of tapir, *Tapirus*; C, D, right manus and left pes of *Equus*, the modern horse; E, F, right manus and pes of *Hyracotherium*, ancestral horse, drawn to the same scale. (All after Scott.)

phasize the middle digits while shortening or losing the lateral ones (Figs. 201, 202). The feet of edentates are generalized except when modified in some kinds for support of massive claws; in tree sloths the digits are reduced to three or two.

Among lagomorphs and rodents the limbs vary, but not extremely, according to their adaptive use. They are more massive and shortened in burrowing types (as pocket gophers), while the hind legs become lengthened in the runners and leapers; in more than one family of rodents a bipedal habit has arisen (jerboas, kangaroo rats), with the result that the forelegs are very small and the animal is essentially a miniature kangaroo in shape and behavior. At the other extreme among terrestrial mammals come the graviportal Proboscidea, with massive pillarlike limbs to support their weight, digits shortened, and foot bones in parallel series.

THE PECTORAL GIRDLE IN TETRAPODS

We saw that in higher fishes the girdle consists of a deeper *scapulo-coracoid,* preformed in cartilage, and a more superficial *dermal series,* linked dorsolaterally with the roof of the skull, and meeting at the midventral line. In the fish the girdle is a stable base for articulation of the pectoral fins.

In tetrapods the girdle becomes more and more freed from the rest of the skeleton, and progressively simplified by loss of parts. The first step in both of these processes occurred in the early labyrinthodonts, where the *supra-cleithrum* disappeared, leaving the shoulder girdle entirely disconnected from the skull, so that the head obtained some freedom of movement. The *scapula* meanwhile expanded dorsally, providing more room for the enlarging limb muscles which originated on it, and the same factor probably accounts for the expansion of the ventral coracoid region. The dermal parts of this girdle were a rather reduced *cleithrum* and a *clavicle* (on each side, of course), with a median diamond-shaped breastplate, the *interclavicle.*

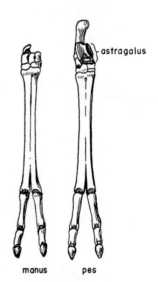

manus   pes

Fig. 202. Right manus and pes of guanaco (South American relative of camel). (After Scott.)

Modern Amphibia have no dermal bones in the girdle except for the narrow cleithrum and clavicle of Salientia. In Caudata the girdle consists only of a scapulocoracoid ossification surmounted by suprascapular cartilage, and extending ventrad as a coracoid plate of cartilage; this usually overlaps its opposite in the median line, and meets, behind, a small cartilaginous sternum. In Salientia there is a separate coracoid bone, properly called *anterior coracoid.* Toads, the primitive frog *Ascaphus* (Fig. 181), and tree frogs (*Hyla*) have the right and left halves of the girdle overlapping at the median line; this loose sort of girdle is called *arciferal.* Advanced frogs (*Rana* and others) enjoy a solid median fusion of the girdle, called the *firmisternal* type.

Reptiles, except those that have lost the pectoral girdle, keep the anterior coracoid (Fig. 203A), but behind this, in mammal-like reptiles, appears the *coracoid* proper; we shall follow it presently into mammals. The clavicle and interclavicle remain in most reptiles, but the cleithrum persists only in cotylosaurs and some mammal-like reptiles. Turtles show an extraordinary condition: the pectoral girdle, starting to develop ante-

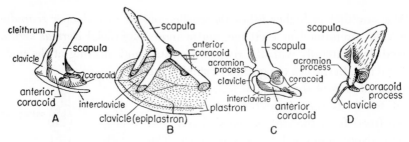

Fig. 203. Pectoral girdles of reptiles and mammals, left side. A, *Dimetrodon* (after Romer); B, turtle, pectoral girdle in relation to plastron; C, *Ornithorhynchus* (monotreme, after Romer); D, gorilla.

riorly to the ribs, becomes internal to them (Fig. 203B). That part to which the humerus is attached is a triple prong, consisting of a slender V-shaped scapula and the bladelike anterior coracoid. The clavicles and interclavicle persist in turtles as paired and median plates of the plastron (ventral shield). Clavicles are absent, however, in Crocodilia.

Birds (Fig. 204) have a strong anterior coracoid reaching from the

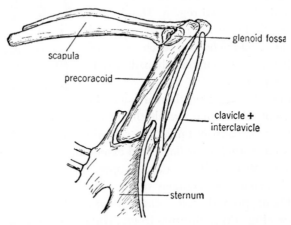

Fig. 204. Pectoral girdle of turkey, right side. (After Adams and Eddy.)

sternum to the head of the humerus (glenoid cavity), and the scapula extends back like a knife blade. The clavicles fuse at their ventral tips with the interclavicle and form the "wishbone," usually attached to the sternum.

The primitive reptilian girdle is passed on, little changed, to the mono-treme mammals (Fig. 203C), where the interclavicle makes a T-shaped breastplate. Higher mammals, of course, have no interclavicle or anterior coracoid; the coracoid itself is present only as a hooked process (Fig. 203D) on the scapula, while the clavicle, if full-sized, goes from the sternum to the acromion process of the scapula. It may, however, be vestigial. The last stage in reduction and release of the pectoral girdle comes by total loss of the clavicle in ungulates, elephants, many carni-vores, and the marine groups, where nothing but muscles serve to con-nect it with the axial skeleton. Thus the scapula enters freely into move-ments of the limb, and is no longer a fixed base.

PELVIC GIRDLE IN TETRAPODS

The *pelvic girdle* in crossopterygian fishes was no more than a pair of small simple bones lying on either side of the cloaca and serving for articulation of their respective fin skel-etons. In *Eusthenopteron*, according to the restoration by Gregory and Ra-ven (1941), these two bones were in contact at their anterior ends, and each bore an iliac process projecting dor-sally but not nearly reaching the ver-tebral column (Fig. 205). The acetab-ulum (socket) was at the posterior end. According to these authors the pelvis was then equivalent to the pubis alone, of tetrapods, and the part which became the ilium grew upward, while that which made the ischium grew posteromediad. The result was to put the acetabulum on the lateral surface, as it is in tetrapods. Of course the enlargement of leg muscles in adaptation to land life may be con-sidered responsible for the extension of the bones, to provide greater sur-faces for their attachment.

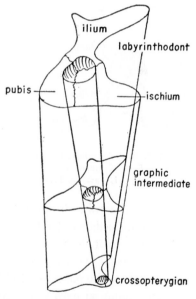

Fig. 205. Probable relationship between pelvis of crossopterygian fish (bottom) and that of labyrinthodont (top), as shown by graphic intermediate form. Left lateral views. (After Gregory and Raven.)

The next step, found in early Am-phibia, was to make a symphysis (union by suture) between the two pubic bones; that of the ischia came somewhat later, but presently a broad flattened ventral plate was established, from which the ilia rose vertically on either side to meet the ends of one pair of ribs and thus produce a true girdle and a sacrum for the first time. The earliest labyrinthodonts did not yet have the sacroiliac connection. A single pair of ribs is involved in Amphibia, but the sacral region contains two pairs in most reptiles. The acetabulum, in all but a few tetrapods, is the meeting place of all three pelvic bones.

The pelvis of Caudata is degenerate, consisting usually of an ischiopubic cartilage with centers of ossification ventrally only for the ischia; the ilia are partly ossified. Sutures may be lacking. In lung-breathing salamanders (Fig. 206A) a Y-shaped (ypsiloid) cartilage extends for-

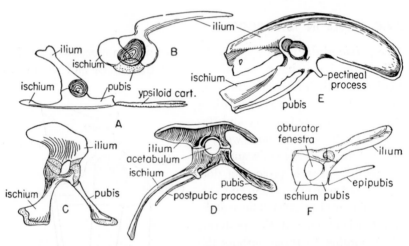

Fig. 206. Pelvis in various tetrapods, right lateral views. A, salamander, *Cryptobranchus*; B, frog, *Rana*; C, young alligator; D, dinosaur, *Iguanodon*, showing bird type; E, ratite bird, *Apteryx*; F, opossum, *Didelphis*. (D and E after Goodrich, F after Romer.)

ward from the pubes in the median line and is movable; by pulling it in (dorsad) the salamander thrusts air forward in the lungs, causing the head to rise as it floats in the water. The ypsiloid cartilage is therefore part of a special hydrostatic mechanism. In Salientia, as part of the leaping adaptation, the pubis and ischium may be much reduced (Fig. 206B), while the ilium on each side extends far forward, parallel with the urostyle.

Early reptiles had a complete ventral plate like that of labyrinthodonts, with the ilia attached to two pairs of sacral ribs. A small foramen in each pubis gave passage for the obturator nerve, and continues to do so in most reptiles, but the obturator foramen as seen in mammals and the Therapsida is the result of union of this pubic foramen with a larger opening which presently developed between the pubis and ischium (properly called puboischial fenestra). The fenestra is wide in most reptiles, so that the pubic symphysis does not connect with the ischial symphysis, and as seen from the side the pelvis is triradiate (Fig. 206C).

Ornithischian dinosaurs and birds share certain peculiarities of the pelvis that possibly indicate relationship (Fig. 206D, E). The ischium and pubis are greatly prolonged caudad, parallel with each other, and do not form symphyses (there is a pubic symphysis in *Archeopteryx*, but in no higher birds). Ornithischia also have a large "prepubic process" forward and down from each pubis; this corresponds to the "pectineal process" of birds, shorter but in the same position. The ilium, of course, is greatly expanded and thinned, as mentioned already in connection with the synsacrum of birds. The acetabulum is partly open, probably reducing weight by eliminating superfluous bone.

There are not many remarkable features of the pelvis in mammals. Monotremes and marsupials have a pair of *epipubic* or *marsupial* bones in the abdominal wall just anterior to the pubes, from which they develop embryonically (Fig. 206F). Usually the ventral symphysis is short, made only by the pubes in some insectivores, carnivores, and Primates. It is absent in other insectivores and in Chiroptera. The pelvis as a whole degenerates to a vestige or disappears in Cetacea and Sirenia, in connection with loss of their hind legs.

CHAPTER VI

Muscles

What Muscles Are and What They Do

Meat is muscle. Nearly all movements of the body are caused by the contraction of muscles. The muscular system contributes more to the bulk of the body than any other. A muscle is an organ of soft, well-vascularized tissue which, when stimulated, shortens itself and thereby pulls toward one another the parts to which it is attached. When the stimulus ceases, the muscle relaxes and regains its original shape passively. Muscles pull; they never push.

In spite of this highly plastic form, the positions and anatomical relations of muscles are as constant in any species of animal as are those of other organs. Therefore it is no more difficult to understand the anatomy of the muscular system than to grasp that of the skeleton or the blood vessels. Yet muscles are rather commonly neglected in books of comparative anatomy.

The reason for this neglect may be that anatomists differ on the homologies and names of many muscles among the classes of vertebrates. Few authors have attempted to follow muscles carefully through a series from fish to mammal. This is not an easy task for two reasons: the fossils give little direct evidence of muscular anatomy, so that we must depend largely on modern types; and only a handful of workers have used evidence from embryology, although this is quite readily obtainable.

Of the three kinds of muscle tissue found in vertebrates (Fig. 207), two can scarcely be treated in a comparative anatomy course because they do not constitute organs in their own right, or because their anatomy is microscopic and shows little significant change. These two are *smooth* and *cardiac* muscle.

Smooth muscle occurs in the walls of the digestive tract as circular and lengthwise layers; in the walls of arteries and arterioles, circularly; in the

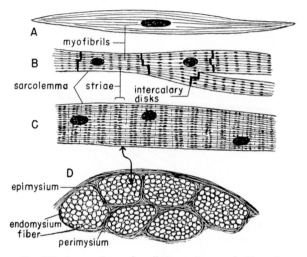

Fig. 207. A, smooth muscle cell; B, cardiac muscle fiber; C, skeletal muscle fiber; D, bundles of fibers in a muscle, cross section.

passages of the urogenital system, in the deep layer of the skin (dermis) and elsewhere. The cells are spindlelike, with a single nucleus, relatively slow to contract, but powerful and activated by the autonomic nervous system; this means that with one or two exceptions they are involuntary.

Cardiac muscle forms the bulk of the heart wall, as well as a part of the pulmonary artery and aorta. The cells are generally branched, interlacing, with many nuclei, and partly striated (cross-banded). Of course they are involuntary and under autonomic regulation, but contraction is initiated *within the muscle itself*, not by a nervous impulse.

The third kind of muscle, **striated** (skeletal or "voluntary"), with which we are concerned from here on, is made of large slender manynucleate cells (more properly called **syncytia**), in which occur a great number of lengthwise **myofibrils**, the actual contractile threads; alternately light and dark regions in these give the muscle cell a cross-banded or striated appearance. Such a cell or syncytium is a **fiber**. A **muscle** is a great bundle of these fibers parallel to one another (Fig. 208). Small groups of fibers within the muscle are more or less set apart by a thin connective tissue wrapping, the *perimysium,* while the common sheath of connective tissue around all is the *epimysium.* By means of the connective tissue in these sheaths the muscle is fastened at either end to, usually, some part of the skeleton. A *tendon* is simply a thick cord or band continuous with the epimysium and serving to attach the muscle to a part which it may not reach by itself. A *fascia* is a sheet of such tissue.

Striated muscles are activated by the "voluntary" nervous system. Its *motor nerves* send branches to all muscle fibers (Fig. 208). Normally any

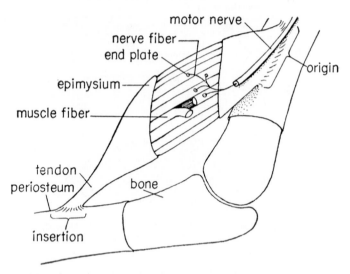

Fig. 208. Diagram of relationship between muscle, nerve, and skeleton.

contraction of a muscle is a response to a barrage of impulses from the central nervous system. The direction in which the fibers lie is, of course, the direction in which they will pull. The sheath or tendon of the muscle is continuous with the connective tissue sheath of the bone (*periosteum*) or cartilage (*perichondrium*).

The more stationary attachment of a muscle is its *origin;* the more movable is its *insertion.* Our chewing muscles, then, *originate* on the cranium and *insert* on the jaw. Usually muscles work in antagonistic pairs or groups, one pulling a bone one way, the other in the opposite direction.

Naturally whenever we see a joint between two parts of a skeleton we can infer that muscles were present in places where they could make movements of that joint. Similarly a solid fusion or immobility of parts of the skeleton implies a lack of muscles between those parts; it would be useless to have a muscle begin and end on a solid piece which it could not move. Further, during development, bones and cartilages adjust their shape to the stress of muscles upon them, and skeletons therefore carry ridges, crests, grooves, or roughened areas by which we can visualize the extent of muscle attachments. It is possible, then, to "restore" a part of the muscular anatomy of animals known only from fossil bones.

Several terms used in the study of muscles should be introduced here, so that we may be able to talk more freely. To *adduct* is to pull a certain part towards an adjoining part of the body, as when the lower jaw is pulled towards the upper, or the arm against the trunk; muscles acting thus are *adductors.* The opposite movement is to *abduct;* hence *abductors.* To bend a joint (increase the sharpness of its angle) is to *flex* it; muscles bending the knee, fingers, etc., are *flexors.* Antagonistic to flexors are others which straighten or *extend,* the *extensors.* Muscles which raise something are *levators;* those that lower are *depressors.* Any so placed as to squeeze a cavity, giving it smaller circumference, are *constrictors.* *Sphincters* are those which constrict an opening, as of the rectum or bladder. There are also muscles which rotate a part, *rotators;* which turn an appendage upside down or supine, *supinators;* and which turn it back again so that the normal lower surface is down or prone, the *pronators.* These last terms are used mostly in connection with rotating the arm and hand.

A particular muscle is almost invariably supplied by a particular motor nerve. During the course of evolution, just as during individual development, the same nerve continues to supply that muscle even if the latter should shift its position, change its action, split into separate parts, or fuse with some other muscle. We therefore need to know the innervation (nerve supply) of muscles in order to be sure that we recognize corresponding muscles when we compare different animals. For example, the muscles supplied by the seventh cranial nerve in man have no resemblance to those so supplied in a fish, yet a study of developmental stages or of the anatomy of intermediate types shows very clearly that they are the same, albeit with numerous changes of position and function, splitting into parts, and fusion with others.

Arrangement and Divisions of the Skeletal Muscles

1. *Segmental* (somatic or myotomic) muscles are those which come from muscle segments or myotomes of the embryo, and are at first segmentally arranged (Fig. 209); in higher vertebrates they quickly lose

this pattern. They are the muscles of the trunk, including neck and tail, and the following groups derived from these: hypobranchial (longitudinal throat) muscles; integumental muscles of the body in mammals, birds, and some reptiles; the muscle of the diaphragm in mammals. Also

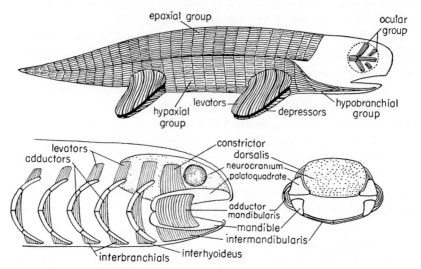

Fig. 209. Diagram of segmental muscles and their derivatives in a generalized vertebrate, at top. Lower left, diagram of primitive branchiomeric muscles (simplified). Lower right, transverse section through jaws of preceding.

derived from myotomes are the muscles which move the eyeball (extrinsic ocular muscles). The muscles of the limbs come directly from myotomes in fishes and are therefore primitively segmental, although they develop within the limbs themselves in all higher groups.

In the neck, trunk, and tail, muscles of the right and left sides are separated dorsally by a *dorsal septum* of connective tissue, and ventrally by a corresponding *linea alba.* Along the body and tail in those animals whose muscle segments show clearly (except cyclostomes) there is also a *horizontal septum* separating the dorsal (*epaxial*) half from the ventral (*hypaxial*); this horizontal septum is usually at the level of the lateral line in fishes, and inwardly it meets the centra of the vertebrae. In birds and mammals the segmentation, as well as the separation of epaxial from hypaxial muscles, is largely lost by fusion.

2. *Branchiomeric* ("visceral") muscles are those of the jaws, hyoid, and throat cartilages (Fig. 209), plus (in mammals) several integumental muscles that move lips, nostrils, ears, eyelids, etc. This group was primitively associated with jaws and gill arches, and is supplied by cranial nerves. It has nothing to do with myotomes, but develops from a

series of paired bands which in turn grow from the embryonic hypomere just in front of the heart (see Chapter II).

Comparative Anatomy of the Segmental Muscles

PROTOCHORDATES

Longitudinal muscles occur in the body wall of Enteropneusta, and in the tail of larval tunicates parallel to the notochord. But in neither of these is there segmentation. The tail muscles of tunicate larvae may be a reduced vestige of segmental muscles of an Amphioxus-like ancestor. *Branchiostoma* (Amphioxus) itself has 60 or more pairs of >-shaped myomeres (muscle segments) along the sides of the body; the point of each > is forward. Myomeres of right and left sides are placed alternately in Amphioxus and hagfishes, instead of opposite, as in all other Chordata. In the wall of the atrium lies a transverse sheet of muscle.

VERTEBRATES

Longitudinal Muscles of Neck, Trunk, and Tail

In nearly all fishes, amphibians, and to a lesser extent reptiles, one can see a segmental arrangement of the longitudinal muscles. Myomeres (muscle segments) are separated from each other by myosepta (connective tissue walls), so that the muscle fibers, running longitudinally, reach only from one myoseptum to the next. The septa attach to the sides of their corresponding vertebrae; hence the myomeres must alternate with the vertebrae. (For development, see Chapter II.)

The mass of longitudinal muscles extends from skull to tail (Fig. 210),

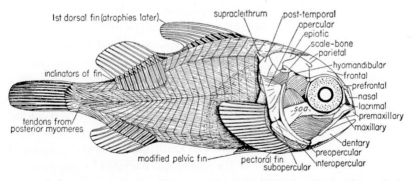

Fig. 210. General pattern of muscles in a fish, young *Cyclopterus lumpus* (lumpsucker), showing relationship to fins and head.

and, as seen in cross section, from middorsal to midventral line. In the tail the upper and lower portions are equal, but in the trunk there must be space for the body cavity and visceral organs below the level of the vertebrae, so that only a thin layer of muscle can surround the abdomen. leaving the bulk of body muscle on the dorsal side (Fig. 211).

Much distortion of this fundamental pattern has taken place. In birds

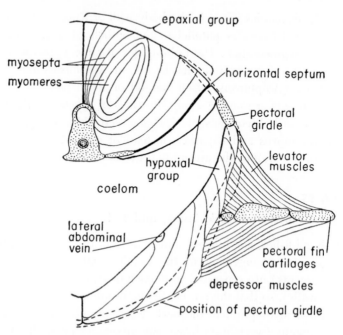

Fig. 211. Diagram of cross section through a shark, showing muscle groups and concentric pattern of myomere cones.

and mammals, which no longer travel by wriggling undulations of the body, the embryonic myotomes blend, myosepta largely disappear, and muscle fibers extend for several segments. Segmentation still shows, of course, in the vertebrae, ribs, spinal nerves, and blood vessels.

Although it may be that the series of myomeres in some remote vertebrate ancestor extended along most of the head, uninterrupted, this is not true in any known vertebrate, because the skull occupies too much of the available space in the head. Therefore the first pair of trunk myomeres attaches to the back of the skull (occiput). In most fishes this comes just behind the location of the tenth cranial nerve (vagus), because the vagus happens to be the last that is enclosed by any part of the skull. But in the degenerate modern cyclostomes the skull terminates behind the position of the eighth nerve. On the other hand, when we come to reptiles, birds and mammals there are 12 pairs of cranial nerves, and it is doubtful, then, whether the first trunk myomere is the same in all cases.

A special feature of segmental muscles is the zigzag form of the myomeres in most fishes. This seems to be related to speed in swimming, for the swiftest kinds, as tuna, swordfish, and mackerel, are those with the most acute angles in their myomeres. Moreover, in any fish the angles become sharper in the more posterior segments (Fig. 210), for the greatest activity is near the base of the tail. Here the myosepta are almost longitudinal and serve as tendons to transmit movement from muscle segments to tail vertebrae. The more nearly the myosepta lie in the direction of the muscle fibers (lengthwise), the more effective is their action. Any young fish shows at first vertical myosepta, but presently they become angled. The more sluggish Amphibia, although a "higher class" of animals than fishes, have only slightly bent myomeres.

Fishes show scarcely any differentiation of the hypaxial muscles into layers, but we find these in Amphibia (Fig. 212) and all higher animals. Ventrally, from pelvis to thorax, runs a ribbonlike paired muscle, the

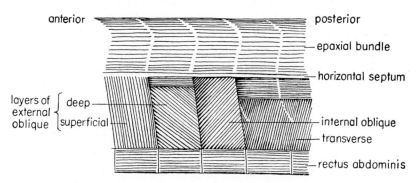

Fig. 212. Muscles of body wall in a salamander, *Dicamptodon ensatus*, partly dissected, left side.

rectus abdominis. Laterally, but below the horizontal septum, are three layers, differing in the direction of their fibers: *external oblique* (runs posteroventrad), *internal oblique* (anteroventrad), and *transversus abdominis* (dorsoventrad). Between successive ribs are segregated the *external* and *internal intercostals,* in higher tetrapods, which take part in breathing movements.

The *diaphragm* of mammals is a membranous sheet between the pleuropericardial and peritoneal cavities, to which has been added a layer of muscle derived from myomeres in the neck; it is supplied by the phrenic nerve, formed by branches of the third, fourth, and fifth cervical nerves. The action of the diaphragm is rhythmically to flatten itself from a dome shape, thereby enlarging the thorax cavity and admitting air to the lungs. This movement synchronizes with that of the intercostal muscles.

Integumental (skin) muscles of the body in reptiles, birds, and mammals are variously derived from segmental muscles directly, or from appendicular muscles. The skin-twitching muscle found in mammals, for instance (*panniculus carnosus*), develops from the *latissimus dorsi,* a shoulder muscle, and from the edge of the *pectoralis* group; it frequently spreads to envelop most of the body.

Development of special activities in certain regions results in a corresponding specialization of muscles. Thus, along with mobility of the head and neck comes the division of epaxial neck muscles into several *occipital* muscles to the skull. Muscles of the back split into three or four groups, each of considerable length. Muscles at the base of the tail may be specialized as tail waggers. The pectoral and pelvic girdles partly interrupt the course of the body muscles. This is especially true of the pelvis in birds and mammals because its bones are enlarged for increased attachment of limb muscles. The pectoral girdle, because it forms the posterior wall of the gill chamber in fishes, acts as a complete barrier to all muscles running forward, *except* those dorsal to it, and a small ventral group which extends to the lower jaw. In tetrapods, where the weight of the body must be borne by the limbs, we find portions of the body muscles attaching to the shoulder girdle internally or on its margins. For instance the *serratus* muscles act as a sling supporting the body between the scapulae, especially in mammals, and the *rhomboideus* takes a part in the same action, at a different angle.

The ventral group of throat muscles, the *hypobranchial* group, is actually a forward continuation of the hypaxial trunk muscles. It consists of paired muscles originating on the pectoral girdle (as in elasmobranchs) or sternum, and inserting on the mandible and hyoid (*coracomandibularis* and *coracohyoideus* of sharks; *sternohyoid* plus *geniohyoid,* etc., of tetrapods). These are the ventral divisions of myomeres which have their dorsal divisions *above* the gill chambers; consequently the nerves which supply them do so by taking a detour back behind the gill region and then forward ventrally. In tetrapods the tongue muscles develop largely from this group.

Eye Muscles

No muscles have departed more widely from their presumed original segmental form than the muscles that move the eyes. Embryonic development shows that they come from the first three myotomes of the head. In completed form they have a remarkably constant arrangement in all vertebrates (Fig. 213). Four *rectus* muscles originate on the wall of the orbit close to the optic foramen, and insert on the edge of the eyeball at

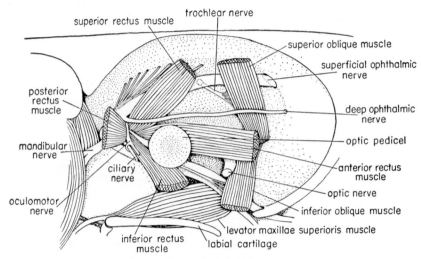

Fig. 213. Muscles and nerves of right orbit of shark, *Squalus acanthias.*

places indicated by their names: *rectus superioris, r. inferioris, r. anterioris* (or *internus* in man), *r. posterioris* (or *externus* in man). Two *obliquus* muscles originate at a point on the anterior wall of the orbit (in man the medial wall), and insert on the upper and lower edges of the eye; hence *o. superioris* and *o. inferioris.* These six, so placed, are found from cyclostomes to birds and mammals.

There is in Amphibia, reptiles, and mammals also a *retractor bulbi,* derived from the external rectus, which helps withdraw the protruding eyes. Reptiles and mammals have a *levator palpebrae superioris* to the upper eyelid, to raise it; this evidently is derived from the superior rectus. A *quadratus* and *pyramidalis,* to the nictitating membrane (third eyelid) of birds, are

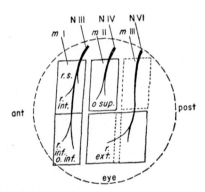

Fig. 214. Diagram of development of ocular muscles from first three myotomes. *m,* myotome; *N,* cranial nerve; *o.inf.,* inferior oblique; *o.sup.,* superior oblique; *r.ext.,* external rectus; *r.inf.,* inferior rectus; *r.int.,* internal rectus; *r.s.,* superior rectus.

derived from the third myotome, like the external rectus. In mammals the superior oblique takes a detour through a pulleylike loop in the wall of the orbit before reaching the eye.

Each of the first three myotomes, soon after its first appearance, splits into a dorsal and ventral half, and each of these gives rise to one or more muscles according to the accompanying table; only the dorsal half of the third myotome degenerates and produces nothing (Fig. 214).

In cyclostomes the myotomes behind these all persist and become

EXTRINSIC EYE MUSCLES

Muscle	Myotome	Nerve
Rectus superioris (+ lev. palp. sup.) R. internus	I, dorsal	III. Oculomotor
R. inferioris Obliquus inferioris	I, ventral	
O. superioris	II, dorsal	IV. Trochlear
R. externus (+ retr. bulbi, + quadr. + pyram.)	II, ventral + III, ventral	VI. Abducens

myomeres, but in gnathostomes, as indicated before, there is a gap in the posterior part of the head where some fail to develop.

Relation of Body Muscles to the Fins in Fishes

The supporting rays of the dorsal and anal fins usually have separate small muscles to move them (Fig. 210). Typically a fin ray has on each side an *erector,* a *depressor,* and an *inclinator* (to pull it sideways); often the fin as a whole will have a *protractor* and a *retractor.*

Muscles of the paired fins, like those of the unpaired, arise directly from the myotomes in all fishes in which their development has been studied. They lie characteristically in two groups for each fin: a ventral, more anterior group, the *abductors* or *depressors,* and a dorsal, more posterior group, the *adductors* or *levators.* Naturally the precise functions of these groups differ according to the position of the fin on the body in various fishes. A shark gives perhaps the simplest picture, where the muscles act as depressors and levators, and are but little divided into separate parts (Fig. 218).

As the limb bud appears in the embryo fish (Fig. 215) the descending tips of the myotomes in the body wall reach the base of the limb bud, and muscle buds grow into it from each myotome in the area concerned. These projecting muscle buds split into dorsal and ventral halves, and each of these again into an anterior and posterior slip. Radial fin cartilages then appear, lying parallel to and between the dorsal and ventral portions. Deeper cartilages (basals) may also arise in the body wall proper; indeed it is likely that the entire pelvis and possibly the scapulo-coracoid part of the pectoral girdle originated in this way. In any case, the fundamental dorsal-ventral division of fin muscles is thus accom-

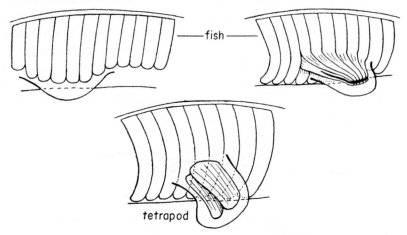

Fig. 215. Relationship of myotomes to limb bud in embryo fish (above) and tetrapod (below).

plished, and the same grouping has been shown to persist, more ob-scurely, in tetrapods.

Muscles of the Limbs in Tetrapods

During development of tetrapod limb muscles there is no direct rela-tionship between them and the body myotomes (Fig. 215). Instead the limb muscles arise from undifferentiated mesenchyme cells in the limb itself. But this is an embryonic specialization, and is not a reason to doubt the derivation of tetrapod limb muscles from those of fishes. Spinal nerves supply the limbs, and the number of nerves to each limb indicates the number of body segments to which that limb is related.

We do not know from direct evidence the intermediate stages between the limb muscle plan of fishes and that of tetrapods, since the soft parts of the appropriate early amphibians and lobefins are not preserved as fossils. But of some points we may be reasonably sure. Unlike most bony fishes the early crossopterygians had the forward edges of the paired fins tilted down; muscles of the dorsal group in these fins were therefore probably abductors and levators, while the ventral muscles were adduc-tors and depressors. They extended out on the fin far enough to cause it to undulate along its axis, as is evident from the axial series of freely movable bones. It is likewise highly probable that the muscles nearest the base of the fin were derived from more anterior myotomes than those distally, and that the whole set of fin muscles arose from five or six body segments.

On the ventral side of the forelimb the more basal muscles became the *pectoral* group primarily, of tetrapods, while on the dorsal side the basal ones produced several of the upper shoulder muscles, including *latissimus dorsi* and the *deltoids*. Farther out, the ventral muscles of the fin formed the *flexors* of arm and hand, while the more dorsal ones became *extensors*, on account of the manner in which the elbow and wrist joints developed as the fin was converted to a walking limb. (See Chapter IV.) In the hind limb similar arrangements took place.

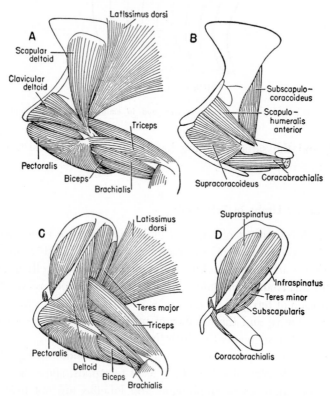

Fig. 216. Shoulder and upper arm muscles in (A, B) lizard and (C, D) opossum, lateral views. B and D are deeper layers. (From Romer.)

The following table summarizes the dorsal and ventral groups of limb muscles among the classes of tetrapods. It is incomplete, and in places probably inaccurate, because our knowledge of development is incomplete, and because the conditions are immensely more complicated than any such table can suggest. The data were drawn from a number of recent authors, especially from Romer (1942, 1944). See also Figs. 216, 217.

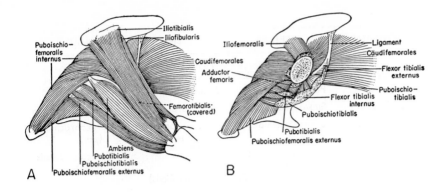

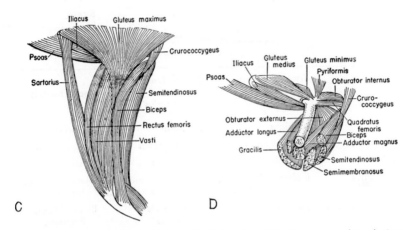

Fig. 217. Muscles of pelvis and thigh in (A, B) lizard and (C, D) opossum, lateral views. A and C, superficial; B and D, deeper layers. (From Romer.)

AMPHIBIANS	REPTILES	BIRDS	MAMMALS
Forelimb, Dorsal			
Latissimus dorsi	Latissimus dorsi + teres major	Latissimus dorsi	Latissimus dorsi + teres major
Subcoracoscapularis	Subcoracoscapularis + scapulohumeralis posterior	Subcoracoscapularis + scapulohumeralis posterior	Subscapularis
Deltoides scapularis	Deltoides scapularis	Deltoides scapularis	Deltoides scapularis
Procoracohumeralis longus	Deltoides clavicularis + humeroradialis	Deltoides propatagialis	Deltoides clavicularis
Procoracohumeralis brevis	Scapulohumeralis anterior	Scapulohumeralis anterior	Teres minor, infraspinatus, supraspinatus
Triceps (Anconeus)	Triceps	Triceps	Triceps
Also forearm extensors and supinators			

AMPHIBIANS	REPTILES	BIRDS	MAMMALS
Forelimb, Ventral			
Pectoralis	Pectoralis	Pectoralis	Pectoralis
Supracoracoideus	Supracoracoideus	Supracoracoideus	Supracoracoideus
Coracobrachialis brevis	Coracobrachialis brevis	Coracobrachialis externus + internus	Coracobrachialis (part)
Coracobrachialis longus	Coracobrachialis longus (Absent in Crocodilia and Birds)		Coracobrachialis (part)
Brachialis	Brachialis	Brachialis	Brachialis
Biceps	Biceps	Biceps	Biceps
Also forearm flexors and pronators			
Hind Limb, Dorsal			
Iliotibialis	Triceps femoris: Iliotibialis	Triceps femoris: Iliotibialis + "Sartorius"	Rectus femoris
	Ambiens	Ambiens	Sartorius
Femorotibialis	Femorotibialis	Femorotibialis	Vastus group
Iliofibularis	Iliofibularis	Iliofibularis	Tenuissimus
Ilioextensorius	Iliofemoralis	Iliofemoralis externus + Iliotrochantericus	Glutei + Tensor fasciae
Puboischiofemoralis internus	Puboischiofemoralis internus	Iliofemoralis internus	Iliacus, Psoas, Pectineus
Also extensors of lower leg and foot			
Hind Limb, Ventral			
	Flexor cruris: Puboischiotibialis		Gracilis
Puboischiotibialis	Flexor tibialis internus	Ilioflexorius	Semimembranosus, Semitendinosus, Biceps femoris
	Flexor tibialis externus	Caudilioflexorius	
Pubotibialis	Pubotibialis		
Adductor femoris	Adductor femoris	Puboischiofemoralis	Adductores femoris
Puboischiofemoralis externus	Puboischiofemoralis externus	Obturator	Obturator externus Quadratus femoris Obturator internus
	Ischiotrochantericus	Ischiofemoralis	
Caudofemoralis	Caudofemoralis brevis + longus	Coccygeofemoralis	Caudofemoralis
Also flexors of lower leg and foot			

Comparative Anatomy of the Branchiomeric Muscles

In embryos of the lower vertebrates the branchiomeric or visceral muscles appear first as slender bands running parallel to the jaw and gill bars; that is, from the cranium down to the mid-ventral line of the throat. At least this was the generalized plan; we have noted already that jaws were developed from the anterior gill arch. (See Fig. 209.)

In cyclostomes (lamprey, hagfish) the cartilaginous gill basket is external to the muscles that move it. Being elastic but not jointed, this gill basket yields to the contraction of the muscles as they squeeze the gill pouches within, and then it springs back, outward, as the muscles relax; thus the cartilages serve as antagonists to the constricting action of the muscles.

But in gnathostomes the cartilages (or bones) of the visceral arches are always jointed and lie internally to the muscles that move them. No one questions that the gill pouches, gills, blood supply, and nerves in these two major divisions correspond. To the author it seems probable that the muscles also correspond, but that the skeletal parts in the gill region do not; in other words, that the internal, jointed visceral arches of gnathostomes were not derived from the external, nonjointed arches of cyclostomes, but that both arose in ostracoderms.

Branchiomeric muscles seem to be derived embryonically from the hypomere. They probably have nothing to do with myotomes. They are supplied by cranial nerves, as follows:

Jaws	V. Trigeminal
Hyoid	VII. Facial
First branchial	IX. Glossopharyngeal
Second and succeeding branchials	X. Vagus

As the visceral arches of the embryo become movable, the simple embryonic muscle bands break into corresponding muscles, so arranged as to raise, flex, constrict, or otherwise move the parts to which they attach. For instance in a shark the embryonic jaw muscle becomes, on each side, a group of three, all supplied by the trigeminal nerve (Figs. 218, 219A):

Constrictor dorsalis—Cranium to upper jaw
Adductor mandibulae—Upper to lower jaw
Intermandibularis—Lower jaw to mid-ventral line

Likewise the hyoid muscle band forms several muscles, a *levator* of the hyomandibular cartilage, a ventral *interhyoid*, a superficial *hyoid constrictor*, etc., all supplied by the facial nerve. For each of the branchial arches there is a similar differentiation of muscles from its embryonic muscle band.

Essentially the plan just described occurs in fishes wherever the upper jaw (palatoquadrate) is not immovably fused with the cranium; that is,

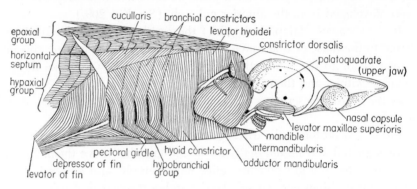

Fig. 218. Head muscles of shark, *Squalus acanthias*.

in the majority of bony fishes and in elasmobranchs except for Holocephali. Wherever there is a movable operculum a **dilator operculi** (from the jaw muscle group) and an **adductor operculi** (from the hyoid group) are present to move it.

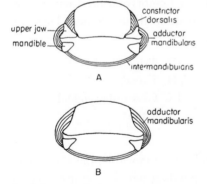

Fig. 219. A, arrangement of muscles (cross section) when upper jaw is movably articulated to cranium; B, when upper jaw is fused to cranium, showing spread of area of origin of adductor mandibularis, and loss of constrictor dorsalis.

The **adductor mandibulae** tends to divide into two, three, or more parts, one of which (Fig. 220), in most teleost fishes, inserts on the loose maxillary bone instead of the lower jaw, and takes part in the familiar protrusion of the mouth practiced by most fishes. Fishes such as Holocephali and Dipnoi, which do not have a movable palatoquadrate, have lost at the same time the **constrictor dorsalis** usually found between upper jaw and cranium. This encourages the adductor mandibulae to extend its area of origin upon the cranium itself, just as we find in most tetrapods (Fig. 219B).

The adductors of the jaw, by which we chew or bite, are usually more complex in tetrapods than in fishes. They take origin from the sides of the cranium, or from the inner faces of dermal roofing bones (in case the skull is covered by a "deck"), and insert on the lower jaw; this has an upright crest, the coronoid process, for their attachment. In mammals

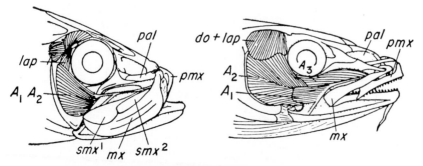

Fig. 220. Modifications of jaw muscles in herring (left) and cod (right), in connection with mobility of upper jaws. (From Eaton, 1935, J. Morphology, Vol. 58 (1): 171, 172.) A_1, A_2, A_3, divisions of adductor; do, dilator of operculum; lap., levator of primary upper jaw; mx, maxillary; pal, palatine; pmx, premaxillary; smx, supramaxillary.

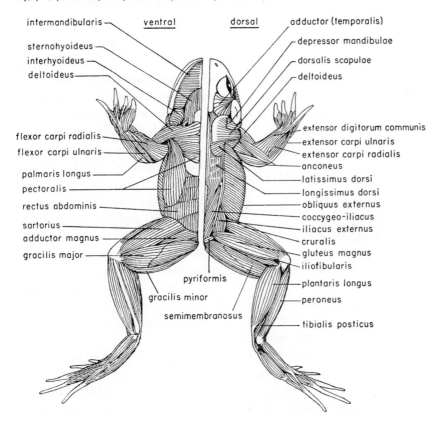

Fig. 221. Muscles of green frog, Rana clamitans; ventral aspect on left, dorsal on right.

and in several other groups which have a large temporal opening bounded by a bridge of bone laterally, there is a deep adductor, the *temporalis,* originating on the cranium and largely filling the temporal

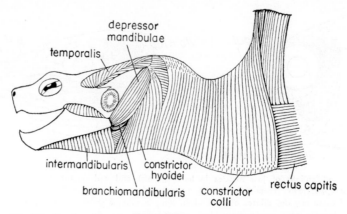

Fig. 222. Muscles of head and neck of snapping turtle, *Chelydra serpentina.*

fossa, while a more superficial *masseter* originates on the arch laterally; there are also one or more *pterygoid* muscles, coming from the floor of the cranium and inserting diagonally on the inner face of the lower jaw.

At the time of transformation from fish to amphibian the levator of the hyoid arch (in fishes) shifted its insertion forward slightly so that it attached to the lower jaw and became the *depressor mandibulae,* to open the mouth. This change of function and position can be seen also in the metamorphosis of salamanders from larvae to adults. The depressor so formed is present in Amphibia, reptiles, and birds (Figs. 221, 222). But in mammals the muscle to open the mouth is the *digastric* (Fig. 223), which develops in part from the embryonic hyoid group and partly from the intermandibularis or mylohyoid muscle of the lower jaw; it is therefore compound, and is innervated by both the fifth and seventh nerves.

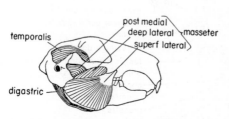

Fig. 223. Jaw muscles of rabbit. (Modified from Parker and Haswell, after Tullberg.)

We have seen before that the hyomandibular bone of fishes became the stapes, a sound-transmitting bone of the middle ear of tetrapods. With it there went also a small vestige of the levator hyoidei of fishes, to become the *stapedius,* which is the smallest skeletal muscle we have; it is served, of course, by a branch of the seventh nerve.

From the ventral portion of the hyoid muscle series there develops a broad thin sheet, the **constrictor colli,** enclosing most of the neck in reptiles (Fig. 222) and birds. This corresponds in part to the **platysma** of mammals, which inserts on the skin of the neck. From the platysma have

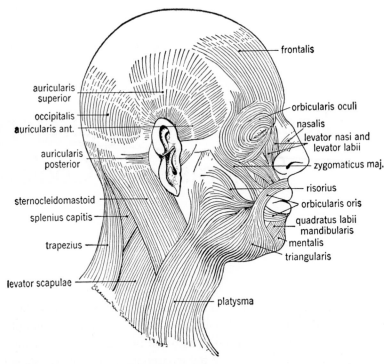

Fig. 224. Human facial muscles. (Reproduced by permission from *Comparative Anatomy* by L. A. Adams and S. Eddy, published by John Wiley & Sons, Inc., 1949.)

arisen numerous small dermal muscles concerned with movement of the face, ears, nose, eyelids, and lips in many kinds of mammals. They are especially important as the **muscles of facial expression** in Primates (Fig. 224). Their hyoid origin is betrayed by innervation from the seventh (facial) nerve.

CHAPTER VII

Digestive and Respiratory Systems, and Coelom

THE SURFACE of the body turns in at the mouth, to run as a tube through to the anus; this surface is everywhere continuous, an unbroken epithelium, and therefore anything taken into the passage is still actually external to the body, still a part of the environment (Fig. 225). Since the outer integument of most animals cannot serve to absorb food, even if this is present in contact with the body, the digestive system is specially equipped both to hold prospective food and to absorb, through its unbroken lining, any materials to which this is permeable. Here is the crux of the problem: food becomes usable only if it can pass through the semi-permeable membrane into the blood, lymph, or tissue fluid.

Water can do this; so can most salts, simple sugars, amino acids, and some other substances, without change except that they must be in solution. But proteins, starch, and the more complex sugars, fats, etc., do not pass through such a membrane, and the main reason is the relatively great size of their molecules. These must therefore be broken, by hydrolysis or other reactions, into smaller ones; this is *digestion.* As soon as any of the products of these reactions appear, they are absorbed, but the *absorption* and *transportation* of food to the tissues is not a part of digestion. Furthermore, the separation of big molecules into their smaller components (as proteins to amino acids) may be only a temporary matter, for many of the latter, after passing through the membrane, recombine to make big molecules, sometimes in the plasma of the blood, most often in the protoplasm of cells to which they are brought. Naturally the re-

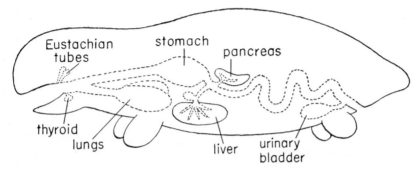

Fig. 225. Digestive canal and its derivatives, in which the lining originates from endoderm.

combining usually follows different patterns so that the compounds produced are not those from which the materials were first obtained.

Since protochordates and fishes all live in water and obtain their food and also their oxygen from it, any system developed for the digestion and absorption of food would be available without too much inconvenience for respiration as well. Thus the digestive and respiratory organs are usually specialized parts of the same canal, and in lower chordates it is difficult to consider their anatomy separately. An organ of respiration is one in which blood with low oxygen concentration is given access, as closely as possible, through semipermeable membranes, to oxygen of higher concentration dissolved in water outside the body. Even in the lungs of air-breathing vertebrates this is still the case, for oxygen from the air must dissolve in the film of water within the alveolar spaces before it can actually diffuse through and enter the blood.

Digestive and Respiratory Organs of Protochordates

In each group of protochordates and in the larvae of cyclostomes there is a feeding mechanism fundamentally different from that of the familiar vertebrates. It has these characteristics: sticky mucus secreted by cells in or near the beginning of the digestive canal, entanglement of microscopic food by this mucus, transportation of the mucus and food into the digestive tract by continuously beating cilia on the mucous surface, and openings in the wall of the pharynx through which a current of water produced by the cilia can escape. Since this mechanism and the micro-phagous (microscopic feeding) habit are present in Hemichorda, Uro-chorda, Cephalochorda, and up into the lowest vertebrates, they must enter any discussion of the origin of Chordata, and we shall refer to them again in that connection.

In the sessile group of Hemichorda there are two genera, *Cephalo-discus* and *Rhabdopleura;* in both of these food is conveyed into the mouth by ciliated tentacles (Fig. 5) and in the former water escapes by a single pair of "gill slits" whose function can scarcely be conceived as respiratory. The wormlike types, *Balanoglossus* and its relatives, have no tentacles but burrow in, and swallow, sea mud or sand. They retain, how-ever, the ciliary feeding device, ac-cording to Barrington (1940), who finds that when the animal protrudes from its burrow, the ciliated epithe-lium of the proboscis and collar catches food particles (Fig. 226) and passes them towards the mouth, "the mobile lip of the collar providing a re-jection mechanism." Inside the phar-ynx there is a partial division into up-per and lower passages, the former

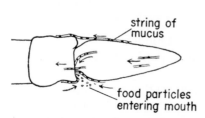

string of mucus

food particles entering mouth

Fig. 226. Direction of ciliary feeding cur-rents on proboscis and collar of *Glosso-balanus minutus,* a hemichordate. (After Barrington.)

running between the two series of gill slits where water runs out, and the latter towards the opening of the simple straight intestine. But Barrington believes that there is no distinction between these passages so far as food is concerned, and that the gill bars help trap food just as in Amphioxus.

Amphioxus (Cephalochorda) and the tunicates (Urochorda) are much alike in their pharyngeal basket. The *pharynx* of these (Figs. 8, 9), and of lower vertebrates as well, might be defined as the anterior region of the alimentary canal where food is separated from the water by a sieve or basket arrangement in its walls. When this sort of pharynx had become established, the persistent water current through the sieve made it pos-sible to use the bars for gills. In Amphioxus most of the food-catching mucus originates in a trough on the floor of the pharynx, the *endostyle,* from which cilia carry it forward, then laterad along *peripharyngeal bands* to the dorsal side, where an *epipharyngeal groove* transmits it back to the esophagus. Nothing is changed from this in the simple tunicates (Ascidia) except the orientation, for a tunicate grows on a surface so that the mouth is farthest up or away from that surface, and the intestine is bent around to bring the anus likewise away from the substratum. In both Cephalochorda and Urochorda the water escapes from the pharynx through a large number of minute slits separated by very delicate bars, and is then in an outer chamber, the *atrium,* from which it leaves by the *atriopore.*

As to the gills in protochordates: in *Balanoglossus* (Figs. 3, 4) and its relatives the slits open from the dorsal part of the pharynx into an external dorsal groove. Each slit is U-shaped because, having developed as an oval opening, it is nearly cut in two by a *secondary gill bar* growing down from its dorsal rim. Between these secondary bars and the *primary* ones (separating the original slits) there usually extend little bridges, the *synapticulae.* The number of gill slits is indeterminate, increasing with age.

A similar arrangement of primary and secondary bars is seen in Amphioxus, except that here the secondaries completely cut the original openings into two. Synapticulae are numerous. The whole basket is more complex and delicate. In tunicates the pharyngeal basket appears to stand upright, as mentioned above, and this means the original slits are now horizontal, while the synapticulae, far more numerous than before, are vertical, and the basket seems to contain many rows of very small slits.

"Ammocoetes" and the Thyroid Gland

The larva of a lamprey is radically different from the adult and was described as another genus, *Ammocoetes,* before its relationship was known; this name is still used as a convenience in speaking of it. The *Ammocoetes* looks and behaves much like Amphioxus, burrowing in the sand of rivers and creeks, but it has no atrium, and fewer (seven pairs of) pouched gill clefts. It feeds, however, by a ciliary and mucous mechanism essentially the same as in Amphioxus; there is an epipharyngeal and a hypopharyngeal ciliated groove, connected anteriorly by two peripharyngeal bands (Fig. 227). But midway in the hypopharyngeal groove is a ventral slit leading down into a complex glandular sac (Leach, 1944). This has been called the endostyle; it develops as a pocket from the ciliated epithelium of the groove. Evidently the hypopharyngeal groove as a whole corresponds to the endostyle of Amphioxus, and the sac may be called the *subpharyngeal gland.*

During transformation from the microphagous larva to the parasitic adult lamprey, the sac closes and in part becomes the *thyroid gland.* In sharks the thyroid originates likewise as an open pouch in the floor of the pharynx of the embryo, retaining a duct in the primitive shark *Chlamydoselachus,* and it also develops from ventral pharyngeal epithelium in higher vertebrates. This important endocrine gland takes the form of scattered follicles in *Amia* and many teleosts, while in others it forms two to four masses. Amphibia generally have two lobes in the thyroid gland, and it is either simple or lobed in the reptiles, birds, and mammals.

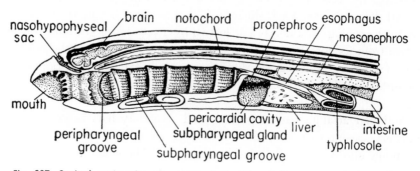

Fig. 227. Sagittal section through anterior half of larval lamprey, *Ammocoetes*. (After Goodrich.)

The transforming lamprey loses the ciliated bands, enlarges the anterior part of the head into a sucking disc with horny teeth (Fig. 101; compare with Fig. 228), and develops a hydrostatic pumping apparatus (Reynolds, 1931), of which the major elements are a complete separation between the esophagus (dorsally) and the respiratory part of the pharynx (ventrally); a valve called the **velum** to block the latter passage while blood is being sucked into the mouth; and a toothed, pistonlike "tongue" for cutting the skin of the fish on which the lamprey clings. The esophagus leads to the straight, slender intestine, whose inner surface is increased by a somewhat spiral fold, the *typhlosole* (Fig. 227). There is a liver, but the gall bladder, present in *Ammocoetes*, is lost; there is no distinct pancreas.

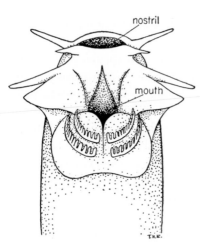

Fig. 228. Hagfish, ventral side of head, showing nostril, tentacles, mouth, and horny teeth. (Sketch from model in American Museum of Natural History.)

It is important to add that the gills are in pouches, each opening by a small passage inward to the pharynx and by another pore outward to the surface (Fig. 239). Using the muscular outer wall, the lamprey pumps water in and out of the pouches through the external pores. This is the only way to supply a breathing current while the lamprey feeds or clings to stones with its mouth.

Digestive Organs of Gnathostomes

When we recall that protochordates are microphagous, that the earliest known vertebrates were jawless ostracoderms, and that the first fishes to develop jaws (acanthodians) did so by placing upon a gill arch the additional labor of bearing teeth, it becomes clear that the coming of jaws had something to do with a change from microscopic to larger units of food. These larger units, usually whole animals, take an appreciable time to digest, and so must be held in an elastic pouch, the *stomach*, until this is nearly accomplished. Most chemical phases of digestion and the greater part of absorption then take place in the remainder of the canal, the *intestine.*

Some important features of the digestive system of vertebrates in general should be noticed here. The mouth enters an *oral cavity*, the lining of which is derived from the ectoderm of the stomodeum in the embryo, and this is the region in which teeth may be found. The *pharynx* is the beginning of that part of the digestive canal whose lining is derived from endoderm. It is the part concerned with gill respiration (gills, gill arches, clefts) in fishes and larval Amphibia, and with related features (as the Eustachian tubes) in higher vertebrates. Also it is the region in which "voluntary" action in swallowing ends and the food is passed on to the involuntary control of the esophagus. Because of numerous mechanical devices for carrying out these functions of swallowing and of respiration, the pharynx contains much of interest to the comparative anatomist.

From the esophagus down to the end of the intestine, the mechanism for propelling food along the tract consists of layers of smooth muscle under control of the autonomic nervous system. Since these comprise two of the five generally recognizable layers of the wall of the tube, we should notice these as diagrammed in Fig. 229. Innermost, next to the lumen of the esophagus, stomach or intestine, is the *mucosa*, an epithelium derived from endoderm; frequently it is ciliated and nearly always it is glandular, as its name suggests. Folds, villi, and pitlike digestive glands occur in various parts of the canal as modifications of the mucosa. Next is a *submucosa*, filled with fibrous tissue, blood and lymph vessels, a few smooth muscle cells, and nerve endings. Now a strong layer of *circular muscle* follows, and this becomes greatly thickened at the entrances to, and exits from, certain parts of the tract; such ringlike thick constrictors are called *sphincter* muscles. ***Longitudinal muscle*** covers the circular layer on the outside, its function being, obviously, to shorten parts of the tract and resist stretching by large objects within. The *serosa* (peritoneum) covers the outside of all digestive organs. It is simply connective tissue, continuous with that which makes mesenteries and the lining of the coelom.

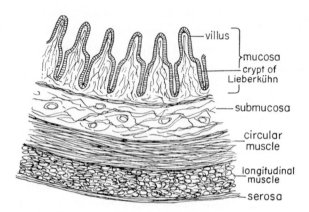

Fig. 229. Layers of wall of small intestine, diagrammatic.

(All these layers except the mucosa are derived from embryonic mesoderm.)

At the end of the tract the *anus* and its lining are formed by the pushing in of the embryonic proctodeum (ectoderm). In most classes of vertebrates the excretory and reproductive systems also employ the same opening; that is, a portion of the lower end of the digestive tract, called the *cloaca*, receives the ducts from these systems.

FISHES

Mouths of fishes are usually terminal (at the end of the head), but in several groups, as sharks and rays, sturgeons, some catfishes, etc., they are ventral. In a few (e.g., halfbeaks) the mouth is dorsal. It varies in size from the immense gape of angler fishes and gulpers to the tiny tube of a sea horse or pipefish. All these and other modifications are correlated with the nature of the food and manner in which it must be obtained. A fish has no movable tongue and no salivary glands, but taste buds and mucous glands are widely distributed in the mouth and often on the skin of the head.

While a simple opening and closing of the mouth, by abducting and adducting the mandible, is a sufficient mechanism in primitive fishes to get food into their mouths, many progressive groups develop additional complex movements of the upper jaw. The marginal jaw bones, premaxillary and maxillary, both carry teeth in such teleosts as herring, but in the perchlike fishes the premaxillary alone forms the margin of the jaw, and the toothless maxillary is incorporated into a system of levers, with the palatine, for protracting and retracting the premaxillaries. The movement is brought about partly by a ligament to the lower jaw, and partly by a separate division of the adductor mandibulae muscle, inserting on the maxillary. The general significance of this protractile mechanism is that the fish, having no independent mobility of head and neck, can bite or nibble at its food with the jaws alone, without involving the entire body in each part of the action. In at least three groups other than perchlike teleosts, a protractile mechanism occurs with a contrasting and obviously independent pattern.

On the internal faces of the gill bars most fishes have rows of toothlike or comblike *gill-rakers,* so placed as to overlap the gill clefts except when the pharyngeal walls are distended. Evidently this is an arrangement to prevent loss of food through the gill-clefts with the respiratory current. The form, number, and relative sizes of the gill-rakers are quite constant for a species, but show differences among species and genera, so that they are useful in classification. Some marine teleosts, such as herring and menhaden, have complex pharyngeal screens, formed by the gill-rakers and gill-bars, for straining plankton from the water; this makes it possible to take advantage of the great supply of microscopic food in the sea and thus accounts for the tremendous numerical success of these teleosts, which in turn serve as food for the predatory species.

The esophagus is a short passage from pharynx to stomach, usually equipped with a sphincter strong enough to shut out water, except when it is relaxed for swallowing. The epithelium is stratified. The entrance to the stomach is indefinite as a rule, marked only by the presence of gastric glands, columnar epithelium, and increased diameter. The lining of esophagus and stomach may both be folded. Gastric glands are usually deep and flask-shaped. The stomach in fishes is most often J-shaped, but may be a blind sac with both openings placed anteriorly. Some deep-sea fishes have a stomach so distensible as to hold prey larger than themselves. It is thick and gizzardlike in mullets (Mugilidae) and the gizzard-shad (*Dorosoma*). The exit from the stomach is the *pylorus;* usually but not always there is a *pyloric valve* (sphincter muscle). The majority of teleost fishes have blind pouches or tubes at this point called *pyloric ceca,* which are thought to secrete digestive juice. Ammodytes (sand-lance) has one; flatfishes have two, three, or several; salmon, cod, and mackerel have a great many, up to 100 or 200; catfishes, pike, and pipefish have none.

The *liver* and *pancreas,* digestive glands of great importance, empty their ducts into the beginning of the intestine. Ordinarily the liver is large, filling most of the body cavity in some sharks, and has two or three lobes. Within the liver are great numbers of branching **hepatic ducts,** which secrete bile. The ducts converge into a **common bile duct** (**ductus choledochus**), which then connects with the intestine near the pyloric valve. The **gall bladder** is simply a nonglandular pouch out of the common bile duct, serving for retention of bile; its wall contains a small amount of smooth muscle so that it can be contracted. The neck of the gall bladder, entering the common bile duct, is the **cystic duct.** Thus the liver is a very large gland with a supplementary reservoir for its secretion,

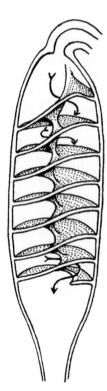

but bile contains no digestive enzymes. Certain salts in it have a physical effect on fat in the food, causing large drops to break into smaller ones by a reduction of their surface tension, thus increasing enormously the surface area exposed to fat-digesting enzymes. But the liver is much more than a digestive gland. It is the organ to which the hepatic portal vein carries all absorbed food from the digestive canal, where sugar can be removed and stored as glycogen, and where broken-down hemoglobin from the red blood cells is cast off in the form of bile pigments. Therefore the tissues between the hepatic ducts consist largely of capillaries and venous sinuses, many of them of considerable size. Blood brought to the liver by (1) the hepatic portal vein, and (2) the hepatic artery, is drained from the hepatic sinuses into the postcaval vein.

The *pancreas,* like the liver, starts embryonically as a pouch from the gut, presently developing into a soft glandular organ containing branching ducts. It is essentially a magnified intestinal gland secreting a fluid containing enzymes. But interspersed among its branching ducts are clusters of endocrine tissue, the *islets of Langerhans,* which secrete insulin into the blood. The pancreas is a distinct, two-lobed gland in sharks, but may be very hard to find in a teleost, where

Fig. 230. Spiral valve in *Raja.*

it is sometimes hidden in the liver and may use the same duct for its secretion.

The *intestine* of primitive fishes has a feature of great interest, the *spiral valve* (Fig. 230). It is a fold of the inner wall, usually running spirally down like a winding stairway. The turns may so far overlap as to resemble a scroll. This "valve" is represented in cyclostomes by the nearly straight typhlosole, and there is evidence that it occurred in a placoderm, *Bothriolepis*, of the Devonian period (Denison, 1941). It is best developed in Chondrichthyes but continues in lungfishes, *Polypterus*, sturgeons, and *Amia*, finally vanishing in the most primitive teleosts. It is a device to increase the absorptive area of the intestine. The same object is served among plant-feeding or mud-grubbing teleosts by lengthening and looping the intestine; in the mud-eating stone-roller minnow, *Campostoma*, the intestine coils around the air bladder. As a general rule

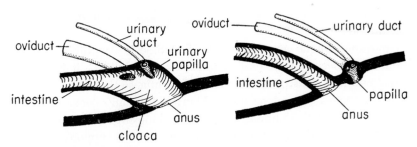

Fig. 231. Relationship of urinary and genital ducts to intestine in fish with cloaca, such as shark (left), and fish without cloaca, as teleost (right).

among vertebrates the herbivorous types have a long intestine, the predatory or carnivorous types a short and simple one.

There is little point in trying to distinguish a small and large intestine in fishes, but there is often a **rectum,** from which in elasmobranchs a dorsal blind pouch, the **rectal gland,** is given off. The elasmobranchs and Dipnoi have a *cloaca* (Fig. 231), as no doubt the crossopterygians did also, but in Actinopteri the anus lies in front of the urinogenital opening. The anus in a few teleosts is brought far forward, even to the throat in the electric eel and pirate perch (*Aphredoderus*).

AMPHIBIANS AND REPTILES

The digestive organs of these animals are usually simple and quite comparable with those in mammals. But certain innovations appeared with the adaptation to terrestrial life. A tight fit is necessary between the upper and lower margins of the mouth, usually obtained by a pliable fleshy edge, outside of the rows of teeth. These lips are not muscular, however, except in mammals. Sometimes, as in turtles, a horny beak makes the rim of the mouth. Here the loss of water by evaporation is minimized partly by the close fit and partly by reducing the area of mucous membrane in the lining of the mouth.

With life on land there came also multicellular salivary glands in the mouth, secreting a sticky mucus. These are not conspicuously developed until we come to mammals, but some reptiles, especially snakes which swallow large prey, have a copious secretion of saliva. Among poisonous snakes these glands, opening through or in proximity to teeth in the upper jaw, become enlarged and secrete a powerful venom. This is either **hemolytic** (destructive to blood cells and capillaries), as found in nearly all the pit-vipers, or **neurotoxic** (causing nerve paralysis), as in the cobras, coral snakes, sea snakes, etc. The poison glands and grooved teeth of Gila monsters are in the lower jaw; their venom has both hemolytic and neurotoxic effects.

A movable **tongue** appears for the first time in Amphibia. Although absent in primitive frogs (Aglossa: *Xenopus* and *Pipa*) it is normally present and free at its posterior edge in Salientia, so that it can be flipped out of the mouth to catch an insect. Many but not all salamanders of the lungless family Plethodontidae have a stalked mushroomlike tongue (Fig. 232), which they shoot out for the same reason; it is supported by cartilages of the hyoid apparatus and propelled by specialized muscles. In

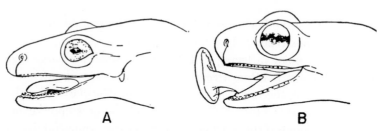

Fig. 232. Tongues of two plethodontid salamanders: A, *Desmognathus fuscus*, tongue attached in front; B, *Eurycea bislineata*, tongue free and stalked. (From *Biology of the Amphibia* by Noble.)

one Central American genus this apparatus extends in the abdominal wall as far back as the pelvis.

The tongue remains short in turtles, Crocodilia, the iguanid lizards, and geckoes, but is a long, forked, tactile organ in the monitors, whiptail lizards, and snakes. In the Old World chameleons it is stalked, with a pad at the end, and can be shot out to an astonishing distance. Each group with a protractile tongue has a pit or groove in the floor of the mouth to receive it when it is retracted; with snakes and the monitor lizards the opening of this pit and also the glottis are located well forward, for the animal swallows large prey slowly and must be able to continue breathing while doing so.

The stomach, usually simple among amphibians and reptiles, becomes gizzardlike in Crocodilia; that is, a thick-walled lower portion with a smooth lining receives food from the upper, glandular, and thinner-walled *proventriculus.* That this was true also in some of the dinosaurs is suggested by the discovery of little heaps of "gizzard stones" in the location of a stomach in some cases, these smooth pebbles having been swallowed and used as a grinding mill in the same way that grain-eating birds use gravel.

Following the general rule already mentioned, the intestine is longer and more complex in herbivorous than in carnivorous types. A good example of the difference is shown by tadpoles and adult frogs. Most tadpoles (e.g., *Rana*) are algae-feeders, and their intestines, much longer than the body, wind spirally; the frog, however, eating insects and other animal food, has a short and simple intestine. When tadpoles are reared on a partial meat diet, the intestine shortens accordingly. Often a distinction appears in amphibians and reptiles between the small intestine and the expanded *colon.* An intestinal pouch, the *cecum,* is present in some lizards. A cloaca is characteristic of all reptiles. Among freshwater turtles this is often provided with thin-walled vascular sacs just inside the anus, in and out of which water can be pumped; they serve as accessory breathing organs, which we might call "cloacal gills" by analogy with the rectal gills of dragonfly larvae.

BIRDS

Since birds, like reptiles, usually swallow food whole and with great rapidity, they have little use for salivary glands, but mucous glands are present, in the secretion of which ptyalin occurs. The beak, a horny epidermal structure, takes the place of the toothed jaws of archosaurian ancestors, except in the early fossil birds where teeth still hung on.

The tongue is ordinarily simple and spear-shaped, not the fleshy type found in mammals. In parrots it is club-shaped and solid enough to help in manipulating and cracking nuts or seeds. In woodpeckers it is long and highly protractile.

The *crop,* present in many birds, is a distensible pouch out of the esophagus, serving the same function as cheek pouches in a hamster, namely to receive a large quantity of food quickly, for temporary storage, so that the bird can get away in a hurry if need be. Pigeons have a crop secretion, "pigeons' milk," as supplementary food for the young, and oddly enough, this secretion can be stimulated by the anterior pituitary hormone, prolactin, which is responsible for inducing milk secretion in mammals.

The stomach is of the simple reptilian type in flesh-eating or fish-eating birds (Fig. 233), but among seed-eaters it becomes divided into an upper, thin-walled, glandular *proventriculus* and a lower, muscular *gizzard*, with a horny lining. Here, with the help of grit, resistant seeds and grain can be milled. (Incidentally the fact that endoderm, which normally forms a mucosa, can produce locally a stiff horny layer, is worth special notice.)

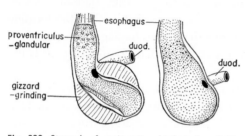

Fig. 233. Stomach of grain-eating bird, turkey (left), and carrion eater, buzzard (right). (Redrawn from Kingsley, *Outlines of Comparative Anatomy of Vertebrates*, 3rd ed., Blakiston.)

The intestine, sometimes divided into *duodenum, ileum,* and *rectum,* leaves the stomach near its middle or upper end, then receives one or two bile ducts (the gall bladder is often lacking), curves back under the slender, lobed pancreas, and then forms several close loops before reaching the cloaca. Most frequently a pair of ceca are developed near the lower end, and they may be ciliated or contain villi; those of owls are especially long. Some birds have only one, although that of ostriches is about as large as the rest of the intestine; woodpeckers, parrots, and some others have no ceca. The *bursa Fabricii* is a dorsal pouch out of the cloaca, connecting with the proctodeum, found in many birds (e.g., ducks). The cloaca is commonly in three parts: *coprodeum,* receiving the rectum; *urodeum,* into which empty the excretory and reproductive ducts; *proctodeum,* next to the anus, and lined with ectoderm because it forms in the embryo as a pocket from outside.

MAMMALS

Among the most distinctive characters of mammals are those of the mouth. We have seen that *heterodont dentition* and a *hard palate* (Fig. 234), separating the oral and nasal cavities from each other, were established, or nearly so, in the mammal-like reptiles. These imply that the habit of holding food in the mouth for gnawing or chewing had also begun, and from this it is perhaps a fair inference that the advanced Therapsid reptiles had fleshy lips and cheeks, as well as a slight side-to-side mobility of the lower jaw. It is impossible, of course, to be certain of details of the soft parts in extinct reptiles, such as mucous and salivary glands, but these are more extensively developed in mammals than in the other vertebrate classes, again in correlation with the activity of the mouth and jaws in starting digestion.

Mucous glands are abundant on the inner surface of the lips (*vestibule*), and also in the lining of oral cavity and pharynx. The *salivary glands* represent massive outpocketings of the mucous lining, secreting either a mucous or a watery saliva, or both, with the carbohydrate-digesting enzyme *ptyalin*. (This enzyme has been demonstrated in many mammals, some birds, and frogs.) In man and many

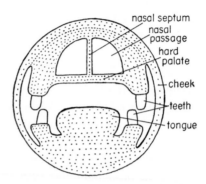

Fig. 234. Diagram of relationship between teeth, tongue, cheeks, and hard palate in mammals.

other mammals there are three pairs of salivary glands: the large *parotid* gland, located behind the masseter muscle and below the articulation of the mandible, opening by *Stenson's duct* inside the cheek; the *submaxillary* along the lower edge of the mandible, opening through *Wharton's duct* just under the front of the tongue; the *sublingual,* which opens by several *ducts of Rivinus* on the inner face of the gums. Both sympathetic and parasympathetic nerves supply the secretory cells of these glands, except the parotid, where the secretion is induced only by the parasympathetic. The significance of this is that a watery or serous fluid comes from the cells with parasympathetic innervation, and a thick mucus from those with sympathetic; stimulation of the latter nerves causes the more anterior glands to secrete mucus, but stimulating parasympathetic nerves (facial and glossopharyngeal) brings about a serous secretion from all three.

The tongue of mammals, equipped with mucous glands and both tactile and chemical sense-receptors, is a mobile organ to manipulate food in chewing, to propel it back to the pharynx, to reject, and to discriminate. Among some herbivores it is prehensile (giraffe, cow, etc.), to pull grass or leaves into the mouth. It is commonly used for lapping or for grooming (as in cats), and with anteaters it is a sticky tool for licking up ants and termites. Such an organ is obviously very different from the stiff, bony, often tooth-bearing "tongue" of a fish. The latter may be called the *primary tongue* among vertebrates. With life on land there is usually formed some sort of muscular *secondary tongue,* variously specialized as we have noted, and this reaches its most complex structure in mammals, its bulk being largely due to muscles derived from the longitudinal group between mandible and hyoid. *Taste buds* are aggregations of neuro-epithelial cells, either placed at random on the surface or clustered in and around *papillae;* their sensory nerves are (anteriorly) the facial and (posteriorly) glossopharyngeal.

In the mucous lining of the pharynx, back of the tongue, are sensory endings stimulated by contact with food or water, which thus act as a trigger setting off the swallowing reflex; included in this reflex is a dropping of the epiglottis (to prevent food going the "wrong way" into the larynx), relaxation of the esophageal sphincter, inhibition of breathing movements, and contraction of pharyngeal muscles. The *uvula* or "soft palate" in man is a part of the sensory trigger mechanism, and is not involved in propelling the food. Nearly always the smooth circular and longitudinal muscles of the esophagus, under autonomic control, take over the transmission of food from here to the stomach, but in a few mammals, as the cud-chewers, the esophagus is supplied by striated muscle and its action can be reversed voluntarily to regurgitate the cud for additional grinding. In the long neck of a camel, for instance, one can watch the passage both ways, as the cud makes a traveling bulge that shows through the skin.

The stomach is simple in most mammals, with a folded lining that allows for expansion and increase of surface area. That of man (Fig. 235) is a good example. It has no fixed shape, since in life it is active and mobile, but its most distinct landmarks are these: *cardia,* where the esophagus opens through an easily forced sphincter, and where the stratified epithelium of the esophagus changes to one with tubular glands; *fundus,* the swollen pocket on the left, which, like the *body* below it, secretes gastric juice containing hydrochloric acid, pepsin, rennin, and sometimes lipase;

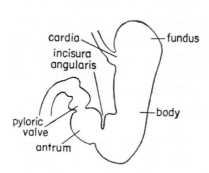

Fig. 235. Outline of human stomach.

pylorus (*antrum*), the narrower, lower right side, more active mechanically than chemically; *pyloric opening,* with a strong valve or sphincter, which can be forced under considerable pressure when food is ready to enter the intestine. A constriction, the *incisura angularis,* frequently appears in the *lesser curvature* (right-hand margin), but it is not an anatomical feature, since it moves along towards the pylorus and a new one appears above it; this is simply a special form of peristaltic movement, a wave of constriction of circular muscle passing slowly around the bend to mix the food and create a pressure in the direction of the pyloric exit.

Multicellular glands are scattered throughout the epithelial lining, but especially in the fundus and body, to the number of about 35 million. Each gland (Fig. 236) has a short *neck* and a *body,* which is often branched. In the neck are *mucous neck cells;* the body contains *zymogenic cells* and *parietal cells,* the former producing pepsin and the latter hydrochloric acid. In the fundus and body of the stomach, then, the glands supply mucus, pepsin, and hydrochloric acid. In the pylorus, however, only mucous neck cells occur in the glands, so that their secretion has no pepsin and is alkaline instead of acid. The same is true of glands adja-

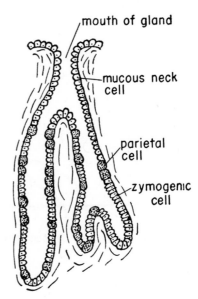

Fig. 236. A gastric gland.

cent to the cardiac opening. The esophagus is mostly nonglandular but has mucous glands near its lower end.

Some idea of the relationship between stomach parts in various mammals can be gained by seeing the distribution of these glandular regions. In *Hyrax* the fundus and a large part of the body are without digestive glands, although the stomach is shaped like that of man. In a porpoise, the stomach has three or four distinct chambers, of which the first, likewise, resembles the esophagus in its nonglandular lining. The well-known four-chambered stomach of a cow (Fig. 237) contains three parts in which glands are absent: *rumen,* a large smooth-walled cavity; *reticulum,* a smaller space lined with honeycomb pouches (tripe); and *omasum* or

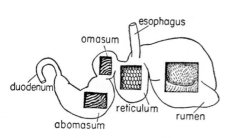

Fig. 237. A ruminant stomach. (Modified from Parker and Haswell, after Flower and Lydekker.)

psalterium, lined with folds like the leaves of a book. Only the fourth part, the *abomasum,* contains glands corresponding to those described in the human stomach. The rumen and reticulum are simply reservoirs from which swallowed vegetation, formed into a ball, can be regurgitated as a cud up the esophagus for repeated chewing. Camels have numerous small sacs emerging from the walls of their stomachs where they store water after a long drink and hold it there by sphincter muscles.

The liver usually has two large divisions, each split again into two or more lobes, and the gall bladder is present in all but a few mammals (perissodactyls, cetaceans, hyracoids, and such rodents as rats). The pancreas is a slender forked or bilobed gland with one to three ducts opening into the duodenum close to the bile duct (Fig. 238).

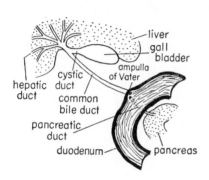

Fig. 238. Connections of liver, pancreas, and intestine (human), simplified.

Herbivorous mammals have not only a relatively long intestine but often an immense **cecum** at the beginning of the colon, while carnivores tend to reduce or lose the cecum and have a short intestine. The small wormlike **appendix** in man and apes is considered to be a vestige of a more extended cecum. The *Hyrax*, peculiar in so many ways, has two extra ceca along the colon. The small intestine of mammals can be divided into **duodenum** (loop below stomach and pancreas), **jejunum,** and **ileum** (the greater part). Most of its lining is well supplied with folds and microscopic **villi,** fingerlike projections of the mucosa, each containing a capillary loop and a lacteal vessel. The latter is a minute branch of the lymphatic system, serving to absorb fat from the contents of the intestine, while the blood capillaries absorb digested amino acids, carbohydrates, salts, etc. Between the longitudinal and circular muscle layers lie plexuses of autonomic nerves, responsible for the slow wavelike contraction of the intestinal walls, called **peristalsis,** which urges the food along. Such movement, with local modifications, takes place throughout the tract from esophagus to rectum. The **colon** is mainly a place for water absorption. A **cloaca** persists in the monotremes and in female marsupials; otherwise mammals have the anus separate from the urinary and reproductive openings.

Gills in Fishes and Amphibians

The arrangement of gill pouches in the pharyngeal wall as seen in such ostracoderms as *Cephalaspis* is probably very near to the ancestral pattern from which the gill clefts of more advanced fishes were derived. The external openings were small pores, and the internal ones (from the pharynx to each gill pouch) not much larger. On the anterior and posterior faces of each pouch presumably there was a series of gill filaments, designated **pretrematic** and **posttrematic** respectively. The number of pouches, 10 pairs in *Cephalaspis*, went up to 15 in some Anaspid ostracoderms, and this may be more primitive; in many others the external openings seem to have combined into a longitudinal canal on each side opening posteriorly.

Modern cyclostomes retain the pouches, hence the alternative name Marsipobranchii ("pouch gills") for the class. But both lampreys and hagfishes have made certain adjustments in connection with the parasitic habit. Hagfishes have the external pores relatively far back (6 to 14 pairs in *Bdellostoma* and a common opening from 6 or 7 on each side in *Myxine*). In lampreys the pharynx itself is specialized, being split off from the

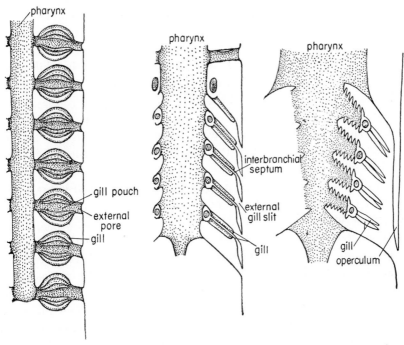

Fig. 239. Pharynx, gill pouches, and gill openings in lamprey (left), shark (center), teleost (right).

more dorsal esophagus, and going only far enough to serve the 7 pairs of internal gill pores (Fig. 239). As noted earlier, this allows the lamprey to cling to its prey and suck blood while continuing to breathe by pumping water in and out of the external pores. The gills proper consist of shelf-like folds of epithelium on the anterior and posterior walls of the pouches, each fold supplied by a capillary loop.

At first sight the plan in sharks and other gnathostomes seems utterly different. The gills are in double sets of filaments (*holobranchs*) supported on the *inner* side by cartilaginous or bony *branchial arches.* (Those of cyclostomes were external.) Sharks and rays have a complete *interbranchial septum* from each gill arch to the outer wall, so that one set of filaments (a demibranch) is on the front and one on the back of each septum. This makes four holobranchs (complete gills) in sharks with five external clefts. In addition there is a demibranch on the hyoid arch (front of the first full-sized cleft) and a vestigial demibranch (called *pseudobranch*) in the spiracle; this one is the nonfunctional remnant of the mandibular gill present in early placoderms.

But, comparing these clefts and gills with those of cyclostomes, it becomes clear that a gill slit in a shark, from pharynx to exterior, corresponds fully to a gill pouch with inner and outer pores. The interbranchial septum therefore is the much reduced partition between one pouch and the next, and a demibranch on the front of the septum is *posttrematic* so far as its cleft is concerned, while the other demibranch of the same gill is *pretrematic* (for the cleft behind). The only real difference is that the branchial arches are internal in gnathostomes, external in cyclostomes, and this suggests that they are not homologous.

Bony fishes (Dipnoi, Actinopteri, etc.) as well as the peculiar chimaeras (Holocephali) no longer have separate external slits, but the gill chamber is covered by a flap, the *operculum;* consequently the interbranchial septa do not reach to the outside, nor even beyond the tips of the gill filaments; they undergo progressive shortening until virtually absent in teleosts. The latter generally do not have a hyoid demibranch.

Common to the lungfishes and primitive Actinopteri (e.g., *Polypterus*) are temporary bushy *external gills* (Fig. 240) in the larva, developed from the outer epithelium over the gill arches. These occur also in larval salamanders, persisting throughout life in the permanently aquatic kinds like *Necturus;* they become hidden in *Cryptobranchus* and *Megalobatrachus.* Newly hatched tadpoles have external gills but presently conceal them under a broad fold of skin, the *operculum,* and then develop true internal gills on their gill bars. Water escapes through a small pore, usually left-sided, the *spiracle* (not to be confused with the spiracles of many fishes).

Other devices for breathing should be mentioned here before we touch on the lungs and air bladder: The African "hairy frog" (*Astylosternus*) has vascular filaments on its thighs and abdomen. The skin as a whole is a respiratory organ in many Amphibia, especially those like the lungless salamanders that live in damp situations where the skin is always moist; many adult salamanders and frogs breathe through the lining of the mouth and throat, its floor moving in regular respiratory rhythm. This is

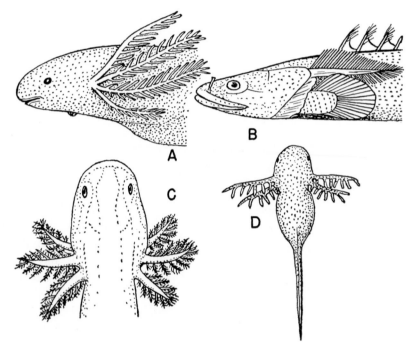

Fig. 240. External gills. A, larval lungfish, *Lepidosiren;* B, *Polypterus;* C, salamander, *Siren;* D, frog, *Rana.* (A after Goodrich; B and D after Parker and Haswell; C after Noble.)

probably true in some aquatic turtles as well; their cloacal breathing sacs have already been mentioned.

Lungs and Air Bladders

Almost all terrestrial vertebrates (exceptions among salamanders) use lungs for respiration, while the majority of fishes have a simple air bladder that is usually an organ of buoyancy rather than breathing. But we have ample evidence that both lungs and air bladders were derived from paired sacs in ancient fishes, serving both respiratory and hydrostatic functions. We may call these organs *lungs* if air is inhaled for respiration, even when the animals that do so happen to be fishes.

Among bony fishes the more primitive kinds have either one sac or a pair connected to the esophagus on its ventral side by a duct (Fig. 241). In lungfishes, judging by existing kinds, two sacs were present primitively, as now in *Protopterus* and *Lepidosiren*, but these are reduced to one in *Neoceratodus;* lungfishes are known first from the Lower Devonian. *Polypterus*, most primitive of living ray-finned fishes, has likewise a pair, one usually longer than the other. The presence of lungs can

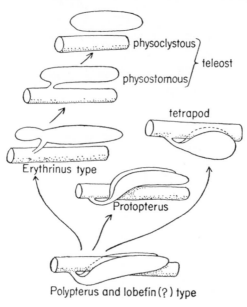

be inferred with reasonable certainty in Rhipidistia, the ancestral lobefins with nostrils entering the mouth, and there is evidence (Denison, 1941) of paired lungs in the Devonian placoderm *Bothriolepis.*

The use of the word **lung** for these organs in fishes is justified by the evidence that they have a respiratory function, and it has been shown that even in the Holostei, *Amia* and *Lepisosteus,* and several kinds of teleosts living in swamps or stagnant water (e.g., the South American *Arapaima,* the African *Gymnarchus,* and the European and American mud minnows, *Umbra*) the same is true of the single air sac. No doubt its function in all these is partly hydrostatic as well; that is, for buoyancy to offset the weight of bones, scales, and teeth, making the specific gravity of the fish equal to that of the water. Embryonically, it has been shown that lungs originate in Amphibia as paired internal pouches behind the last (sixth) gill arches in the floor of the pharynx. They may have started as gill pouches primitively, which happened to trap and retain air. This is in accord with the derivation of pulmonary arteries from the sixth aortic arch. In higher vertebrates there is a single ventral pocket or groove from the embryonic pharynx, and the developing trachea then bifurcates to make the two lungs.

Looking now at the teleost fishes, we find the air bladder provided with an open duct (homologous with the trachea, evidently), in the more primitive half of the group, which are roughly those with soft-rayed fins,

Fig. 241. Air bladders and lungs. (In part from Romer, after Dean.)

cycloid scales (if any), and the pelvic fins in abdominal position. These are called *physostomous,* in relation to the duct. *Erythrinus,* shown in Fig. 241, is also physostomous, but it does not have the duct completely brought around to the dorsal side of the esophagus, as it is in others. *Erythrinus* is a South American characin, belonging to the very large order Ostariophysi (characins, catfishes, minnows, carp, suckers), in which the air bladder becomes constricted midway into two divisions, the anterior of which connects with the inner ear of the fish by means of a curious series of **Weberian ossicles** (Fig. 246). These bones develop from lateral parts of the anterior vertebrae and quite clearly act as a mechanical lever system moved by the changing volume of the air bladder. But

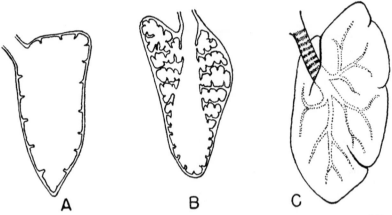

Fig. 242. Lungs. A, toad; B, lizard (after Goodrich, *Studies on the Structure and Development of the Vertebrates,* The Macmillan Company); C, mammal.

this may be interpreted in more than one way. Presumably in some cases, at least, the increase or decrease in size of the air bladder according to depth and pressure of the surrounding water may be sensed through the ear, and a reflex mechanism enables the fish to secrete into or absorb from the bladder enough gas (oxygen primarily) to maintain a constant specific gravity of the body as a whole. But in shallow streams and lakes where most Ostariophysi live, this seems less likely than that the apparatus is for hearing, transmitting vibrations to the ear from the resonating air bladder.

More advanced teleosts lose the pneumatic duct during development; these are *physoclystous.* Some groups, such as flatfishes, have lost the air bladder altogether. In a considerable number of teleosts (drums, toadfishes, certain catfishes, etc.) there are devices for making sounds by vibration of the walls of the air bladder.

Chondrichthyes apparently branched off from placoderms which never had lungs, for there is no evidence of either lung or air bladder in them.

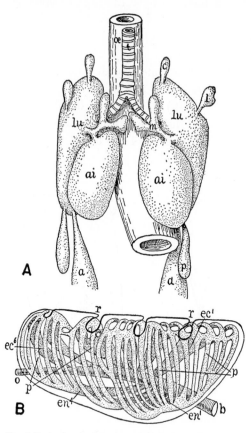

Returning now to the crossopterygians, the living genus *Latimeria,* a coelacanth, inhabiting deep water off the east coast of Africa, has a single "lung" apparently serving as a fat reservoir, and no nostrils. But the origin of Amphibia can be traced from Devonian Rhipidistia instead of coelacanths, and there can be no doubt that these had both lungs and nostrils. Most modern Amphibia have simple, saclike lungs with varying degrees of pocketing internally, to increase their absorptive surfaces (Fig. 242). Among salamanders this is true of most of the families, but the largest family, Plethodontidae, is without lungs, and so is the Olympic salamander, *Rhyacotriton,* in the Ambystomidae. This condition is thought to have originated in cool, well-oxygenated mountain brooks, and it seems to have been quite compatible with terrestrial life as well, for many Plethodontids live in moist forests, under bark of trees or in rotting logs.

Fig. 243. A, developing air sacs in 12-day chick embryo (from Kingsley, *Outlines of Comparative Anatomy of Vertebrates,* 3rd ed., Blakiston).

a, abdominal sac; *ai,* anterior intermediate sac; *c,* cervical sac; *l,* lateral moiety of interclavicular sac; *lu,* lung; *m,* mesial moiety of interclavicular sac; *oe,* esophagus; *p,* posterior sac; *t,* trachea.

B, diagram of bird lung (from Kingsley, *Outlines of Comparative Anatomy of Vertebrates,* 3rd ed., Blakiston).

b, bronchus; *ec,* ectobronchi; *en,* entobronchi; *o,* connection with abdominal air sac; *p,* parabronchi; *r,* notches occupied by ribs.

Breathing, of course, is done through the lining of the mouth and the skin; the heart is secondarily two-chambered, since it needs no left auricle to receive blood from the lungs. In frogs and toads (except *Ascaphus*) the voice of males is produced by resonance of air entering single or paired *vocal sacs* in the throat. These are pouches from the pharynx but have no direct relationship to the lungs. Air may be passed rapidly back and forth from lungs to sacs, however, producing a trill, a peep, or some multiple call.

Most reptiles still have simple lungs with a moderate amount of pocketing (Fig. 242B). In chameleons several blind pouches emerge into the body cavity from each lung, by which the body can swell up with air. In the extinct pterosaurs some of the limb bones were hollow and are thought to have carried air sacs, as in birds. Snakes and Amphisbaenia

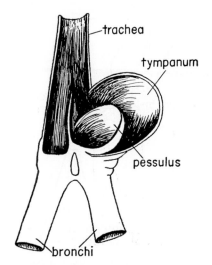

Fig. 244. Syrinx of canvasback duck. (Redrawn from Kingsley, *Outlines of Comparative Anatomy of Vertebrates,* 3rd ed., Blakiston.)

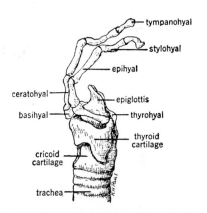

Fig. 245. Larynx of dog. (Reproduced by permission from *Comparative Anatomy* by L. A. Adams and S. Eddy, published by John Wiley & Sons, Inc., 1949.)

(limbless tropical lizards) have only the right lung, for evidently the linear body does not allow room for two.

The lungs of birds are much more elaborate, being spongy internally. Their most distinctive feature is the series of *air sacs* (Fig. 243) which extend from them into many parts of the body, as between viscera, between muscles, and even into some of the limb bones. Recent work shows that many flying birds, such as grebes and loons, as well as the flightless ones, lack the spaces within bones, so that this is by no means a character of the whole class. Probably air sacs are of greater value in respiration than in merely lowering the specific gravity of the bird, since they make it possible for a more complete change of air in the lungs to take place with every breath, thus increasing the availability of oxygen, as compared with the partial change which occurs in other vertebrates.

In bird lungs a series of *parabronchial tubes* with looped *air capillaries* carries on respiration, instead of alveoli. At the point where the bronchi meet the trachea in most birds there is an enlargement, the *syrinx,* in which a *semilunar membrane* (or *pessulus*), vibrating as air passes it, produces the voice (Fig. 244).

In mammals, however, the lungs have innumerable microscopic pockets, the *alveoli,* reached by *bronchioles* (branches from the bronchi). The development of a muscular *diaphragm* between the thorax and abdomen was undoubtedly a major contribution to the rapid metabolism

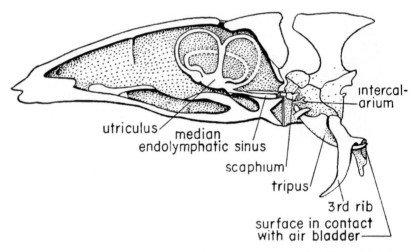

Fig. 246. Weberian ossicles of carp in relation to inner ear and skull. (Modified from Goodrich.)

and high activity of most mammals, because it supplements the movements of the body wall in breathing. The voices of mammals are produced in the *larynx* (Fig. 245), at the beginning of the trachea, by vibration of paired folds, the *vocal cords.* Cartilages supporting the larynx in mammals are greatly modified derivatives of the more posterior branchial cartilages of amphibians and reptiles.

Coelom and Mesenteries

The coelom is a cavity, or more than one cavity, separating the viscera from the body wall. No actual vacant space may be present, of course, but the organs may move, change their shape, or slide past one another with a minimum of friction. Their surfaces are wet with a serous fluid.

The body wall itself can also change shape and position relative to the viscera, which is an equally important consideration.

Most phyla of metazoan animals have a coelom. Among echinoderms and the Enteropneusta (Hemichorda) it starts to develop as a series of paired pouches out of the sides of the archenteron (embryonic gut). It is therefore bilateral and segmented. In Hemichorda the proboscis cavity develops from one of the first pair of pouches (the other degenerating), the two collar cavities come from the second pair, and the trunk coelom by an extension of the third. In *Branchiostoma* the method of formation is essentially the same, but a much larger series of segments is formed by continuing the separation of mesoderm into segments behind the first three pairs of pouches; these more posterior ones develop their cavities independently of the archenteron.

A separation of each segment into an upper part (epimere) and a lower (hypomere) then takes place, after which the hypomeres along each side of the body fuse so that their cavities are continuous, but the epimeres remain segmented, develop into myomeres, and lose their cavities entirely. Therefore the coelom consists of whatever cavities may be formed by the united hypomeres. In vertebrates, the hypomeres are not segmented at any stage.

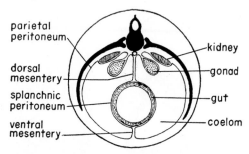

Fig. 247. Diagram of coelom in relation to other parts of vertebrate.

As the hypomeres, with their right and left coelomic cavities, grow downward in the early embryo, they rest against the gut inwardly. If there is no longer any yolk remaining under the gut, then the hypomeres meet each other in the middle line ventrally as well as dorsally, and a median *mesentery* results, part above and part below the gut. This, of course, is a double rather than a single membrane, since the median walls of both hypomeres meet in it. If the embryo contains a large quantity of yolk (reptiles, birds, etc.), the hypomeres cannot come together below the gut but must spread laterally at first, carrying the coelom over the surface of the yolk, beyond the limits of the body of the embryo. Hence it is called extra-embryonic coelom. Later the reduced yolk is surrounded and engulfed by the body wall, and the hypomeres come to their normal position below the gut. In any case that part of the mesentery above the gut is called *dorsal mesentery,* and that beneath is *ventral mesentery.*

Much of the dorsal mesentery remains, although modified, in adult vertebrates. Its divisions, according to the portions of the digestive tract to which they attach, are the *mesogaster* (stomach), *mesoduodenum* (duodenum), *mesentery* (small intestine in general), *mesocolon* (large intestine), *mesorectum* (rectum). The dorsal mesentery is incomplete in most vertebrates, however; for example in elasmobranchs there is a mesogaster, more or less reduced, a part (or none) of the mesentery proper, and a mesorectum. (A torpedo ray, *Hypnos,* is exceptional in retaining a nearly complete dorsal mesentery.) In other vertebrates likewise we find variability but usually a great reduction. Among mammals there is a special modification, the *greater omentum,* which is a broad, delicate pouch of mesentery developed from the posterior part of the mesogaster.

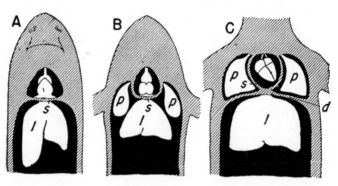

Fig. 248. Coelom (black). A, fish; B, amphibians, reptiles, and birds; C, mammals. (From Kingsley, *Outlines of Comparative Anatomy of Vertebrates,* 3rd ed., Blakiston.)

As the stomach becomes curved toward the left side of the body, and its lower edge becomes transverse, leading to the duodenum, the mesogaster is thrown into a leftward fold, which then grows much larger until it hangs down as a double-walled blanket over the ventral surface of the intestine. Its edges are usually attached to the greater curvature of the stomach and the duodenum (in man the transverse colon), and in it are supported the pancreas and spleen.

Very few vertebrates (lungfishes, garpike, eels) retain an extensive ventral mesentery in the adult. Usually it breaks through and only two or three fragments persist: *falciform ligament* (from base of liver to linea alba, in the ventral body wall); lesser *omentum* (from stomach and duodenum to liver, supporting the bile duct, hepatic portal vein, etc.); *median ligament* of the bladder. The *mesocardium* is a temporary part of the ventral mesentery, in which the embryonic heart is, for a while, suspended.

Most characteristic of the several special cavities (Fig. 248) developed in the coelom of vertebrates is the *pericardial cavity* (enclosed by *pericardium*), a space in which the heart can beat without friction against other organs. In fishes this lies far forward under the esophagus, just behind the branchial arches; its posterior wall is the *transverse septum,* a nearly upright membrane that accompanies the large veins (ducts of Cuvier) which run in from both sides to the heart. Above these veins, however, small openings persist from the pericardial to peritoneal cavities in hagfishes, larvae of lampreys, and in elasmobranchs and Holostei. Otherwise, in all vertebrates, the pericardium is complete. Among tetrapods, with the development of a mobile neck, the heart and pericardium retreat into the thorax, and the transverse septum draws back into an oblique position as a result.

The liver develops in the embryo as a median ventral outgrowth of the gut just behind the stomach and transverse septum. It bulges into the transverse septum, and of course remains enclosed in a single layer of serosa derived from this. A part of the ventral mesentery then remains as a strap from the duodenum to the liver, supporting the bile duct; this is the *lesser omentum.* The pancreas arises partly from ventral and partly from dorsal outgrowths of the gut, and so is attached to the stomach and duodenum by a portion of the dorsal mesentery. Now the lesser omentum and bile duct

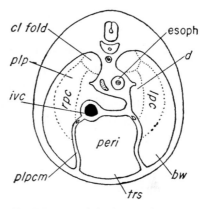

Fig. 249. Face of diaphragm of mammal, showing sources from which its parts are derived. (After Goodrich.)

bw, from body wall; cl fold, from posterior closing fold; d, from median mesentery and tissue dorsal to liver; esoph, esophagus; ivc, inferior vena cava; lpc, left pleural cavity; peri, pericardium; plp, from pleuroperitoneal membrane; plpcm, pleuropericardial membrane; rpc, right pleural cavity; trs, transverse septum.

anchor the duodenum, so to speak, to the liver, and as the growing stomach bends to the left, the dorsal mesogaster bends with it, forming a cavity (*bursa omentalis*) with an opening (*foramen of Winslow*). This pouch, as noted before, becomes a large thin sac in mammals, the *greater omentum,* and the foramen of Winslow lies in the lesser curvature of the stomach, or better, on the morphological right side now turned dorsally.

The lungs as they grow out from the foregut push ahead of them a covering derived from the splanchnic peritoneum of the gut, and usually remain attached by *pulmonary folds* to the esophagus, dorsal mesentery, and transverse septum. These connections may be partly or wholly lost (the left pulmonary fold is lost in mammals). The Müllerian ducts (oviducts) and kidney ducts may be supported by *nephric folds* attached to the dorsal body wall.

In reptiles (Crocodilia, etc.) there is partial but rarely complete separation of the *pleural cavities,* containing the lungs, from the rest of the coelom. This is completed in birds, however, by a *pulmonary aponeurosis,* which extends more or less horizontally from the transverse septum to the sides of the thorax and dorsal wall in front of the kidneys. This, plus the median mesentery, gives a pair of pleural cavities.

The *diaphragm* of mammals (Fig. 249) accomplishes much the same thing in a different way. It results from the spreading of a *pleuroperitoneal membrane* across the body cavity to the transverse septum, while the liver withdraws somewhat from the latter, remaining attached to it only by the coronary and falciform ligaments. The sides of the diaphragm spread more posteriorly down the body wall, and it acquires thus the shape of a dome. It receives a sheet of muscle from the myotomes, evidently in the neck region during very early development, for the *phrenic nerve* which supplies it is composed of branches of cervical nerves 3, 4, and 5.

CHAPTER VIII

Circulatory System

ONE requirement for developing a many-celled body is that the individual cells have access to a watery medium which will transport solutes to and from them, and indeed provide the liquid basis of their own protoplasm. In all the higher Metazoa the body carries such a fluid within itself. It is further necessary, in all animals beyond a certain minimum size, that the fluid be in motion so that dissolved food and oxygen can get to every part and not be wasted on the few tissues lying near the surface where they were absorbed, and that excretory products may not destroy the cells that make them, but be carried off. This is accomplished in many animals without circulatory systems by the incessant movement of the body, as, for example, in nematode worms. But in more complex or less vigorous creatures the fluids must be propelled by some pump-and-valve mechanism.

Speaking of vertebrates especially, there are three body fluids (extracellular), distinguished mainly by their location: *tissue fluid,* which occupies spaces among cells or tissues, including the coelom and cerebrospinal canal, but is not within any vessel; *lymph,* which is the same fluid carried in the lymphatic system of vessels; *blood plasma,* which is the same fluid again, in the blood vessels, with the addition of red corpuscles and a higher proportion of proteins (7 percent in man, as compared with 3–4 percent of protein in lymph and tissue fluid). Minor chemical differences exist between these fluids on account of their relationship to various tissues, but it is important to understand that they are fundamentally the same, and that a nearly free interchange goes on between them all the time. This we illustrate in Fig. 250, which diagrams the relationship between a capillary, tissue spaces, and a lymph vessel.

Leucocytes, the white phagocytic blood cells, are present in blood, tissue fluid, and lymph because, by diapedesis (squeezing through) they can penetrate a capillary or lymphatic wall. **Erythrocytes,** the far more abundant red cells which carry oxygen for respiration, are limited to the blood proper. Except for brief references, we shall be concerned here primarily with the blood vessels and heart, for, as a well-defined system of tubes and a pump, these display the evolutionary progress of all the vertebrate groups.

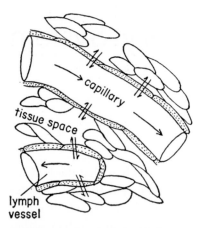

Capillaries are the microscopic vessels through whose single-layered walls (Fig. 251) nearly all the work of the blood goes on; virtually everything that enters or leaves the blood does so here. It is for these capillaries that the veins, arteries, and heart exist. In an animal the size of man there are hundreds of millions of capillaries, averaging less than a millimeter in length, and permeating all the tissues. The lumen of capillaries is but little wider than the blood cells, so that these may slip through in single file. Since blood, on account of its dissolved proteins and other solutes, has a higher viscosity than water, its flow is impeded in capillaries to the extent that it almost stops, for the amount of surface (hence the friction) relative to the volume of blood becomes maximal. Another important factor in slowing blood flow in capillaries is that the blood stream, as it divides into a multiplicity of branches, comes to have a very much greater total *area of cross section* in the smallest vessels than it did in the largest; in man the difference is over 600 times.

Fig. 250. Diagram of relationship between blood capillary, tissue spaces, and lymph vessels. Arrows show flow of blood and lymph; double arrows show diffusion through membranes.

Capillary walls are of a single layer of cells, the endothelium, which continues into veins, heart, and arteries as the internal lining. This is elastic but is not contractile; therefore the pressure of blood entering capillaries (normally about 25–30 mm. of mercury) determines the expansion of their walls. The last ends of arterioles leading to capillaries

are *metarterioles,* where only a few muscle cells lie on the outer surfaces; by constriction, one of these metarterioles may reduce or stop the
flow of blood into its dependent capillaries, or by dilation cause them to
fill.

Arteries have thick, elastic walls with a lining, the *intima* or *endothe-*
lium (continuous, as noted above, with the capillary walls), a *media* or
muscularis, of circularly arranged muscle fibers, and an *adventitia,* or
connective tissue sheath. There is usually a layer of elastic fibers (*elas-*
tica interna) between media and intima, and in the larger arteries an
elastica externa between media and adventitia. In the finer branches
these outer layers diminish until the last to remain is a muscularis of a
few scattered cells; the small branches, hardly visible to the naked eye,
are *arterioles.* Always arteries carry blood *away from the heart,* regard-

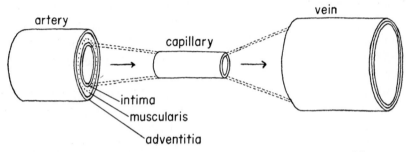

Fig. 251. Differences between artery, capillary, and vein, and continuity of lining.

less of its oxygen or carbon dioxide content. (For example, the big vessel
going from heart to lungs in higher vertebrates is the *pulmonary artery,*
even though its blood is not "oxygenated.")

The reason for the elasticity of arterial walls is that blood is being
pumped into arteries by the heart with a high but fluctuating pressure;
for each contraction (*systole*) of the ventricle in man and related animals
the pressure reaches more than 100 mm. of mercury, and the wave of
pressure advances much more rapidly through the artery than the moving
blood itself. This systolic wave is followed by a reduced pressure as the
ventricle relaxes (*diastole*), but even so the figure may be 60–80 mm.
Thus the arterial walls yield but immediately "take up the slack" and
continue to press on the blood within. This is, of course, necessary in
order that the blood shall continue along through the rest of the circulatory system. (No peristaltic action is implied; the output of the heart
maintains the current at considerable velocity.)

Veins and their finer tributaries, the *venules,* collect blood from the
capillaries and return it *toward the heart.* Since it is moving slowly and

has lost the pulse pressure it had in the arteries, venous blood must occupy bigger vessels, but their walls need not be elastic. Veins, therefore, are usually larger than corresponding arteries but have a very thin muscular layer or none; often they expand into large chambers or *sinuses.* The larger veins contain valves to prevent a back flow of blood.

Protochordates and Cyclostomes; The Vertebrate Plan

The general plan of the vertebrate circulatory system seems to have been established with the appearance of pharyngeal respiration, but it has not yet become clear in the Hemichorda, which we may just mention in passing. *Balanoglossus* has both a dorsal and ventral vessel, each longitudinal and each giving off short branches to the pharynx and intestine. Blood runs forward above and back below, the connection being made by peripharyngeal vessels in the collar. The "heart" is a contractile chamber at the anterior end of the dorsal vessel, corresponding in development to one in echinoderms, but obviously not to the heart found in other chordates.

Amphioxus has a plan more nearly comparable (Fig. 252) to that of vertebrates. Blood flows forward beneath the branchial arches in a pulsating vessel, the *ventral aorta* (no actual heart), then up the primary arches as *branchial arteries* to enter paired (right and left) *radices aortae,* which carry it back to the united *dorsal aorta.* It continues in this to the posterior part of the body, including the intestine, where it enters capillaries. Then going forward in a *subintestinal vein,* the blood has to pass through capillaries again in the liver (partly *hepatic portal system*) before entering the ventral aorta. On either side at this point there enters also a *common cardinal vein* or *duct of Cuvier,* formed laterally by junction of an *anterior* and *posterior cardinal.* In tunicates the same arrangement is present, with a distinct heart, but no liver and no cardinal veins, and the direction of blood flow can be reversed.

In cyclostomes, as in higher fishes, the ventral aorta gives off paired *afferent branchial arteries* (eight pairs in lampreys) which go up between successive gill pouches, each dividing completely into capillaries to the demibranch before and behind it. Then *efferent branchial arteries* collect this blood and bring it to the *dorsal aorta.* This runs forward, becoming paired and producing the *carotid arteries* of the head, and also back beneath the notochord into the tail, en route sending off a *coeliacomesenteric artery* to digestive tract and paired branches to the body wall, gonads, and kidneys. The *subintestinal vein,* running forward, enters the liver as a *hepatic portal vein* (that is, breaking up into capillaries there, which unite again), and thence a single *hepatic vein* enters the heart. From the tail the *caudal vein,* embryonically an extension of the subintestinal, splits and sends blood into two *posterior cardinal (postcardinal) veins* which go forward in the roof of the body cavity beside the notochord. At the level of the heart they meet *anterior cardinals* from the head and unite to form a *common cardinal* entering the right side (in lamprey) of the heart (left in hagfishes). Other fishes have two common cardinals, left and right.

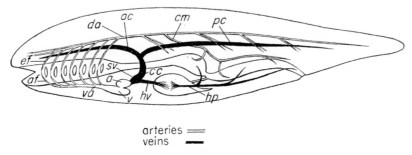

arteries ===
veins ━━

Fig. 252. Diagram of circulation in a generalized vertebrate.
a, auricle; *ac,* anterior cardinal vein; *af,* afferent branchial artery; *cc,* common cardinal vein; *cm,* coeliacomesenteric artery; *da,* dorsal aorta; *ef,* efferent branchial artery; *hp,* hepatic portal vein; *hv,* hepatic vein; *pc,* posterior cardinal vein; *sv,* sinus venosus; *v,* ventricle; *va,* ventral aorta.

This pattern, with the two common cardinals, is the *primitive* one for vertebrates (Fig. 252), and should be learned as something different from the *embryonic* arrangement of vessels seen in the early life of an individual fish, bird, or mammal. The embryonic pattern contains some special features, like the vitelline arteries and veins, never present in any adult ancestor, and also eliminates a few details which were present in adults of primitive forms.

Heart

In fishes the heart has two chambers (Fig. 253), a thin-walled, more dorsal *atrium (auricle),* receiving blood from behind, and a thick-walled *ventricle,* which propels it forward. Two valves in the opening between permit the flow of blood into, but not back out of, the ventricle. In addition there is a funnel-shaped *sinus venosus,* to which all blood from veins is brought and thence poured into the auricle between *sinauricular valves.* A *conus arteriosus* receives blood forward out of the ventricle;

this is the contractile, enlarged base of the ventral aorta, and contains *semilunar valves*, to prevent the return of blood into the ventricle. In elasmobranchs and the lower bony fishes there are several of these valves in three or more (*Lepisosteus,* seven) rows. In teleosts the conus is no

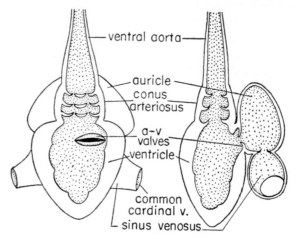

Fig. 253. Heart of shark, in frontal and sagittal sections.

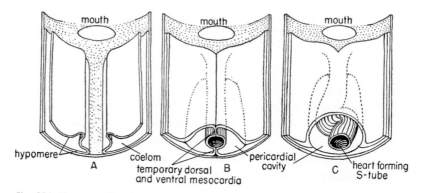

Fig. 254. Diagrams of early development of heart. A, hypomeres approaching midventral line; B, median walls meet, forming mesocardia and tubular heart, with pericardial cavity formed as pocket of coelom on each side; C, mesocardia disappear, leaving heart free to bend in S-shape.

longer recognizable, and the swollen *bulbus cordis* at the base of the ventral aorta contains usually only one set of valves; it is frequently as large as the ventricle, and acts as a supplementary pumping chamber maintaining blood pressure to the gills.

Among these lower vertebrates the heart begins its development as a single median tube, formed from mesenchyme between the right and left coelomic cavities (Fig. 254). It is thus supported, very briefly, by the mesocardium, a portion of the ventral mesentery, but as the pericardial cavity becomes shut off behind by the transverse septum, the mesocardium disappears, leaving the heart as an S-shaped vessel crossing this cavity. The presence of a yolk sac in teleosts and in reptiles, birds, and mammals prevents the early meeting of hypomeres; the heart in these groups results from the fusion of two vitelline veins converging from the yolk, but of course this is not primitive.

Lungfishes have almost a three-chambered heart (Fig. 255) like that of Amphibia, because with the development of a circulation to the lungs, blood returns by pulmonary veins which enter as one into the left side of the atrium, while the sinus venosus enters the right, and there is an almost complete interauricular septum between. Then by means of a spiral ridge within the conus arteriosus, blood from the right auricle tends largely to veer towards the last (fourth to sixth) aortic arches, from which some of it can get to the lungs, while blood from the left auricle is deflected towards the openings of the arteries leading to the head.

Recently it has been discovered that the heart of the modern coelacanth, *Latimeria*, is secondarily two-chambered, in correlation with the absence of lungs in this lobefin. Ancestral lobefins (Rhipidistia) must (in all prob-

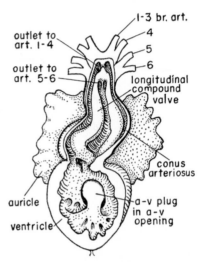

Fig. 255. Heart of lungfish, *Protopterus*, open from ventral side, showing plug valve in a-v opening. (After Goodrich.)

ability) have possessed a ventricle and two auricles as do the lung-breathing amphibians.

In Amphibia (Fig. 256), where the adults may lose their gills, the auricles are entirely separate, pulmonary ("arterial") blood entering the left, systemic ("venous") the right. The conus arteriosus contains an elaborate spiral fold to induce the former to enter systemic arteries on its circuit, and the latter to get to the lungs. What happens in lungless salamanders? The interauricular septum does not develop, and the heart remains two-chambered, as it is in the immature stages of Amphibia.

The sinus venosus is much reduced in adult Amphibia and reptiles, and is merged with the right auricle in higher animals. The ventral aorta has been shortening progressively until it almost disappears, especially after the loss of gill respiration, and the pulmonary and systemic arteries tend to carry their separateness back into the ventricle itself, by intensification of the fold already mentioned. This is the situation in most reptiles, where a septum is carried down into the ventricle, seemingly an extension of that between the auricles. In Crocodilia the heart is four-chambered, showing only a very small opening between the right and left ventricles (Fig. 257).

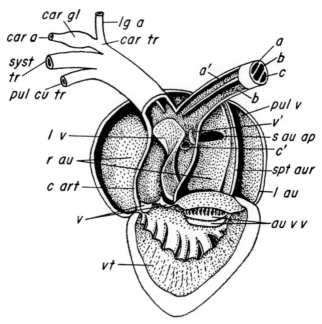

Fig. 256. Heart of frog, *Rana temporaria*, dissected, from ventral side. (Redrawn from Parker and Haswell, *Textbook of Zoology*, 6th ed., The Macmillan Company.)

a, a′, left carotid trunk; au v v, auriculoventricular valves; b, b′, left systemic trunk; c, c′, left pulmocutaneous trunk; car a, carotid artery; car gl, carotid "gland"; c art, conus arteriosus; car tr, carotid trunk; l au, left auricle; lg a, lingual artery; l v, longitudinal valve; pul cu tr, pulmocutaneous trunk; pul v, opening of pulmonary veins; r au, right auricle; s au ap, sinuauricular aperture; spt aur, auricular septum; v, v′, valves; vt, ventricle.

Independently of each other, since their common ancestry goes far back among primitive reptiles, the birds (Fig. 257) and mammals attained a four-chambered heart, in which the right auricle sends systemic blood to the right ventricle and it can then go *only* to the pulmonary artery, while the left auricle receives pulmonary blood, sends it to the left ventricle, and thus *only* to the systemic arteries. Here is another instance of structure perfected in the service of higher physiological activity. No blood has to go twice around the systemic circulation without being brought to the lungs. In mammals before birth (and for a while after, in the case of blue babies) there is a *foramen ovale* between right and left auricles, allowing a small amount of mixing to take place.

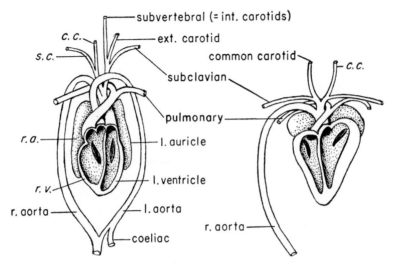

Fig. 257. Heart of crocodile (left, modified after Greil), and chicken (right).

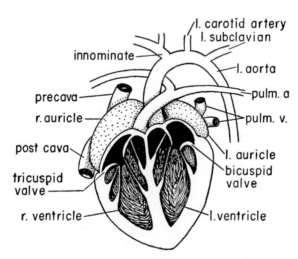

Fig. 258. Heart of mammal, diagrammatic.

We may now summarize the main features of the heart of mammals (Fig. 258). The auricles are thin, and flaccid when empty, while the ventricles have a heavy muscular wall, that of the left being much thicker than the right. This is because more pressure is required to circulate blood through the systemic vessels than on the shorter course to the lungs. The auriculoventricular valves are, on the right, the **tricuspid;** on the left, **bicuspid** or **mitral.** The openings into the pulmonary artery and aorta are provided each with three **semilunar** valves. In the muscular walls of the heart, especially the ventricles, is a system of coronary circulation; the **coronary artery** emerges from the aorta near its base, while the **coronary vein** returns blood to the **coronary sinus** (a vestige of the right duct of Cuvier), and thence to the right auricle. The inner walls of the ventricles are strongly ridged with muscular **trabeculae,** from which tapering **papillary muscles** give off numerous tendons, the **chordae tendineae,** to the margins of the tricuspid and bicuspid valves, to sustain them against the pressure of ventricular contraction.

The heart appears, at first glance, to contract as a whole (**systole**) and

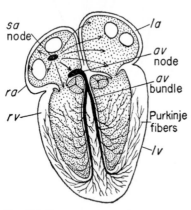

Fig. 259. Neuromuscular mechanism of the mammalian heart. Arrows show spread of contraction wave.

then relax (**diastole**), with a very brief resting interval before the next contraction. But when watching a slow-motion picture of the heartbeat (**cardiac cycle**) we see that each systole begins at a point in the wall of the right auricle, the **sinauricular (s.a.) node,** where the sinus venosus long since disappeared; that is, at the entrance of the systemic veins (Fig. 259). The sinauricular node consists of cells with some properties of neurons, including the ability to cause contraction in otherwise quiescent muscle cells, even though they themselves are derived from cardiac muscle. A wave of contraction spreads quickly out through the wall of the right and then the left auricle, but between these and the ventricles a barrier of connective tissue has developed in Amniota, and the only way for the contraction wave to pass is for it to stimulate the **atrioventricular (a.v.) node,** a cluster of neuromuscular cells like those in the right auricle. Thence two **a.v. bundles (bundles of His)** conduct the **impulse to contract** (not the contraction wave) down the middle septum and out from this, by way of **Purkinje fibers,** to the ventricular walls. Thus the ventricles are induced to contract simultaneously, although a little later than the contraction of the two auricles. Blood will therefore be pushed from auricles into ventricles while the latter are still in diastole, and systole follows immediately, sending it out into pulmonary artery and aorta at the same time.

Now the ability of the heart to initiate each beat is the property of the heart muscle (that is, it is myogenic rather than neurogenic), and in lower vertebrates the isolated heart, or parts of it, will beat rhythmically without nervous connections. But in birds and mammals this property seems to be localized to a large degree in the "pacemaker" (sinauricular node) of the right auricle. Nerves that go to the heart regulate but do not initiate its action. The *vagus* nerves (*parasympathetic*) retard or inhibit, while the *sympathetic* nerves accelerate the beat. These effects can be duplicated by extremely small quantities of the drugs acetylcholine and adrenalin, respectively.

Arteries

The history of the arteries in vertebrates centers about the *aortic arches* which supply the gills in fishes and Amphibia, and their later derivatives in Amniota, because evolutionary changes in these vessels are

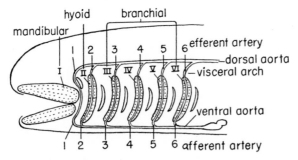

Fig. 260. Customary system of numbering visceral arches and aortic arches.

diagrammatically clear. They form a classic illustration of the method of comparative anatomy.

Primitively, the **ventral aorta** led forward from the heart in the midventral line of the gill region, giving off a right and left **afferent branchial artery** to the outer side of every visceral arch including the jaws, for all these bore gills and were essentially identical. The branchial arteries (or **aortic arches**) are numbered (Fig. 260) like the visceral arches: I (to upper and lower jaw), II (hyoid), III–VI or more (branchial arches). In some ostracoderms there was a premandibular arch, but to give this the number I would unnecessarily confuse the familiar sequence applied to those of other vertebrates, so it might just be kept in mind and tagged, if need be, as O. Capillaries in the gills receive blood from the afferent arteries and return it to corresponding **efferent** arteries, although early in embryonic development each branchial artery is continuous. The efferents go to the dorsal aorta.

In most Chondrichthyes the pattern is much like that shown in Fig. 261, but in the seven-gilled sharks (*Heptanchus*) there are seven aortic arches (i.e., numbers 2–8); *Chlamydoselachus*, the frilled shark, has six (2–7). Features to notice especially are: (1) While there is *single* afferent artery to each gill, there are *two* efferents from those gills which consist of a double set of filaments, but one efferent from the first

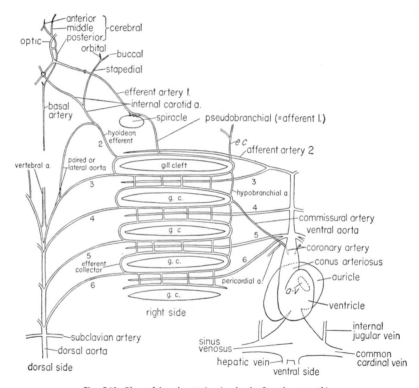

Fig. 261. Plan of head arteries in shark, *Squalus acanthias.*

(hyoid) gill, since this has only one set of filaments. (2) Above and below each gill cleft the efferent arteries connect, making an **efferent loop** surrounding the cleft. (3) From the ventral end of the second efferent loop a **commissural artery** goes to the heart wall and pericardium; this, of course, carries oxygenated blood. (4) From the first efferent loop an **external carotid** supplies the lower jaw and face. (5) The primitive afferent artery of the first (mandibular) arch is still present, going, as the **pseudobranchial**, to the vestigial gill in the spiracle and thence in to supply the brain; since it cannot receive oxygen from a gill on the way, its origin has shifted to the efferent artery of the second (hyoid) arch, which has just obtained oxygenated blood from the hyoid gill.

In most Osteichthyes, including lungfishes (Fig. 262B), the hyoid arch does not retain a functional gill, and therefore aortic arches I and II are both missing. (A pseudobranchial persists in some which have a spiracle and vestigial gill, or pseudobranch, as the sturgeons.) This

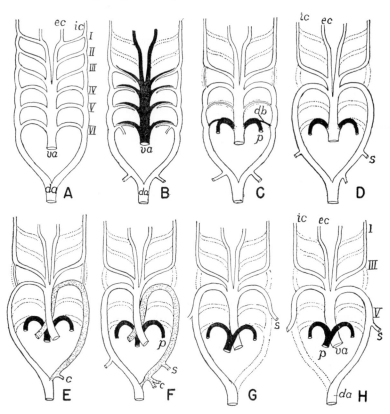

Fig. 262. Aortic arches of vertebrates from ventral side, diagrammatic. A, primitive scheme; B, lungfish; C, salamander; D, frog; E, snake; F, lizard; G, bird; H, mammal. (From Kingsley, *Outlines of Comparative Anatomy of Vertebrates*, 3rd ed., Blakiston.) c, coeliac artery; da, dorsal aorta; db, ductus Botalli; ec, external carotid; ic, internal carotid; p, pulmonary; s, subclavian; va, ventral aorta.

means that the external and internal carotids arise from the ventral and dorsal ends, respectively, of the *third* arch, which supplies the first functional gill. There are generally four such gills, each a holobranch, and supplied, therefore, by aortic arches III–VI. The afferents are always one per arch; in Dipnoi as in sharks each holobranch carries two efferents, but in teleosts only one. From near the dorsal end of each sixth arch in Dipnoi there arises a *pulmonary artery,* to the lungs.

In larval lungfishes and again in larval salamanders the external gills are supplied by capillary loops from the branchial arches (IV–VI in lungfish, III–V in salamanders); the sixth, with its pulmonary artery, is also present in larval Amphibia (Fig. 262C). The transformation of salamander larvae to adults entails the loss of gill capillaries, but not of the arteries that supplied them, as these continue to the dorsal aorta; that portion of the dorsal aorta between arches III and IV (called *ductus caroticus*) disappears, and the result of this is that the external and internal carotids now arise from a common carotid on each side (the base of the internal carotid is really the third arch). Blood to all parts of the body behind the neck goes through arches IV, V, and VI in adult salamanders. Naturally these changes do not occur, or are not completed, in neotenic or permanently aquatic types like *Necturus*.

In frogs and toads, besides the loss of the ductus caroticus, arch V vanishes at metamorphosis (Fig. 262D), and VI loses its connection with the dorsal aorta (*ductus Botalli*), thus becoming solely a pulmonary artery. This leaves arch IV to carry all systemic arterial blood to the body and limbs. The ventral aorta is now split back to the heart.

Here we quote a paragraph from Goodrich (1930, 524–525): "Since . . . the ductus caroticus still persists in Apoda, in some adult Urodela, such as *Triton*, and some adult Reptilia (Sphenodon, Alligator?), and many Lacertilia, its obliteration has probably taken place independently in Amphibia and Amniota. The same may be said of the ductus Botalli (ductus arteriosus), that dorsal part of the sixth aortic arch which joins the pulmonary artery to the dorsal aorta. Closed and reduced to a fibrous strand in adult Anura and the majority of Amniotes, it survives as an open vessel in Apoda, Urodela, *Sphenodon*, *Alligator* and some Chelonia. *Sphenodon*, indeed, is the only Amniote normally preserving both these ducts in the fully developed adult."

Now in modern reptiles the arrangement somewhat anticipates that of birds, in having a large *right aortic* arch (IV) and a reduced *left* arch; the common carotids unite to form a *carotid trunk* which emerges near the base of the right aorta. Arch V, of course, is absent except in the embryo. Birds have only the large right aorta; they lose the left one.

Mammals, derived from reptiles more primitive than any now living, preserve the *left aorta* but not the right. The embryos of mammals and birds show, very rapidly and in much reduced form, the presence of all six pairs of arches, and repeat broadly the evolutionary changes outlined here. The ductus Botalli (Fig. 263) closes at the time of birth in mammals, and of hatching in birds.

The arteries to the body wall and limbs, as well as those to the gonads and kidneys, are paired segmental branches of the aorta, variously enlarged or modified. On the other hand, the main arteries to the viscera (*celiac, superior,* and *inferior mesenteric*) are single, and there is no reason to suppose that they ever were paired in adult vertebrates. This is because the gut itself, which they supply, is a single median tube primitively, no matter how many diverticula and accessory parts it may come to have. But in animals in which the egg has a large yolk and the embry-

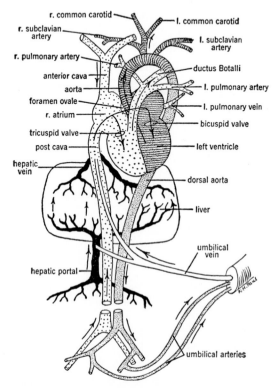

Fig. 263. Embryonic circulation in a mammal. (Reproduced by permission from *Comparative Anatomy* by L. A. Adams and S. Eddy, published by John Wiley & Sons, Inc., 1949.)

onic body must be built upon the upper surface of this, the gut arteries first appear as irregularly paired branches of the aorta, just as the heart itself in such cases comes from a pair of vitelline veins. This is another illustration of the divergence in ontogeny from the actual sequence followed in adult evolution. The superior mesenteric, to the small intestine, is the survivor of a pair of *vitelline* (*omphalomesenteric*) *arteries* to the yolk sac, which occur temporarily even in mammals. The *umbilical arteries* of the mammal embryo arise near the caudal end of the aorta and go out to the placenta; they actually represent special, temporary branches of the two hypogastric arteries, but the latter become recognizable a bit later, as the allantois is being formed.

Veins

VEINS ANTERIOR TO THE HEART

The primitive arrangement has been outlined already. In Chondrichthyes the *anterior cardinal veins* of the embryo run from the region of the eyes back along the sides of the brain and notochord, passing above the gill pouches and finally meeting the *common cardinals* or *ducts of*

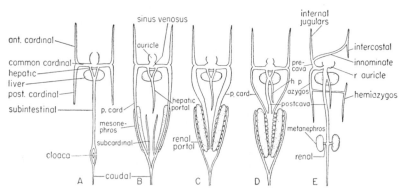

Fig. 264. Development and relationships of principal veins in vertebrates. A, fish, early development; B, fish larva; C, fish adult; D, lungfish, amphibian; E, mammal.

Cuvier, which in turn enter the sinus venosus. In adults the anterior cardinal has become the *lateral head vein* (*vena capitis lateralis*), receiving blood from the *orbital sinus* medial to the eye, from *cerebral veins* emerging from the skull, and from various other tributaries. In most vertebrates such a lateral head vein persists, external to the cranium but receiving cerebral tributaries and also, more posteriorly, veins from the lower jaw and facial region; the latter may be called *external jugulars*, but the lateral head vein proper does not correspond wholly to the *internal jugular*. This is developed in placental mammals, mainly inside the cranium where it drains the sinuses located among the meninges of the brain and the cerebral veins. But the old lateral head vein disappears, and the new internal jugular emerges beneath the skull, running down to join the external jugular. Below this point on each side is the anterior cardinal, essentially unchanged except as described in the next paragraph.

Returning to the shark (Fig. 264C), we find that both the anterior cardinal (lateral head vein) and the posterior cardinal vein enter the common cardinal at the level of the pectoral girdle; here the **subclavian vein** from the fin enters the posterior cardinal. But as the heart in higher vertebrates takes a more posterior location relative to the pectoral girdle, the subclavians associate themselves with the anterior cardinals. Now also the blood from the head, neck, and pectoral limbs is brought directly to the right auricle, and the **left common cardinal** disappears during early development. Blood from the left anterior cardinal must be brought across to the right side nevertheless; to do this a new vein appears, the **left innominate.** Thus we come to the condition in adults of higher vertebrates; a **left innominate** meets a **right innominate** (which was the right anterior cardinal), and together they enter the **precava** (or **superior vena cava**), which goes to the right auricle. This precava, then, is the survivor of the right common cardinal (Fig. 264E).

Behind the heart are two major divisions of the venous circulation, one concerned exclusively with the digestive organs (the **hepatic portal vein** and its tributaries), the other with the body wall, tail, hind limbs, and the excretory and reproductive organs (**postcardinal veins, postcava,** and their tributaries).

POSTCARDINALS, POSTCAVA, AND THEIR TRIBUTARIES

At the earliest stages of development in fishes (Fig. 264A) the **subintestinal vein** continues into the tail as the **caudal,** making a split around the anus to do so, but when the hepatic portal system, arising from the subintestinal, begins to function, the caudal drops this connection and drains into two new channels, the **posterior cardinals,** along the dorsal side of the body cavity. These postcardinals also receive segmental branches from muscles, gonads, and kidneys. As the latter organs develop (mediad to the postcardinals), a pair of **subcardinals** appears between them (Fig. 264B). Now blood from regions posterior to the kidneys begins to detour through capillaries in the kidneys into the subcardinals, which meanwhile connect with the more anterior part of the postcardinals (Fig. 264C). The kidney vessels supply in their passage the renal tubules. (Arterial blood goes to the glomeruli.) Thus is formed the **renal portal system,** in association with the mesonephric type of kidney, found in fishes and Amphibia. The **renal portal veins,** of course, are the original posterior portions of the postcardinals, linked to the caudal vein.

Beginning in lungfishes, a new, important vein, the **postcava** (*inferior* *vena cava*), extends back and dorsad from the hepatic vein, just in front of the liver, to meet the right subcardinal (the left disappearing) near the anterior ends of the kidneys (Fig. 264D). No doubt this postcava existed in the earliest Choanichthyes, for we find it present in Amphibia much as in the lungfishes. It is bigger now than both postcardinals put together, and usurps their function to a large extent, draining kidneys (via the cardinal), gonads, and posterior parts of the body. In adult frogs and toads the postcardinals have disappeared entirely, and they occur only during early development in amniotes (except *Sphenodon*, which bears here another sign of its exceedingly primitive position among tetrapods). The postcava tends to reach farther back between the kidneys, so that the subcardinal becomes indistinguishable from the rest of it. Then, owing largely to the appearance of a new type of kidney, the nonsegmental, highly efficient metanephros (see next chapter), the renal portal system as such gradually declines in reptiles and birds, and vanishes in mammals. All blood to the kidneys is brought by renal arteries under strong pressure, and discharged into the postcava by renal veins. This means that the postcava is the major vein of the body posterior to the heart. Incorporated in it is the hepatic (liver to heart), the extension of this reaching from liver to dorsal wall, and the single channel surviving from the embryonic subcardinals. Into it, too, run the caudal, the common iliacs (from hind limbs and pelvis) and the more posterior segmental veins of the trunk wall.

A part of the dorsal body wall was abandoned by the atrophy of the anterior parts of the postcardinals, yet skipped by the postcava. Here *vertebral veins* appear in reptiles, partly from segmental branches of the embryonic postcardinals, and they constitute a *supracardinal* system. This, in mammals, survives as the *azygos vein,* sometimes paired, which enters the precaval.

The *lateral abdominals* are conspicuous veins in fishes, draining lateral and ventral parts of the body wall. In tetrapods these connect posteriorly with the *iliacs* (pelvic limbs) and renal portals, but unite forward to form a single *ventral abdominal* which meets the hepatic portal. In the embryos of placental mammals the separate lateral abdominals become *allantoic* or *umbilical veins;* these fuse in the umbilical cord, and presently only the left umbilical survives, bringing blood from the placenta to the embryo. At birth, of course, it is shut off and atrophies.

HEPATIC PORTAL SYSTEM

Primitively this system of collectors from the digestive organs is represented by a *subintestinal* vein (Amphioxus), and we have mentioned that it connects with the caudal vein temporarily in fish embryos. On severing the connection, as the stomach, intestine and liver become differentiated and functional, the subintestinal develops into (1) a group of veins bringing blood from the walls of the gut into a single large *he-patic portal vein* (Fig. 265) and (2) a complex pattern of sinuses and

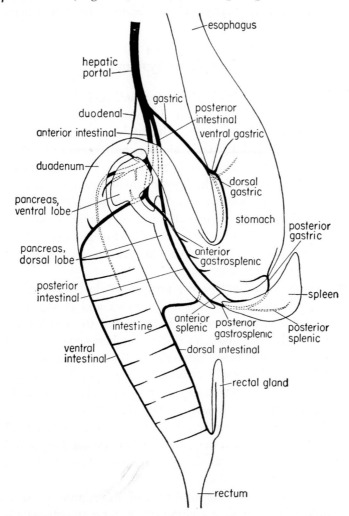

Fig. 265. Tributaries of hepatic portal system in a shark, *Squalus acanthias.*

venous capillaries inside of the expanding liver; from these the blood drains into the *postcava* if present (as it is embedded in the liver), or into the one or two *hepatic veins* in fishes, which go to the sinus venosus. This portal system ensures that all blood from the stomach and intestine is brought into close contact with the liver tissues, where some of the absorbed sugar and amino acids can be stored.

In embryos of all vertebrates that have yolk sacs two *vitelline veins* enter the body from the surface of the yolk, become enclosed in the liver as the *omphalomesenteric* veins, and then, as the intestine develops, they produce branches along it which presently combine to form the hepatic portal. This, however its ontogeny may vary, is one of the most constant features in the circulatory system of vertebrates, from fish to man.

Lymphatic System

At the beginning of this chapter was mentioned the relationship between blood, tissue fluid, and lymph; the latter drains in thin-walled vessels away from the tissue spaces, ultimately entering the veins. The lymphatic system includes vessels, sinuses, hearts, nodes (not glands), and lymphoid organs, such as tonsils and spleen. The earliest embryonic evidence of this system is in the form of small sacs associated with the anterior cardinal veins and the veins of the mesonephros. Probably the evolutionary origin of the lymphatic system was by separation from the veins, with which, however, it retains direct connections. The distinction between the two is still incomplete in cyclostomes and sharks. Protochordates have no lymphatic system.

Lymph sinuses (sacs, or spaces) are present in all groups of vertebrates, especially between the skin and muscles, and among the muscles next to the skeleton. Some authors have treated the coelom as a lymphatic space, and some make no distinction between these and tissue spaces in general, but it seems advisable to think of lymph as a fluid en route from intercellular spaces (tissue spaces proper, not discrete mesodermal cavities) to the veins. Lymph vessels may open from such spaces or, more often, commence blindly among them (Fig. 250) and receive fluid osmotically. Along the way, lymph vessels contain many valves, so arranged that pressure from the movement of surrounding muscles and other organs forces the lymph along, and so close to each other that the vessels themselves look beaded.

Some fishes, probably all amphibians, and also reptiles possess saclike *lymph hearts,* which by slow contraction of their smooth-muscle walls propel the lymph. Commonly these hearts have two chambers, an atrium and ventricle, with valves at their entrances and exits.

Scattered through many parts of the body in mammals and birds are *lymph nodes* (better not called glands or ganglia), where lymphatic vessels meet in spongy clumps of tissue of any size from scant visibility to an inch or more in length. These have an important function in trapping bacteria and other invaders of the body fluids. Here, in mammals, are produced the lymphocytes, a type of white blood cell which circulates freely, and here too occurs much of the phagocytic action by which infections are subdued in the body. The *tonsils,* on sides and posterior wall of the pharynx, are quite comparable to lymph nodes. The *thymus body,* lying between the two membranes of the mediastinum, is lymphoid in appearance but its function is uncertain, possibly endocrine, as it is relatively large in young animals (and man), decreasing or disappearing with age.

The *spleen,* an important organ in the body cavity of nearly all vertebrates (but not cylostomes or Dipnoi), contains pulpy "lymphoid" tissue in which are irregular sinuses. But these hold blood, and the spleen communicates with arteries and veins rather than with lymph vessels. A high concentration of red corpuscles can be maintained here, and the spleen by contracting can release them into the circulation when the oxygen-carrying capacity of the blood is impaired by hemorrhage, or a decrease of atmospheric oxygen calls for more than the normal amount of hemoglobin. The spleen takes a part in forming both red cells and leucocytes during embryonic development.

The general pattern of the lymphatic circulation in vertebrates is like this: (1) From the body wall, tail, trunk, and limbs lymph is gathered by small tributaries into longitudinal vessels located (a) *superficially* (external to the muscles), or (b) *deep* (near the vertebral column and ventrally along the abdomen, but internal to the body wall). The superficial vessels collect from subcutaneous spaces, segmental lymphatics, fins, muscles, etc., and often communicate with the deep vessels. Of the latter the most constant appear to be a pair of subvertebral trunks, sometimes single as in lampreys, and these collect from the body wall, kidneys and gonads; also they receive vessels from (2) the digestive organs. Here again is a superficial and a deep division, the latter containing the plexus of small *lacteal* vessels which occupy the submucosa of the small intestine and collect minute droplets of fat just after it is absorbed by the villi. Larger superficial vessels extend across the mesenteries, usually in company with veins, to meet the subvertebral trunks. Usually the lymph vessels of these first two divisions of the system run forward to the pectoral region where they enter sinuses, and these, or the vessels themselves, open into anterior cardinal veins, ducts of Cuvier, or sometimes also the postcardinals. (3) There are also head lymphatics, with *superficial* (orbital, facial, hyoid) and *deep* (adjacent to brain) branches and sinuses. These drain back, usually into anterior cardinals or their equivalents, the innominates, jugulars, etc.

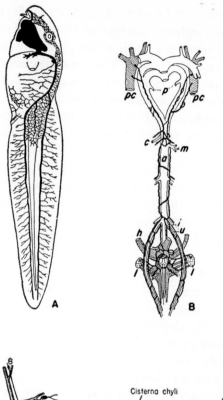

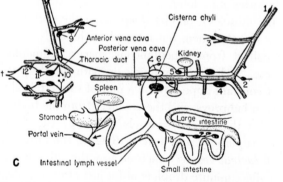

Fig. 266. A, superficial lymph vessels of tadpole; B, thoracic ducts of 17-day chick embryo; C, deep lymphatic vessels of rat. (A and B from Kingsley, *Outlines of Comparative Anatomy of Vertebrates*, 3rd ed., Blakiston; C from Romer.)

a, dorsal aorta; *c*, coeliac artery; *h*, hypogastric vein; *i*, ischiadic artery; *l*, lymph hearts; *m*, mesenteric artery; *pc*, precava; *u*, umbilical artery.

In C, anterior end is left; lymphatic nodes numbered as follows: 1, knee; 2, tail; 3, inguinal; 4, lumbar; 5, kidney; 6, nodes around cisterna chyli; 7, intestinal; 8, elbow; 9, axilla; 10, thoracic; 11, cervical; 12, submaxillary; 13, mesenteric; t, lymphatic plexus of tongue and lips. Arrows show where lymph vessels enter veins.

Many fishes and Amphibia have connections posteriorly as well as anteriorly between the lymph vessels and the veins (caudal, postcardinal, and postcaval). *Myxine*, the hagfish, and a number of teleosts have two lymph hearts to pump lymph into the caudal vein. In salamanders (larvae especially) and Apoda there may be dozens or scores of segmentally placed, paired lymph hearts communicating with lateral longitudinal trunks, and in addition a pair of axillary and of inguinal hearts. The subvertebral trunks become, anteriorly at least, a single *thoracic duct* in mammals (Fig. 266C); this enters the left innominate vein at the base of the internal jugular.

CHAPTER IX

Urinary and Genital Systems, and Endocrine Organs

THE KIDNEYS excrete metabolic wastes, especially urea and uric acid, derived from proteins. But this is not the only, nor perhaps even the primary, function of these organs. In most vertebrates, at least, they regulate the water content of the body, keeping the rate of loss approximately equal to the rate of intake. Among animals living in fresh water the concentration of dissolved materials in body fluids is greater than in the surrounding water; hence any membranous surface absorbs water by osmosis and it is necessary to excrete the surplus by a mechanism sufficiently powerful to balance the osmotic pressure. In the sea, on the other hand, it is difficult to avoid the opposite condition, since the surrounding water contains about 3.5 percent of dissolved salt, and there must be either an active intake of water or some device for increasing the concentration of solutes in body fluids, to compensate for the osmotic loss of water from the body. On land the problem is usually one of conserving water while excreting nitrogenous compounds, since the tendency is to lose water by evaporation from lungs and skin. The work of Homer W. Smith (1937) on comparative physiology of the kidney has illuminated the whole subject of kidney evolution.

A system of paired *coelomic pores,* opening from the coelomic cavities to the outside, is present in the lowest chordates (Hemichorda), in the larvae of echinoderms, and some other invertebrates. It undoubtedly originated far back among the earliest coelomate animals, not necessarily for excretion or for reproductive passages, but perhaps merely to prevent the development of too great a difference in osmotic pressure between the coelom and the sea water. In primitive vertebrates paired ducts from the coelom are arranged segmentally, and clusters of capillaries (*glomeruli*), supplied by arterial blood, make contact with the ducts as a means of releasing water from the plasma of the blood. Therefore these ducts, in more advanced vertebrates, have come to be almost the only available outlets for metabolic wastes from the body. Likewise they were available and near to the **gonads,** so that by appropriate changes the tubes could be used for emission of eggs or sperms. Thus it is difficult to separate the study of urinary organs from that of reproductive organs, but we shall begin with the former because the kidneys and their ducts show most clearly what the primitive structure was.

Excretory and Genital Organs of Protochordates

Among protochordates there is little suggestion, in these systems, of anything found in vertebrates, but for an adequate picture of the Chordata they should be mentioned. In some but not all Hemichorda the proboscis contains a small glandular organ, the **glomerulus,** supplied by blood sinuses. It is thought to be excretory, and if so it discharges into the proboscis cavity, a coelomic pouch, from which a pore provides exit. Since glomeruli in vertebrate kidneys also discharge into capsules derived from embryonic coelom, the comparison between these similarly named organs may not be too far-fetched. *Branchiostoma,* alone among chordates, has an excretory system in which **flame cells (solenocytes)** are the essential part (Fig. 267). Although many lower invertebrates have these, the paired tubular **protonephridia** which bear them in *Branchiostoma* most nearly resemble protonephridia of some marine polychaete worms (Annelida). It is highly improbable that any close relationship exists between chordates and polychaetes, however. About 90 pairs of these nephridia are present, located above the gill clefts and opening into the atrium; there is no connection with the coelom and the nephridia are derived from ectoderm instead of mesoderm. In tunicates it is uncertain what organs are excretory; this function has been attributed to the **"neural gland,"** a blind pouch in the dorsal wall of the pharynx, and also to a vesicular organ without any duct, along the intestine.

The reproductive organs in the wormlike Enteropneusta (Fig. 4) are very numerous paired pouches lying in rows along the dorsolateral part of the trunk, including the gill region. They open by pores to the outside, and the sexes are separate. This is the rule also in Pterobranchia, but two species of *Cephalodiscus* are known to have hermaphroditic individuals besides the males and females. The gonads of *Branchiostoma* are segmentally arranged in the inner surface of the body wall, actually within coelomic cavities, but they break open when mature, letting the gametes fall into the atrium. The sexes are separate. Sexual reproduction among

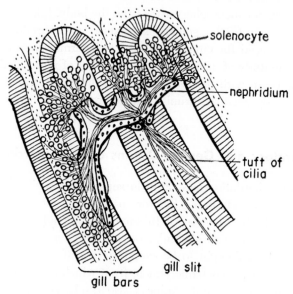

Fig. 267. A flame cell nephridium of Amphioxus, with part of pharynx. (Redrawn from Parker and Haswell.)

tunicates is hermaphroditic, the single or paired gonads having their own ducts to the atrium, but many tunicates add to this an asexual budding, sometimes most complex and remarkable, so that either sessile or drifting colonies may result. Some (*Salpa, Doliolum*) alternate sexual with asexual (budding) generations, as if they had no more ambition than a jellyfish.

The Vertebrate Kidney

Among vertebrates it would be difficult for segmental coelomic pores to open separately to the outer surface of the body, because muscles occupy the body wall as far down as the midventral line. The pores must then become tubes, going out of the coelom to a longitudinal duct along either side of it, and this runs back to the best available external opening, the cloaca. On the theory that such an arrangement is the primitive one in adult vertebrates, we may refer to this longitudinal duct as the **archinephric** duct. The segmental tubes entering it from the coelom are **renal tubules.**

The kidneys of different vertebrates are fundamentally alike in structure and development, but may appear different because of their positions in relation to the body cavity, their longitudinal extent, or the nature of the ducts which serve them. Recent writers tend to emphasize the uniformity of the vertebrate kidney, calling it a **holonephros,** and minimize the distinctions formerly made between both evolutionary and developmental stages under the names of **pro-, meso-,** and **metanephros.** Nevertheless these terms convey certain useful meanings, and need not be discarded.

In early embryos the first appearance of prospective kidney tissues is in a portion of each somite lying just below the epimere but above the hypomere, called the **nephrotome,** or **intermediate cell mass.** A series of nephrotomes, then, is found along each side, and each nephrotome contains a pocket of coelom open to that in the hypomere below it (Fig. 268). The opening becomes a ciliated **peritoneal funnel,** while the cavity within the nephrotome is the **nephrocoel.** Beginning in the more anterior trunk segments, several of the nephrocoels put out tubules laterally; the ciliated opening to each of these is a **nephrostome.** The tubules unite to form a longitudinal duct. As soon as this duct is complete to the exterior, in larval fishes and amphibians, the kidney can begin to function; it is a **pronephros.** The duct, so long as it serves only anterior tubules which have peritoneal funnels, may be called the **pronephric duct** (Fig. 269). In most cases the pronephric tubules become associated with **glomeruli** (capillary tufts), and this is done by converting the nephrocoel into a **renal capsule** (**Bowman's capsule**), which is cup-shaped, the capillaries occupying the cup. Now, through the relatively high pressure of blood delivered to these capillaries, a partial filtration of plasma from the blood into the tubule takes place; this is added to the coelomic fluid coming through the peritoneal funnel under the action of its cilia. The tubule, likewise ciliated, propels the fluid into the pronephric duct.

A functional pronephros is found in early larvae or unhatched embryos of most kinds of fishes and Amphibia, but in nearly all it degenerates as soon as the more posterior nephrotomes have given rise to a different type of kidney, the **mesonephros.** The condition in cyclostomes probably sheds a good deal of light on that of ancestral vertebrates. Pronephric tubules in the larva of a lamprey begin to develop as far forward as the branchial region, and some three, four, or five pairs of them become functional and project into the pericardial cavity. (It may be recalled that in

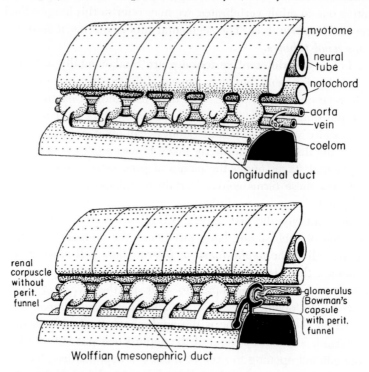

Fig. 268. Development of renal corpuscles and tubules to mesonephric type. Direction of development is read from right (posterior) to left (anterior); lower figure older than upper.

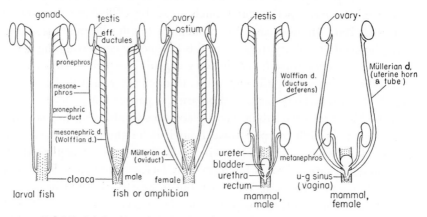

Fig. 269. Relationships of excretory and reproductive ducts among vertebrates.

lampreys the heart is later enclosed in a cartilage wall confluent with the branchial basket, and also that the pericardial cavity is a part of the coelom.) Actually the pericardial space in the lamprey larva includes the expanded nephrocoels of these anterior pronephric tubules; therefore the openings which lead into the tubules are **nephrostomes** instead of peritoneal funnels. A large compound **glomus,** bulging into the nephrocoel, supplies each group of tubules. Nephrotomes posterior to the heart produce, at first, only a pronephric duct. In transformation of the larva to the adult, a series of tubules develops farther back (leaving a gap of several segments without tubules); these are at their first appearance segmental, one for each nephrotome, but soon they become much too numerous and convoluted to retain a segmental pattern; they do not open to the coelom, but have capsules and glomeruli. Thus is formed the **mesonephros,** the adult kidney. At the same time the pronephric tubules and pronephric duct degenerate as far back as the mesonephros, and the remainder of the duct, now serving this kidney, is called a **mesonephric** or **Wolffian duct.**

Hagfishes produce a more elaborate pronephros, consisting (in *Bdellostoma*) of about 18 tubules opening from the pericardium in a cluster. The mesonephros has but one tubule per segment, each with capsule and

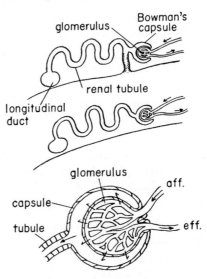

Fig. 270. Upper figures: renal tubule and corpuscle with and without ciliated funnel from coelom. Lower figure: renal corpuscle, showing filtration from glomerulus into capsule.

glomerulus but no funnel. In the adult hagfish, however, the pronephros is still present in a highly modified condition. Its tubules now open, not into a pronephric duct, but into the cardinal vein near the point where this enters the heart; thus pericardial fluid apparently is added directly to venous blood. The pronephric duct has degenerated back to the level where the mesonephros begins. In its simple segmental arrangement the mesonephros of a hagfish is the most primitive known in vertebrates, but we cannot say this for the pronephros.

To summarize our information to this point: The **archinephric duct** is a supposedly ancestral type of longitudinal duct serving tubules in a series extending nearly the whole length of the body cavity; the **pronephros** is an embryonic or larval kidney consisting of segmental tubules in the anterior part of the trunk, usually with funnels opening into the coelom, and with a duct (equivalent to the archinephric duct) extending back to the cloaca; the **mesonephros** is a more posterior, but primitively segmental, kidney in which the tubules do not have funnels but receive fluid only from glomeruli in capsules. The pronephros does not occur in adults of any vertebrates except hagfishes (where it is modified), but the mesonephros is the adult kidney of fishes and amphibians. (See, however, further comments on terms used for types of kidneys, on page 261.)

Blood to the glomerular capillaries in all vertebrates comes from the renal arteries, but in addition the renal tubules of fishes (except cyclostomes), amphibians, reptiles, and birds are served by a network of capillaries carrying venous blood from the renal portal veins. This, of course, is under much lower pressure than that in the glomeruli; consequently much of the water and plasma solutes filtered from the blood into the capsules can be returned here to the blood, partly by osmosis and partly by selective work of the cells in the tubule walls, a "reverse secretion." The renal portal system, then, characterizes not only the mesonephric kidney of fishes and Amphibia, but also, in part at least, the metanephros of reptiles and birds, but it is no longer present in mammals.

Returning now to fishes, the sharks are known to have lived in fresh water during the early part of their history, and then to have spread into the sea prior to the divergence of rays and chimaeras from the shark stem. The blood of sharks contains about 1.7 percent NaCl, plus other dissolved substances, but not enough to make it isotonic with sea water (3.5 percent NaCl), were it not for the retention of a large amount of urea. This is reabsorbed from particular sections of the mesonephric tubules into the renal portal blood, after having been passed by the glomeruli into the capsules in the course of filtration. Thus the elasmobranch fishes have met the problem of keeping an osmotic balance between the blood and sea water.

All, or nearly all, of the work of excretion is handled in the more posterior part of the shark kidney, from which some four or five separate ducts lead to the basal portion of the mesonephric duct. This arrangement is comparable to (but independent of) the metanephros of Amniota. In males the greater part of the mesonephric duct serves as a **vas deferens** (sperm duct), which in mature specimens is enlarged and twisted in its course along the kidney. Anteriorly it receives a few fine **vasa efferentia** (or **efferent ductules**) from the testis; these are outgrowths of early mesonephric tubules but no longer serve for excretion. In females the mesonephric duct in some cases is still an excretory duct for the more anterior part of the kidney.

Some of the actinopterous fishes, such as sturgeons and gars, show a condition more primitive than that of sharks in that the male uses the mesonephric duct for both excretion and conveyance of sperm. In *Polypterus* there is a partial sharing, but in teleosts the testes open only to the basal part of the mesonephric ducts, which otherwise are wholly excretory. These excretory ducts, by the way, join each other to make a single urinary passage, separate from the intestine, so that there is no cloaca in teleosts. At the point of junction there is often a urinary bladder, but this includes no part of the embryonic gut wall (endoderm); it is mesodermal only, and evidently not homologous with the bladder in tetrapods.

Perhaps the most distinctive feature of the kidney in teleosts is the reduction of glomeruli and tubules which occurs in some of the marine kinds, and finally their complete loss in certain specialized groups (most deep-sea fishes, sea horse, pipefish, toadfish, angler, etc.). This is a device for preventing too great a loss of water from the body, since the concentration of salt in the blood is much less than it is in sea water. (We have just seen that the elasmobranchs solved this problem by increasing the urea in the blood.) Marine teleosts must therefore secrete chlorides and urea from their gills, since the kidney mechanism has frequently atrophied. Just as with sharks, the ancestors of teleosts were apparently fresh water fishes, in which this difficulty did not arise.

The mesonephric duct in lungfishes and Amphibia receives vasa efferentia from the testes in the male, but is at the same time excretory. The mesonephros is long in lungfishes, caecilians, and salamanders, but short in most frogs, on account of the reduced number of segments in the trunk. There are about 2000 glomeruli in *Rana*, each filtering plasma (minus proteins and cells) into a capsule at the beginning of a tubule. Blood to the glomerulus comes from the renal artery. In the tubule are two convolutions, proximal and distal, with a short ciliated portion between. The renal portal vein supplies capillaries to the walls of the tubules, through which some water, salts, glucose, and a slight amount of urea are reabsorbed into the blood. Nevertheless the frog releases in its urine enough water to compensate for that absorbed into its body osmotically through the skin and digestive tract. In aquatic frogs this amounts to far more (in proportion to body weight) than would be the case with tetrapod kidneys. On the other hand, desert toads must conserve water; the Australian *Chiroleptes* fails to develop any glomeruli in its kidneys and cannot, therefore, filter its blood plasma. The **urinary bladder** in amphibians, as in higher tetrapods, forms as a pouch on the ventral side of the cloaca, lined with endoderm, and is not directly connected with the mesonephric ducts (Fig. 271).

Among Amniota a new kidney appears, replacing the mesonephros after the embryonic stage; this is the ***metanephros.*** The more posterior embryonic nephrotomes, which have not contributed to the mesonephros, commence the formation of great numbers of renal tubules (Fig. 272). Up towards this cluster of tubules grows a new duct, from the posterior end of the mesonephric duct. This ***ureter*** or ***metanephric duct*** expands distally and produces many short branches which connect with the metanephric tubules, thus forming a kidney separate from and posterior to the mesonephros (Fig. 269), but both, of course, are functional during the time of transition. The mesonephric duct remains as a vas deferens in the male, but disappears in the female, as the mesonephros degenerates.

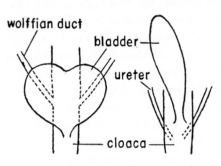

Fig. 271. Relationship of excretory system to cloaca in frog (left) and lizard (right), ventral view.

The metanephros is distinguished by an enormous number of renal tubules and corpuscles (glomeruli in capsules); there are a million or more

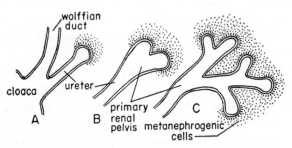

Fig. 272. Embryonic origin of ureter and renal pelvis, human. (Redrawn from *Manual of Embryology* by Frazer.)

of these units in the average human kidney. The metanephros shows no sign of segmentation, and no peritoneal funnels. The tubules, by entering collecting tubules as twigs enter the branches of a tree, conduct urine to a common cavity in the kidney, the renal ***pelvis,*** formed by the expanded end of the ureter. The blood supply to the glomeruli, of course, is arterial, but that to the tubules is largely from the renal portal veins in reptiles and birds, while in mammals these veins disappear and the efferent vessels from the glomeruli themselves give rise to the capillary network on the surface of the tubules. This presumably increases the efficiency of reabsorption in the mammal kidney, as the blood in these capillaries contains a higher proportion of plasma proteins than any other blood in the body (on account of the loss of water into the tubule in filtration); therefore the osmotic difference favoring return of water from the convoluted tubules is relatively great. Also the kidney in mammals has introduced a thin-walled hairpin loop between the proximal and distal convoluted portions, called **Henle's loop,** in which much reabsorption takes place.

In reptiles and birds the cloaca is differentiated into, usually, three sections, a **coprodeum** (in which water can be reabsorbed from the feces), **urodeum** (which receives the ureters and, in the male, vas deferens), and **proctodeum** (with a sphincter muscle). The ureters do not enter the bladder directly, and no bladder is present in Crocodilia, snakes, and birds. Urine therefore tends to accumulate in the urodeum, where most of the remaining water in it can be reabsorbed into the blood. But this would interfere with the excretion of urea, which, returning with the water, would become toxic in the blood. Reptiles and birds, therefore, excrete most of their nitrogen in uric acid rather than urea, for uric acid crystallizes as the water is withdrawn from it in the urodeum, and it is released as a white, semisolid mass with the feces. This arrangement, then, permits nitrogen excretion while conserving nearly all the water in the body.

SUMMARY OF VERTEBRATE KIDNEY TYPES

Nephrotomes in the trunk region of vertebrate embryos appear to have potentialities for making kidney units (**nephroi**) and ducts in an essentially similar manner along the whole series of segments. Owing, perhaps, to the axial gradient in developmental rates, those anteriorly become functional first and form the **pronephros** in primitive vertebrates; this generally contains at least some tubules with tunnels open to the coelom, undoubtedly a heritage from the earliest vertebrates. Succeeding this type of kidney in adult fishes and amphibians is one employing closed tubules, the **mesonephros;** the longitudinal duct it uses is the same, but since the mesonephros is farther back in the trunk, the anterior part of the duct disappears at the same time that the pronephros does. In reptiles, birds, and mammals no functional pronephros occurs, or but very briefly; the first active embryonic kidney is of the mesonephric type, and is followed by a *metanephros,* which is far more elaborate and uses a new duct, the ureter; the metanephros occupies the same location in the body as the more posterior part of the kidney of fishes and amphibians.

Reproductive Organs of Vertebrates

Vertebrates reproduce sexually, by the fusion of *sperm cells* (male gametes) with *egg cells* (female gametes). Not only does this union of gam-

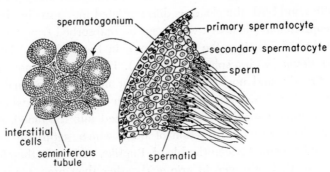

Fig. 273. Structure of testis in mammal. Left, section through several seminiferous tubules; right, detail of part of one tubule, showing maturation of sperm cells.

etes bring together in a single fertilized egg the hereditary factors from both parents, but it induces the egg, otherwise inert, to start division and the formation of an embryo.

Gametes are made in the *gonads* (*testes* in the male, *ovaries* in the female) where primordial germ cells transform through a series of stages into sperms or eggs (Figs. 273, 274). But the ultimate source of these germ cells appears to be in the endoderm of the embryo, from which they migrate to the prospective gonadal tissue in the roof of the coelom. The gonads develop from paired but not segmental *genital ridges* near the median line, above the peritoneum, which is pushed downward into the coelom as they grow. A few of the lower vertebrates are *hermaphroditic,* having both male and female gonads in the same individual, but these mature at

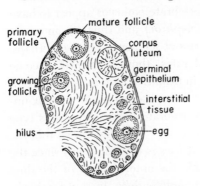

Fig. 274. Ovary with follicles (human).

different times, the testes first; such a condition, found in hagfishes and a handful of teleosts, is not primitive.

Many differences in form and function arise between male and female. A part of these, the *primary sex characters,* have to do with the reproductive organs directly: the production of eggs or sperms, their passage to the exterior, organs for retaining the embryo in the female when the latter is viviparous, and so on. But there are also a great many *secondary sex characters,* which may involve almost any part of the body, including structure, physiology, and behavior, and are likely to be most conspicuous in the breeding season. These features will be discussed in the last part of this chapter. They are induced by *sex hormones* carried in the blood, and these hormones originate, partly, in the gonads. Thus a gonad is an endocrine gland as well as a source of gametes.

The reproductive systems must transmit gametes to a place where their union is possible, perhaps in the open water of sea, lake or stream, or perhaps only as far as the oviducts of the female, to which sperm must be brought from the male. Egg-laying animals are *oviparous,* their eggs being fertilized externally in most fishes and some amphibians, but internally in other vertebrates. Animals whose development begins within the body of the female and whose young are "born alive" (not hidden in an egg shell) are *viviparous.* Of course these always have internal fertilization, and the oviducts must be enlarged and specialized to contain the embryos.

MALE REPRODUCTIVE ORGANS

In early stages of development the testes and ovaries of vertebrates are much alike, consisting of mesenchymal cells to which are added primordial germ cells, scarcely distinguishable, and an outer covering of peritoneum. Numerous separate *testis cords* of prospective epithelial cells form in the interior of the testis, connecting basally in a network, the *rete testis.* The cords split repeatedly, develop internal cavities, and become *seminiferous tubules;* the strands of the rete do likewise, and from them efferent tubules make a connection, in most cases, with some of the anterior tubules of the mesonephros.

In the walls of the seminiferous tubules (Fig. 273) are *spermatogonia* (derived from the large primordial germ cells), and *Sertoli cells,* also called *nurse cells.* Most vertebrates have well-defined breeding seasons, during which the seminiferous tubules have open lumina and the spermatogonia are in continual multiplication, forming *spermatocytes* in two successive divisions. During the first of these the number of chromosomes

is reduced to a single set (haploid) instead of the diploid number characteristic of most cells. The haploid cells, **spermatids**, resulting from the
second division, lose much of their cytoplasm, either into the lumen of
the tubule or into the nurse cells to which they attach temporarily, and
then take on the flagellate form of sperm cells. But between breeding

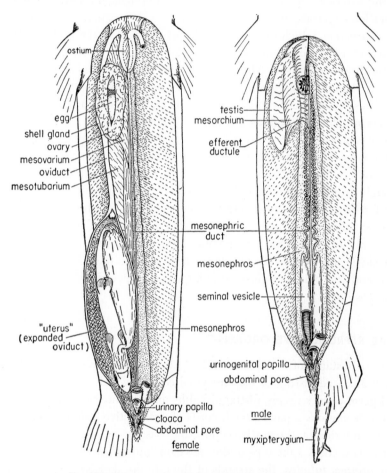

Fig. 275. Urinary and genital organs of shark, *Squalus acanthias.*

seasons the factory may be shut down completely, the tubules lose their
lumina and in some cases deteriorate altogether, while the remaining
tissue of the testis also decreases in volume. With a few types, including
man and some of his domestic animals, no such interruption occurs.

Between adjacent seminiferous tubules is a loose connective tissue of
interstitial cells, the source of the male hormone, and among them are
nerves, blood vessels and lymphatic vessels.

Cyclostomes have a single gonad, resulting from a fusion of the right and left. There are no tubules in the testes, which thus more nearly resemble ovaries, and sperm cells emerge from ruptured follicles into the coelom. Since there are no ducts, they must escape by way of the abdominal pores into the urinogenital sinus just behind the anus; the mesonephric ducts, not available to the testes, also open here.

In primitive Actinopteri and in Amphibia the mesonephric or Wolffian duct is used as a sperm duct as well as for excretion, but in sharks, on account of the development of accessory ducts from the kidney, it is mostly or entirely a

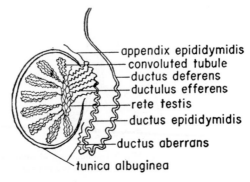

Fig. 276. Diagram of testis and its ducts (human). (Partly after Romer.)

sperm duct. A similar (but of course independent) arrangement is found in teleosts. The posterior end of the Wolffian duct enlarges in male sharks to form a seminal vesicle.

If the eggs of a fish or amphibian are fertilized externally, of course no organ for the transfer of sperm from the male is necessary, but among those fishes with internal fertilization, including all the viviparous kinds,

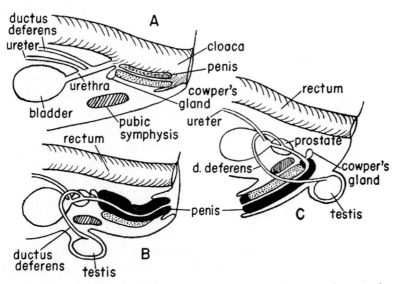

Fig. 277. Relationship between excretory and reproductive ducts in male mammals. A, monotreme; B, marsupial; C, placental.

some sort of copulatory organs occur in the males. In sharks, rays, and chimaeras these are **myxipterygia** (Fig. 16), special grooved and spiny fingerlike projections of the pelvic fins, supplemented by **siphon sacs** which extend forward under the abdominal skin. Many teleosts have intromittent organs, such as the modified anal fins (**gonopodia**) of mos-

Fig. 278. Spermatophores of salamanders. Left, *Diemictylus viridescens;* right, *Desmognathus fuscus.* (After Noble.)

quito fishes and their relatives (Fig. 280), the extended caudal fin of the male swordtail, *Xiphophorus,* or the penislike extension of the urinogenital papilla in some of the tide-pool sculpins.

In salamanders the testes are elongate, but in frogs small and oval. Their vasa efferentia connect with a number of mesonephric tubules. In

Fig. 279. Male of tailed frog, *Ascaphus truei,* showing extension of cloaca, a copulatory device, not a tail. (From *Biology of the Amphibia* by Noble.)

the majority of salamanders fertilization is internal, by an unusual method: the male, during courtship, deposits on the ground or in water small packages of sperms, held together by a secretion from cloacal glands, and the female picks up, in her cloaca, one or more of these **spermatophores** (Fig. 278), retaining them for fertilization of the eggs later. The bell toad, *Ascaphus* (Fig. 279), of the Pacific northwest, has a tubelike extension of the cloaca by which internal fertilization is accomplished, but with other frogs there is emission of sperms over the eggs as they are laid, during amplexus. Male caecilians evert the cloaca for internal fertilization.

Apparently ancestral reptiles, adopting life on land where internal fertilization is necessary, did so without any special copulatory device, for the primitive *Sphenodon* has none. Most modern reptiles have an internal penis in the cloaca, composed of vascular tissue which can be everted under increased blood pressure. There are two types, possibly of independent origin. That in turtles (Fig. 281) and crocodiles is a single organ on the ventral wall of the cloaca, consisting mainly of a pair of soft vascular ridges (*corpora cavernosa*) with a deep *urethral groove* between them.

The entrance of blood into the sinuses of the corpora makes them swell and extend out of the cloaca, while the groove between forms a tube to carry sperm. As this type of penis occurs also in primitive birds, especially Ratitae, tinamous, and the Anseriformes (ducks, etc.), it was undoubtedly characteristic of archosaurian reptiles, from which birds were derived;

Fig. 280. Male of *Phallichthys*, an aquarium fish, showing gonopodium, a modified anal fin.

the Crocodilia are the only modern archosaurs. But in most birds the vas deferens enters the urodeum by a papilla which is erectile, and copulation is by contact of protruded proctodea.

Lizards and snakes (Fig. 281) have paired *hemipenes* in the lateral or

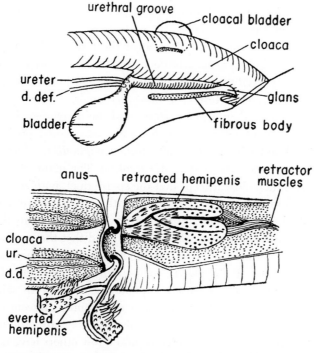

Fig. 281. Upper: cloaca and penis of tortoise. (Redrawn from Romer.) Lower: hemipenis of rattlesnake, *Crotalus*. (Redrawn from Kingsley, *Outlines of Comparative Anatomy of Vertebrates*, 3rd ed., Blakiston.)

dorsal walls of the cloaca; each of these forms as a sac with a vascular wall, kept in a pocket with its outer surface turned inward except when it is dilated and pushed out. The surface is grooved and armed with short spines, the arrangement of which is used to some extent in classification. A retractor muscle draws each hemipenis back into its pocket.

Monotremes show a partial but not complete separation of the penis from the wall of the cloaca (Fig. 277A) but it is essentially of the type described in turtles and crocodiles, withdrawn into a ventral pocket. Instead of receiving the whole urethra it carries only a ventral division thereof. With the separation of urinogenital and digestive canals in higher mammals the cloaca disappears. The urethra now traverses the penis as a tube rather than a groove. In addition to the corpora cavernosa there is a *corpus spongiosum* (or *corpus cavernosum urethrae*), carrying the urethra and ending usually in a slight expansion, the *glans.* This is forked in the opossum and some other marsupials, as is the vagina of the female. A *sheath* may invest the whole penis, or, as in man and a few other mammals, the glans only is covered with a *prepuce.* Many of the carnivores, rodents, and some other groups have a *baculum* (*os priapi,* or *penis bone*) as a stiffening rod; it develops in connective tissue of the corpus spongiosum, not from the pelvis.

We should refer here to the descent of the testes and ovaries from a position near the kidneys, in early development, to the lower (posterior) part of the body cavity in the case of ovaries, and farther, into *inguinal pouches,* in the case of testes of most mammals. Primates, ungulates (with few exceptions), most carnivores, and the marsupials have a complete and permanent migration of the testes into paired pockets of the body cavity, lined with peritoneum (*tunica vaginalis*), which are then enclosed in a common sac of skin, the *scrotum.* The inguinal canals leading to the sacs then close, except that the sperm duct, with accompanying artery, vein, and nerve, wrapped in a sheath of peritoneum, must reach the abdominal cavity from each testis by way of the canal; these parts constitute the *spermatic cord.* It has been found that the production and activity of the sperms is hindered by the normal heat of the body, but is optimum under the slightly lower temperature of the external position. This justifies but does not wholly explain the descent. In some of the rodents, a few carnivores, bats, and the camel family, descent of the testes occurs during the breeding season only, and they are otherwise withdrawn. Monotremes, whales, elephants, and a few others have no scrotum and the testes never migrate out of the abdomen.

Since a testis is supplied by an artery, vein, and nerve, as well as the vas deferens, from its early stages, these are drawn down with it in its descent; as the vas deferens enters the urethra below (or posterior to) the bladder, the descent of the testis leaves the vas deferens looped over the ureter where the latter comes to the bladder on its dorsal side. This accounts for the indirect course followed by the vas deferens to the urethra in most mammals.

Near the distal (urethral) end of the vas deferens there is usually a *seminal vesicle.* The duct from it to the entrance into the urethra is called *ejaculatory duct;* this and the seminal vesicle are enclosed in a *prostate gland,* which has ducts entering the urethra and supplies most of the seminal fluid. *Cowper's* (or *bulbourethral*) *glands* are a pair of small glands on the urethra below the prostate. This group of organs is characteristic of most mammals.

FEMALE REPRODUCTIVE ORGANS

The *ovaries,* each separated from the coelom by a thin covering of peritoneum, lie usually just anterior to the kidneys and are paired, except in a few fishes and in birds. In the tissue of the embryonic ovary *ovarian cords* develop, corresponding to the cords in the testis, but instead of forming tubules the cords separate into clusters of cells, scattered among the interstitial tissue; frequently the original cords degenerate and the outer epithelium of the ovary gives rise to new clusters of cells, pushing inward. Each of these becomes spherical, with or without a well-developed cavity, and so constitutes an *ovarian follicle* (Fig. 274). One cell within this follicle is the *egg.* As noted previously, there seems to be evidence that the eggs arise from embryonic germ cells which have migrated to the gonadal tissue from the endoderm. The only way for a mature egg to escape from the ovary is for the follicle to break open at the surface of the ovary and release the egg into (usually) the coelom.

The cells of the ovary, especially those of the follicles, are occupied in secreting hormones called *estrogens;* these are often described as a single substance with the name estrone (or estrin, theelin, estradiol, etc.). The effects, seen in other parts of the body, are to stimulate and maintain the secondary female characteristics including those of behavior. It should be emphasized here that the sex of an individual has been decided at the time when the egg was fertilized, and that the hormones which control development of either male or female secondary characters are carrying out a decision made through the chance arrangement of chromosomes at fertilization. The sex hormones are not themselves responsible for making an individual male or female. Nevertheless the young of vertebrates are likely to appear "intermediate," or not well differentiated as to sex. This is because the characteristics induced by sex hormones are slow in appearing, since the hormones themselves only gradually are elaborated by the gonads. The rate of these changes may be rapid, causing precocious masculinity or femininity, or it may be slow, so that an individual of mature age may lack the usual secondary distinctions.

The term **hermaphrodite** is not applicable to any of the higher vertebrates, and only by stretching its meaning can it be used for certain fishes. A true hermaphrodite is an animal which is functionally male and female at the same time. In some of the Sparidae (porgies) and Serranidae (sea bass) the gonads are ovaries and testes combined, the testicular ducts opening into the oviduct, but the ovary and testis mature successively. In cyclostomes the gonad (a pair united into one in the middle) contains during its early stages prospective male and female gametes, but those of one sex come to predominate finally, while those of the other degenerate.

Most animals have distinct seasons for breeding, those of temperate countries being usually in spring or summer when food is most available for the young and the temperature is favorable. The gonads, accordingly, undergo seasonal changes of size and activity. Often the ovaries are many times larger in the breeding season, when filled with eggs, and of course the hormonal production by interstitial or follicular cells varies likewise. Some marine teleosts lay millions of eggs in a season; the more numerous they are, the smaller, as a rule, and the more random is their fertilization. But animals producing very large eggs (hagfish, sharks, reptiles, birds) can have but few, and if the young are born in an advanced stage of development the number may come down to half a dozen or less in a lifetime.

In Elasmobranch fishes (Fig. 275) two ovaries normally occur, in which the eggs reach a very large size, up to one or two inches in diameter, before breaking from the follicles. Rays and a few sharks, however, have only the right ovary in the adult, the left having atrophied. Frequently an ovary is extended posteriorly by a long **epigonal cord,** but this part does not contain eggs. In young individuals the ovaries lie closely against the dorsal wall of the body cavity, but as they enlarge the peritoneum covering them is drawn downward and finally makes a mesentery, the **mesovarium,** suspending each. Eggs when released are moved down and forward to a single slitlike opening, the **ostium,** ventral to the anterior end of the liver. From this an egg may go into either the right or left **oviduct,** since the two meet at the ostium, and the first part of the lining of the oviducts is ciliated. The oviducts lead back to the cloaca, but show three distinct portions on the way, the most anterior being that in which the egg is fertilized, and albumen is secreted around it. (The egg itself consists mainly of yolk with a minute quantity of cytoplasm just under its plasma membrane.) After this it passes the **shell gland** and is given a horny shell in the oviparous types, but in dogfishes and most rays the shell gland is vestigial, since the young are born without a shell after passing their embryonic stages. The lower and larger part of each oviduct is either a place for holding a series of eggs before laying them, or a somewhat vascular "uterus" where the embryos of viviparous species spend weeks or months developing. Not only do the vascular folds of the lining of the oviduct supply oxygen from the blood of the mother, but in some rays, at least, the large quantity of material available in the yolk is further supplemented by osmotic feeding, so that the young ray at birth is much larger than the egg from which it came.

Oviducts originate in the embryos of gnathostomes as **Müllerian ducts,** which split off from the pronephric ducts in Chondrichthyes, carrying the pronephric funnels with them, but develop from the mesomere proper in higher vertebrates. The pronephric funnels, expanded, become the ostium and ovarian funnels, but the remaining part of the pronephric duct, as already described, becomes the Wolffian or mesonephric duct. Thus Müllerian ducts, as such, never have anything to do with excretion; the term *oviduct* is applied to them in their functional, adult condition. Their anterior union to make a single ostium, as described above, occurs only in Chondrichthyes where it is a specialization. It is not uncommon for the Müllerian ducts to appear in males, reduced and nonfunctional, but this is *not* evidence that vertebrates were once hermaphroditic.

The bony fishes, Osteichthyes, show several modifications, as would be expected in so diverse a group. Owing, apparently, to delayed development, the Müllerian and Wolffian duct in sturgeons (*Acipenser*) are not separated behind the level of the kidney; therefore the short oviduct opens into an expanded urinogenital canal. In *Amia* a longer oviduct enters the base of the Wolffian duct. Usually in teleosts the ovary contains an internal cavity which extends posteriorly, meeting that of the opposite side to form a median duct (Fig. 282C), and this breaks open through the body wall at a point between the anus and excretory pore, so that there is no cloaca. Properly speaking there is no true oviduct, since the ovarian passages are evidently closed portions of the coelom formed by folds of the peritoneum. In the salmon and smelts (Argentinidae), which are low in the scale of teleosts, the mesovarium extends behind each ovary, folds over and attaches to the body wall, making an enclosed passage, and this may be the way in which the enclosure of the ovaries and their passages in higher types developed first.

The lungfishes (Fig. 282A) show a primitive condition, indeed perhaps more primitive than in any other living gnathostomes, for they are like sharks except that the oviducts do not meet anteriorly, and the eggs are well supplied with yolk; the oviducts do, however, unite just before en-

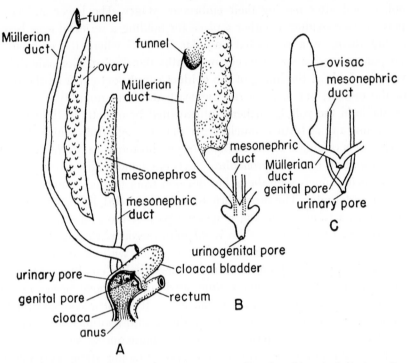

Fig. 282. Female reproductive and execretory systems in various fishes. A, *Protopterus*; B, *Amia*; C, a teleost with closed ovisac and no cloaca.

tering the cloaca. In males the Müllerian ducts occur but are, of course, not functional.

The ovaries of Amphibia are likely to vary with the shape of the body cavity, being elongate in salamanders and caecilians, shorter in frogs and toads, but they are not massive organs, rather appearing thin-walled, pouched or lobed, barely covered with peritoneum. The eggs, emerging into the coelom, enter the oviducal funnels anteriorly, and are covered with jelly secreted by the glandular lining of the oviduct. Since they are generally fertilized just after or just before before emission, the jelly does not prevent access of the sperm cells to the eggs, but a few minutes later, when the jelly has absorbed water and swollen, it does so.

Although in salamanders (*Ambystoma*) the Müllerian duct develops by a splitting of the pronephric duct so that the Wolffian duct is left separated as an excretory passage, in frogs and toads it forms independently and parallel to the Wolffian duct. It also persists as a rather large tube in the males of some frogs, as the bullfrog; to speak of it as a "vestigial oviduct" is a bit misleading, because the word "vestige" implies that the organ was functional in some ancestor, but no male frogs ever had functional oviducts. This situation is comparable to that of the rudiments of mammary glands in male mammals, which likewise do not imply that the males ever had functional milk glands. Usually the oviducts enter the cloaca separately, but they meet each other first in the toads, *Bufo* and *Alytes;* the African *Nectophrynoides* is viviparous and uses the united part of the oviducts as a uterus for the embryos.

The lower part of the separate oviducts, where eggs may be held for a while before laying, serves as a uterus in the viviparous European *Salamandra;* the young pass their embryonic stages there, and in this case the eggs are fertilized as soon as, or even before, they enter the ostium from the body cavity.

Since amphibian eggs are yolky, although seldom large, each follicle in the ovary has its own group of capillaries, bringing blood from the ovarian artery, and this is especially evident in those frogs that lay a few, large eggs, as the tree frog, *Dendrobates.*

Bidder's organ, in all males and some females of the toad, *Bufo,* is a miniature rudimentary ovary located just anterior to the normal testis (or ovary). If either of the latter is removed, it develops into a functional ovary. It is, therefore, an undifferentiated remnant of the embryonic genital ridge, inhibited in development by the presence of a normal gonad.

The fat bodies in Amphibia also develop from the anterior part of the embryonic gonads and serve as a nutrient supply for the gonads. Mutual dependence between the fat bodies and gonads is shown by (1) removal of the fat bodies, which causes degeneration of the gametes; (2) partial removal of the gonads, which causes increased deposition of fat in the fat bodies.

Reptiles are primitive in having a pair of long oviducts, opening separately into the cloaca, but in regard to the egg, and provisions for its development, they have advanced considerably over amphibians and fishes. Since there is no aquatic larval stage, the young must be born or hatched sufficiently well developed to breathe air, run about (or crawl) on land, feed for themselves, and resist dessication. Hence the egg provides a very large yolk, and it follows from this that cleavage must be meroblastic, the embryo forming on the upper surface where the small quantity of cytoplasm is located. But as the eggs, if laid at all, are laid on land additional protection is required. A tough but flexible shell covers the eggs of lizards and snakes, while those of *Sphenodon,* turtles, and Crocodilia have hard shells, as in birds. Further, the embryos of reptiles provide self-enclosing membranes within the egg shell, the amnion, chorion, and allantois, as described in the chapter on embryology. These are partly for maintaining a watery environment for the embryo and partly to provide mechanisms for respiration and absorption of the yolk.

Lizards and snakes are primarily oviparous, as the other modern reptiles are exclusively, but a few lizards and many snakes have become viviparous. For example, the European *Lacerta vivipara* gives birth to live young in warm lowland, but in cooler climates and higher altitude it lays eggs; actually this lizard should be called *ovovipiparous,* for its eggs are brought near to the point of hatching even if they are laid, and when the young are "born alive" it is simply by emerging from the shell while still in the oviducts. Horned lizards (*Phrynosoma*) in our Southwest are mostly viviparous, as are the delicate little night-lizards and a few others. Viviparity is still more common among snakes, where it has come about independently in several different groups: pit vipers (except the tropical bushmaster), boas (but not pythons), the sea snakes (which do not come on land), garter snakes, water snakes, etc. Structures comparable to placentas occur in some of these to give the embryos an added boost beyond that provided by the yolk. There is clear evidence that the extinct mesozoic ichthyosaurs, an order of whalelike marine reptiles, were also viviparous; they could not, of course, have crawled out on land to lay eggs. Skeletons of embryos found inside the adult skeletons show that they reached a shape similar to that of the adults before birth.

Birds have only a left oviduct, and only the left ovary develops while the right remains rudimentary. But this is actually an inhibited testis; if the functional ovary is removed, this will transform to a functional testis, thus changing (physiologically at least) the sex of the bird. The oviduct has a large fringed ostium, an upper portion where albumin and the chalazae are secreted around the egg, then an isthmus where the shell membrane is formed, and finally the enlarged "uterus" in which the egg receives its calcareous shell and shell pigments, if any. All this means, of course, that the egg must be fertilized at the ostium of the oviduct. A short "vagina" holds the egg before laying.

Monotreme mammals might as well be reptiles as regards the female reproductive system. The two oviducts enter the cloaca separately, and the eggs have a large yolk and a tough but not calcareous shell. Unlike reptiles, however, the female attends her eggs and feeds the young after they hatch. The spiny anteater incubates its eggs in the abdominal pouch, but instead of nipples in the pouch, monotremes have aggregations of milk-secreting glands, modified from sweat glands.

Loss of the big yolk in marsupials and placental mammals, on account of the evolution of an efficient system for feeding the embryo during most of its development prior to birth, resulted in a microscopic egg with holoblastic and equal cleavage, but throughout its early stages the embryo shows features reminiscent of a big-yolked reptilian embryo, such as the yolk sac, extraembryonic coelom, amnion, and so forth. In marsupials the oviducts are long, separate almost to the lower end before they unite to form a vagina. But in opossums and kangaroos they also unite halfway up and form a median pouch. This, in kangaroos, grows down and opens, just before parturition, into the median vagina (or urogenital canal). Thus the pouch serves as an exit for the embryos, while the original lateral vaginas were the passages available for receiving sperms. (The penis is forked in many marsupials.) Following a very brief gestation period (8 days in the opossum, 39 in the kangaroo) the premature infants, only a few millimeters long, attach themselves to the nipples and spend a much longer postembryonic period in the pouch, finally emerging as if born a second time.

Since the urinary and genital systems are now separate from the rectum, so that a cloaca no longer exists (marsupials, placentals), the lower end of the united oviducts plus a part of the separated cloaca (or urinogenital sinus) becomes the *vagina.* This is differentiated by thinner walls from the *uterus* above it, and adapted to receive the penis in copulation (Fig. 283). Among most mammals the lower part of the vagina serves also as an excretory outlet, since the urethra meets it internally. But the urethra becomes separated from the vagina in rodents and Primates.

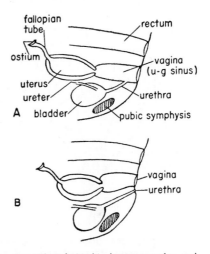

Fig. 283. Relationship between vagina and urethra in female mammals. A, most placental mammals; B, primates, rodents.

The ovaries in mammals migrate to a position below (or posterior to) the kidneys, and the uterus is therefore relatively short. But in primitive placentals which have large litters it is still double, or *duplex,* the two tubes opening into the vagina separately. Oddly enough, this is true of elephants as well as some bats, some rodents, the Hyrax, and the aardvark, although an elephant can scarcely use more than one half at a time, unless it bears twins. In cats and other carnivores, some rodents, pigs, cattle, and horses, the uterine tubes meet each other before reaching the vagina; this type is *bipartite.* Many bats, insectivores, whales, and a few other mammals show a *bicornuate* uterus. That of apes and man, where the "horns" normally are not used for the embryos, is called the *simplex* uterus; it represents the most complete fusion of the formerly separate

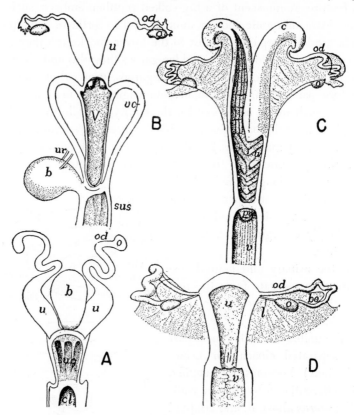

Fig. 284. Uteri of (A) monotreme, *Ornithorhynchus,* (B) marsupial, *Halmaturus,* (C) sheep, *Ovis,* and (D) monkey, *Macaca.* (From Kingsley.)
b, bladder; bo, ovarian bursa; c, cornua of uterus; cl, cloaca; l, ovarian ligament; o, ovary; od, Fallopian tube; pv, vaginal process (cervix); sus, sug, urinogenital sinus; u, uterus; ur, ureter; v, vagina; vc, vaginal canals.

oviducts, leaving only the short, narrow Fallopian tubes to convey the egg to the place where the embryo can develop.

Secondary Sex Characters

Features distinguishing adult males and females from each other, but not a part of the reproductive system, occur commonly in all major groups of vertebrates, but are by no means universal. Their physiological basis is in the hormones originating in the gonads, and therefore such characters must await the development of these hormonal secretions before they can appear. Often elaborate differences of behavior come at the same time, and under the same stimulus. The adaptive uses of these characters are so diverse and overlapping that the best classification seems to be simply by the natural relationships of the animals that show them.

Among fishes other than teleosts, secondary sex characters are rare, unless we include differences in response to individuals of the same and opposite sex. The claspers (myxipterygia) of male elasmobranchs have been mentioned already, as they might justly be considered primary. In Holocephali there is, also, a curious club-shaped hook on the forehead of the male (Fig. 17), armed with denticles and used as an accessory clasper.

In teleosts a great number of kinds show striking differences between the sexes. These are well known in salmon (Fig. 22), for instance. Jordan (1925) wrote, "As the season advances the difference between the males and females becomes more and more marked, and keeps pace with the development of the milt, as shown by dissection. The males have (1) the premaxillaries and the tip of the lower jaw more and more prolonged, both of the jaws becoming finally strongly and often extravagantly hooked, so that either they shut by the side of each other like shears, or else the mouth cannot be closed. (2) The front teeth become very long and canine-like, their growth proceeding very rapidly, until they are often half an inch long. (3) The teeth on the vomer and tongue often disappear. (4) The body grows more compressed and deeper at the shoulders, so that a very distinct hump is formed; this is more developed in the humpback salmon, but is found in all. (5) The scales disappear, especially on the back, by the growth of spongy skin. (6) The color changes from silvery to various shades of black and red, or blotchy, according to the species."

The top minnows, Poeciliidae, and their relatives ("live-bearers" to the aquarist) have very small, brightly colored males, while the oviparous killifishes (Cyprinodontidae) include a number of species in which the male is brilliant, a pugnacious fighter, and takes responsibility for nest building and care of the eggs and young. Many kinds of minnows (Cyprinidae) and darters (Percidae) develop gay colors in the males, especially in the breeding season, to which may be added epidermal tubercles on the head, as in *Campostoma*, the stoneroller minnow. Male sticklebacks (Gasterosteidae) have a special mucous gland in the ventral abdominal wall, used in gumming together bits of plants to make a barrel-shaped nest.

It is significant that these features are common in freshwater fishes but rare in marine kinds, an exception being the brood pouches of male pipe-fishes and sea horses, which live among seaweeds and eelgrass. These abdominal pouches consist mainly of a pair of lateral folds enclosing a groove, in which the male carries the eggs until they hatch (Fig. 285).

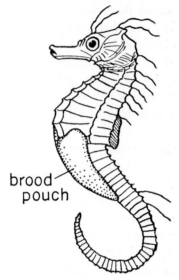

brood pouch

Fig. 285. Sea horse, *Hippocampus*, male with brood pouch. (After Goodrich.)

In tetrapods secondary sex characters are so general as to be rather the rule than the exception. We must judge by modern types, however, for many of the characters do not affect the skeleton, and therefore the sexes can seldom be distinguished in fossil vertebrates. Only a few examples need be used in each large group.

Males of the terrestrial newts, such as *Diemictylus* in North America and *Triton* (Fig. 286) in Europe, on their return to the water for breeding, develop nuptial color, enlarged tail fins, stout hind legs and a swollen cloacal region. Male frogs (*Rana*) have enlarged thumbs which aid in clasping the sides of the female. Practically all male frogs and toads, except Ascaphidae, the bell toads, have single or paired vocal sacs for their "spring chorus." While it seems that almost all these characters are limited to males, we may note here that the female Surinam toad (*Pipa*) carries her eggs on her back in small individual pits

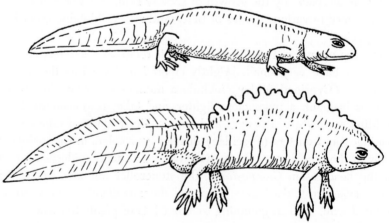

Fig. 286. *Triton cristatus*, male (lower) and female (upper). (After Gadow.)

in the skin, into which the male presses them (Fig. 287). Likewise the female of a Brazilian tree frog, *Hyla goeldii,* carries her egg complement in a sunken area on the back, while females of the Oriental genus *Nototrema* have a dorsal sac opening posteriorly, for the same function.

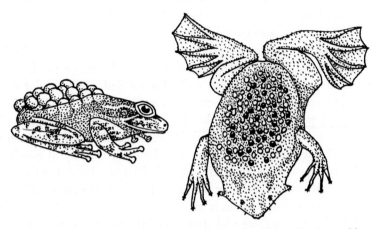

Fig. 287. Females of *Hyla goeldii* (left) and *Pipa pipa* (right), showing modifications for carrying eggs. (*Hyla* after Gadow; *Pipa* after Noble.)

The commonest difference between male and female turtles is that the anus of the male comes much farther out on the tail, in order that in copulation it may reach that of the female, from its mechanically awkward position. In lizards femoral pores (see Chapter III) are always present in males, but reduced in females, while colorful throat patches, throat fans (Fig. 288) and abdominal markings are common in males, as *Anolis* and other Iguanidae.

It is unusual in birds for the sexes to look alike; penguins, gulls, crows, dippers, hawks, and owls are among the few that do. In these the voices, too, are alike, but where a marked difference in voice occurs, there is generally a corresponding difference of color and form. Nearly always the male is larger, more showy, and more

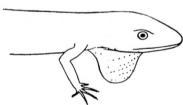

Fig. 288. Throat fan of a male lizard, the "American chameleon," *Anolis.*

vocal. In grouselike birds and many others, he has combs, wattles, crests, ruffs, throat pouches, or ornamental feathering on any part of body, wings, or tail. Birds of Paradise in the Papuan region carry the feather development to incredible extremes. The multitudes of song and perching birds have conservative females in which the ancestral patterns and colors of their families seem reluctant to change, in contrast with the exuberant nonconformity of the males.

With mammals, aside from the mammary glands of the female, the main differences are in size, proportions, voice, and special fighting equipment. Few of these occur in marsupials, insectivores, bats, rodents, or lagomorphs, but they reach an extreme in the polygamous social orders, especially Primates, artiodactyls, and the pinnipeds (sea lions, walrus, etc.). In elephants and swine, large tusks are a mark of the male; in deer, antlers; in sheep, goats, and cattle, the size of horns, or the hump; in lions, the mane. But in monkeys and apes we find a spectacular assortment of anatomical differences, culminating in the baboons. The skin of face and seat pads may become brilliantly colored and swollen out of all normal shape, while the male weighs twice as much as a female and has a notoriously ugly disposition. The male howling monkey of South and Central America carries a greatly expanded larynx, involving the hyoid bone, which gives him probably the loudest voice in the animal kingdom.

The secondary sexual features of apes are somewhat as in man, most marked in the gorilla (size and strength of the male, voice, exaggerated muscle crests of the skull) and orang-utan (size and hairiness of the male, and fleshy cheek pads giving an almost circular outline to the face).

It is important to repeat that these differences become intensified approximately in the degree that the animals are polygamous and social, although certain other factors must be concerned in producing them.

Endocrine Organs

The endocrine organs do not constitute a "system" in any anatomical sense, and it is hardly possible to deal with them in a comparative anatomy laboratory by gross dissection. But physiologically they have much in common, including (1) glandular cells which secrete hormones into the blood, and (2) a certain amount of coördination of their activities, partly through the agency of the hormones themselves and partly through the nervous system. It must be emphasized that hormones are not secreted through ducts or upon any surfaces, but are dispersed in the blood throughout the body; hence the familiar terms *ductless glands, endocrine glands,* or *glands of internal secretion.*

A *hormone* is an organic compound of complex structure, potent in exceedingly small quantities, so that its presence and effects must be studied biologically in most experimental work. That is, chemical analysis could hardly be expected to reveal the presence of a given hormone in the blood in a proportion of, say, one part per 100,000, but variations in this quantity, controlled artificially, produce striking effects which can be standardized and used as indicators. In the study of hormones two points must be kept in mind: (1) the nature of a given hormone is quite constant throughout the series of animals in which it occurs (e.g., thyroxin is alike in fish, amphibian, or mammal); (2) some specific tissue or process in the animal can be influenced by a hormone, while others are completely indifferent to it (e.g., thyroxin has a stimulating effect on the rate of oxidation in tissues, while the adrenocorticotrophic hormone activates only the cortex of the adrenal glands.)

THYROID GLAND

The thyroid in most vertebrates is a soft mass of glandular tissue, subdivided into minute lobules or follicles located beneath the pharynx, although it tends to move more posteriorly in the higher tetrapods. As was mentioned earlier, the thyroid develops from a cluster of epithelial cells in the floor of the pharynx, but soon loses its connection with this in nearly all vertebrates. Its development in sharks takes place by invagination of a small pouch in the embryo, later closed except in the frilled shark, *Chlamydoselachus*. We can trace the evolutionary origin of the thyroid still farther back in cyclostomes, for in the lamprey it develops at metamorphosis by the closing of the subpharyngeal gland, which during the larval stage poured its mucus secretion into the endostylar groove. Thus the thyroid is a heritage from the microphagous feeding device found in the earliest vertebrates, and this in turn apparently goes back to the ciliary-band mechanism in the pharynx of protochordates. Mucus-secreting cells came to secrete a hormone instead, probably without any very radical change.

Iodine is the distinctive component of thyroxin, the thyroid hormone. Removal of thyroid glands in experimental animals results in lowering the metabolic rate, specifically the rate of oxidation in tissues, and thereby the heat production. Thyroid hormone can be restored to such animals either by feeding or by injection, although this must be repeated frequently, and the normal metabolic rate returns accordingly. Naturally the effects of extirpation show most clearly in young individuals, and they demonstrate that processes of development depend upon the metabolic rate. For example, thyroidectomy (removal) in tadpoles or larval salamanders results in the failure of these individuals to go through metamorphosis, and they remain larvae. By the same token, feeding extra thyroid hormone to very young tadpoles induces rapid metamorphosis into miniature frogs.

PARATHYROIDS

Embedded in, or barely separate from, the thyroid in man are a few small clumps of cells which in microscopic section resemble the lobules of the thyroid, although the cells stain differently. The parathyroid hormone is responsible for the level of blood calcium, and this in turn has much to do with contractility of muscle fibers. Removal of the parathyroids will cause an animal presently to go into spasm (tetany) and die. Accidental loss of the parathyroids in early operations to remove goiter was responsible for death of some patients before this function was discovered. In man there are two pairs of parathyroids. These glands originate from parts of the embryonic gill pouches, and apparently occur generally among tetrapods, but are unknown in fishes.

PITUITARY

In its structure and functions the pituitary (Figs. 289, 317A, C) is not one gland but two. Among the vertebrates above cyclostomes the two parts are generally referred to as *anterior lobe* (or *adenohypophysis*) and *posterior lobe* (or *neurohypophysis*). The latter develops as an outgrowth

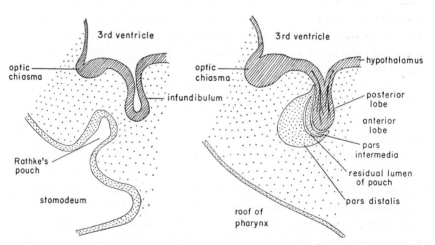

Fig. 289. Diagram of pituitary gland (right) and its embryonic development from Rathke's pouch and the infundibulum (left) in higher vertebrates.

(*infundibulum*) from the floor of the brain, specifically of the hypothalamus, directly beneath the third ventricle in the diencephalon. It contains neurons modified to provide a secretion which, however, originates in the hypothalamus. The name "pituitrin" is used for an extract containing the hormones, at least two and probably more, obtained from the posterior lobe. Among their effects are stimulation of muscle fibers in arteriolar walls (causing a rise of blood pressure), stimulation of smooth muscle in the uterus during labor, and regulation of the ability of kidney tubules to return water into the blood (antidiuretic effect).

The anterior lobe is rather more complex, and has nothing directly to do with the brain, although it lies in contact with the posterior lobe. Its developmental source is **Rathke's pouch,** an invagination of ectoderm in the roof of the stomodeum (embryonic mouth). This pocket of ectodermal cells lies, at an early stage, directly under the diencephalon, and soon becomes separated from the roof of the mouth, making the adenohypophysis (often designated simply **"hypophysis"** in embryology). Typically the anterior lobe contains a lower, larger *pars distalis,* an upper *pars tuberalis* which partially surrounds the stem of the posterior lobe, and a *pars intermedia* (or "intermediate lobe") which is between the pars distalis and the posterior lobe.

Hormones of the anterior lobe are of several types. A *somatotrophic* or *growth* hormone is responsible for the specific rate of growth of the animal, as shown especially in its skeleton; this is, of course, apart from the developmental effects already noted for the thyroid hormone. A *lactogenic* hormone (*prolactin*) induces secretion of milk by the mammary glands after parturition, but, oddly enough, its effect can be seen also in the production of "pigeon's milk" by glandular cells in the crop of a pigeon. Other anterior lobe hormones activate (1) the thyroid, (2) the cortex of the adrenal glands, and (3) the gonads. In the latter category are two *gonadotrophic* hormones; one is called *luteinizing,* since a corpus luteum will not form at the point where an egg escapes from the ovary unless this hormone is present, and the other is called *follicle-stimulating* since it is necessary for the maturation of ovarian follicles. Naturally the effects noted here are seen only in the female, yet the same gonadotrophic hormones occur in the male and are responsible for normal development of the testis and its products.

Turning to the comparative anatomy of the pituitary, we find that in cyclostomes the adenohypophysis is represented only by an open pouch or tube, not apparently an endocrine organ at all, nor is the neurohypophysis clearly differentiated from the floor of the brain. In early stages of a lamprey Rathke's pouch develops in the usual place above the mouth, but here also the olfactory sac develops, and as the head of the lamprey elongates in approaching its adult condition, the olfactory sac and hypophyseal pouch together seemingly migrate dorso-posteriorly on top of the head, so that their common opening, the nostril, is far from the mouth. The hypophyseal pouch in lampreys (and in Cephalaspid ostracoderms) ends blindly beneath the brain, over the pharynx, and immediately anterior to the notochord. In hagfishes (and Pteraspid ostracoderms) it perforates the pharynx. Probably in both cases pressure variations during feeding activities cause a movement of water back and forth past the olfactory epithelium, whereas, if this were not permitted, there could be no quick response to new chemical stimuli in the water.

Among protochordates it seems likely that the hypophysis is represented in the larva of *Branchiostoma* by the ciliated **preoral pit,** originating from the head cavity just anterior to the mouth. But it should be emphasized that the more dorsal "olfactory pit" of *Branchiostoma,* and that of certain tunicates, is a survivor of the embryonic neuropore (anterior end of the neural canal), hence it is improbable that this has any relationship to the hypophysis of vertebrates.

ADRENAL GLANDS

In tetrapods the adrenals are found in proximity to the kidneys, usually anterior to them, and with a copious blood supply. Among fishes some scattered tissue corresponding to the adrenal cortex lies along the mesonephros. Adrenal glands of higher vertebrates are differentiated into a **cortex** and **medulla.** The latter, lying internally, secretes the hormone **adrenalin.** The action of this, throughout the body, is nearly always identical with that of the sympathetic nerves; namely, to increase heart rate, cause contraction of arterial walls (hence raise blood pressure), constrict sphincter muscles of the digestive and urinary tracts, inhibit digestive secretion and peristaltic movements, and so on. It is of great interest, then, to find that the embryonic source of the adrenal medulla is the same as that of the sympathetic neurons; both arise from neural crest cells, at the edge of the neural tube, and migrate to the position in the trunk where they ultimately lie.

The **adrenal cortex,** on the other hand, derives from embryonic tissues related to those of the gonads, and it is not surprising that its several hormones are sterones, related chemically and physiologically to the sex hormones. Among the effects are the maintenance of basal metabolic rate and normal glucose level of the blood, normal vigor of skeletal and cardiac muscle, and the support of the normal balance of sodium, potassium and water by the kidneys.

PANCREAS

Although a complex digestive gland, the *pancreas* also contains interstitial clusters of cells not connected with ducts, called *islands of Langerhans.* Their secretion, appropriately named *insulin,* is a hormone regulating the use of sugar by the cells of the body, whether they remove it from the blood and oxidize it, or, in the case of liver and muscles, retain a quantity of it in the form of glycogen. The pancreas, as a digestive gland primarily, develops in embryos as two or three small diverticula from the gut, partly dorsal and partly ventral; primitively it seems to have been a group of glands along the intestine.

GONADS AND SEX HORMONES

The ovaries and testes, while dependent upon gonadotrophic hormones from the anterior pituitary for their maturation and functioning, are themselves endocrine glands, as well as the source of reproductive cells (eggs and sperms). In the testes, lying between the seminiferous tubules, are interstitial cells which secrete a "male hormone," *testosterone.* Being produced in gradually increasing amounts during the development of the individual, this affects the various parts of the body in which distinctive male characteristics appear, includng such things as coloration (skin, feathers, hair), voice (vocal sacs of male frogs, bird songs produced in the syrinx, the deeper and often louder noises of the males in mammals), muscular and skeletal features, and the peculiarities of male behavior.

In the vast majority of animals reproduction is seasonal. In kinds that breed during more than one year, the gonadotrophic pituitary secretions vary in amount according to length of daylight, amount of daily activity, and probably other factors acting on the pituitary through the nervous system. Thus the testes and ovaries become active in the breeding season, while the secondary sexual characteristics are intensified, and at other seasons there is regression, with shrinking of the gonads, and less obvious difference between the sexes.

In the ovaries the interstitial cells and those of the follicles secrete what is probably a complex of several hormones, known under the collective name of *estrone* (estrin, theelin, etc.). The effects are analogous to those of the male hormone, arising gradually during ontogeny and then subject in many cases to seasonal fluctuation. It is usual for ovulation (release of ovarian eggs) to take place by rupture of the follicles at the surface of the ovary, and in mammals the open follicle then becomes filled with a mass of new cells, the *corpus luteum*, which functions temporarily as an endocrine organ in connection with the cyclical changes in the uterus. *Progesterone*, the hormone of the corpus luteum, induces a thickening of the lining of the uterus (*endometrium*), with increased blood supply, preparing it for reception of developing blastocysts (early cleavage stages of embryos), in case fertilization takes place. If no implantation occurs, then each corpus luteum degenerates and ceases to produce progesterone; presently the endometrium returns to an indifferent state, or may be partially shed (menstruation, in humans and allied primates). On the other hand, when a blastocyst becomes implanted in the uterus and begins to grow, it must somehow convey a message to the corpus luteum which will prevent the degeneration of the latter. This is done by a new hormone, called *anterior pituitarylike*, secreted by the trophoblast cells and by the placenta when it appears; carried in the blood of the pregnant female, it sustains the corpus luteum, which will then be a source of progesterone during most of the period of pregnancy. Thus the placental hormone has the same effect as the luteinizing hormone from the anterior pituitary; hence, its common name. Such, very briefly, are the endocrine relationships between corpus luteum, uterus, and embryo in man and some kinds of mammals.

CHAPTER X

Sense Organs

IT IS a familiar idea that animals which are more advanced in evolution make more different responses to their environment, more precisely, more aptly, than those which are primitive. The rule has exceptions, of course, but usually animal behavior becomes increasingly fitted to a special way of life in each twig of the family tree. This may result in some astonishing abilities, while at the same time it imposes certain limitations. So, too, with the history of any system of organs, and so with the development of tissues and structures in early individual life. This is what "specialization" means—a division of labor and correspondingly increased efficiency.

Nowhere is the rule of specialization more evident than in the study of behavior. The physical basis of behavior in vertebrates is a combination of sense organs (receptors), nervous system (transmitting, associating, coördinating), muscles and glands (effectors), to which we should add the regulating power of hormones. In this chapter we need consider only the first element, but without forgetting the others.

A *sense organ* is one which responds to a particular stimulus by starting an impulse along a sensory nerve. A *stimulus* is simply any influence from the environment or within the animal which will produce such a reaction; without a nerve impulse we usually have no evidence that there has been a stimulus. But this impulse does not affect behavior unless it, in turn, induces a *response* by muscle fibers or the secretory cells of glands, equipped to act when the impulse gets to them. A simple *reflex act,* carried out automatically, is thus an illustration of the coördinated work of different specialized organs.

As a sense organ is made of special tissues which may concentrate or amplify a source of stimulation, so the nervous system is made of special cells, *neurons,* able to carry impulses at high speed. Neurons have their cytoplasm and plasma membranes drawn out into enormously long *fibers,* on the surface of which an impulse is thought to travel as a wave of negative electric charges (but not an electric current). All sense organs are associated with sensory nerves, in which there may be thousands of neurons, but there are also free nerve endings and networks, for example in the skin, which may receive stimuli but are not organs. Many kinds of microscopic organs and receptor cells, however, occur in the skin and internal parts of the body, serving sensations of touch, pressure, heat, cold, pain, etc.

But our concern here is with organs in which a series of significant changes can be traced from the primitive to the higher vertebrates. These are: (1) *organs of chemical sense:* taste buds, olfactory organs, Jacobson's organs; (2) *organs detecting pressure change and movements of the medium:* ear, lateral line organs, pit organs, ampullae of Lorenzini; (3) *organs of vision:* the median and paired eyes.

Organs of Chemical Sense

Essentials for a chemical sense organ in the vertebrates are the epithelial sensory cells, with water from the environment in contact with them, containing dissolved substances which provide stimuli. This water may be that which surrounds any aquatic animal, or it may be on the moist surface of a mucous membrane in a terrestrial animal.

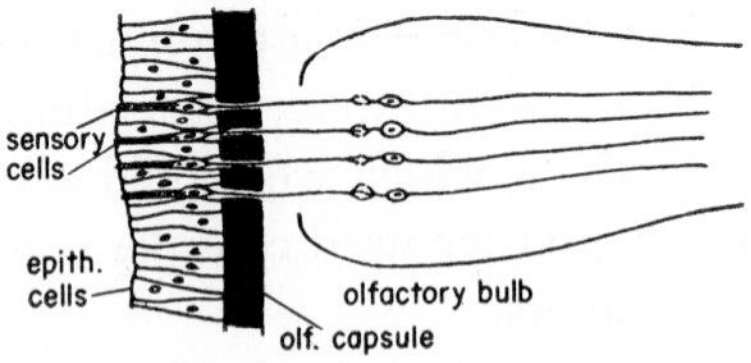

sensory cells

epith. cells

olfactory bulb

olf. capsule

Fig. 290. Diagram of section through olfactory epithelium and olfactory bulb, showing connection of neurons and sensory cells.

The *olfactory organs* are pits or open sacs lined with an epithelium of neurosensory cells from the ectoderm, that is, cells which are sensory outwardly, but at their deeper ends produce nerve fibers that synapse with those of the olfactory tract from the brain (Fig. 290). Although the olfactory sacs are paired in gnathostomes, they are largely fused in the cyclostomes, including many early ostracoderms; but it seems, even in the latter, that the fusion is secondary, since the olfactory tracts are always paired. There can be little doubt that the earliest olfactory organs were paired.

The nostril of cyclostomes (Fig. 291) is single, opening on top of the head in lampreys and some ostracoderms, but just above the mouth in

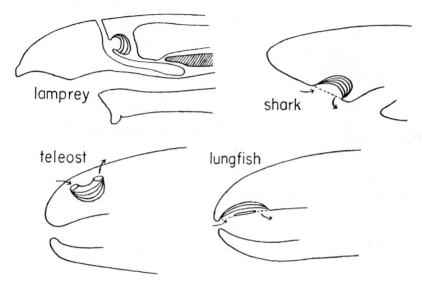

Fig. 291. Diagrams of nostrils and nasal passages in fishes.

hagfishes (Fig. 228) and, presumably, the remainder of ostracoderms. At the bottom of its cavity is the **hypophyseal sac,** extending ventrad beneath the brain until it reaches approximately the tip of the notochord; in hagfishes it goes through into the pharynx. This sac is evidently homologous with the embryonic hypophysis, which becomes the anterior pituitary in higher vertebrates, but its function and structure are different in cyclostomes. It seems to be a mechanical accessory to the olfactory organs, taking water in and expelling it synchronously with the action of the gill pouches. One would not expect such an organ to show a histological similarity to the anterior lobe of the pituitary gland, but this does not constitute evidence against the homology.

Nostrils of gnathostome fishes generally open into pits lined with upright folds of olfactory epithelium. In Chondrichthyes these openings are incompletely bridged by a flap of skin so that the water flows readily through the anterior part and out the posterior. Among Actinopteri as a rule the bridge is complete, so that there are two pairs of external nares. Among many teleosts, especially the advanced types with protractile upper jaws, each olfactory cavity has two accessory pouches (one medial, the other lateral) which are not sensory, but during the movements of the mouth they passively expand and contract, creating a current of water past the olfactory folds in the primary cavity. A single spiny-rayed fish, the stargazer, *Astroscopus,* and a few peculiar eels, have also internal nares communicating with the mouth (Atz, 1952).

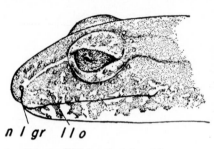

Fig. 292. Head of purple salamander, *Gyrinophilus porphyriticus.* (From *Biology of the Amphibia* by Noble.)

n l gr, naso labial groove; *l l o,* lateral line organ.

In Choanichthyes, however, external and internal nares are the rule (this accounts for the name of the group). Although lungfishes come to the surface of water at times to breathe air, it has been shown that they do so by opening the mouth, and also that the African lungfish, which estivates through a dry season in a mud "cocoon," receives air through the mouth rather than the nares. Evidently the nasal organs of these fish, then, function under water in olfaction but have no special significance for air breathing. The primitive lobefins, but not the living coelacanth, *Latimeria,* had external and internal nares, the openings showing as notches in the margin of the upper jaw. There can be no assurance that they were used in air breathing any more effectively than those of lungfishes, but with the emergence of Amphibia on land these notches withdrew dorsad, closing beneath so that the rim of the jaw became complete and the nasal passages went through the snout. Plethodontid salamanders show a nasolabial groove below each nostril, but it is a special adaptation within the family (Fig. 292). The human ab-

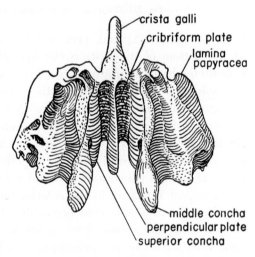

Fig. 293. Human ethmoid bone, from below. (Redrawn from Millard and King.)

normality called harelip (usually single, rarely double) results from delayed closure of the gaps in the rim of the embryonic upper lip.

Beginning in reptiles, especially lizards, the surface available for olfactory epithelium is increased by folds in the walls of the nasal passages. These amount to very little in birds, except *Apteryx*, which has an extraordinary development of the nasal organs, in correlation with its nocturnal search for worms and insects. The **turbinal bones,** supporting

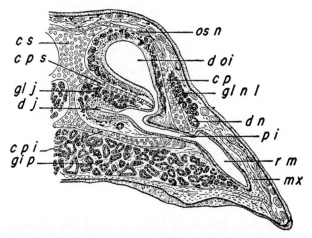

Fig. 294. Transverse section of Jacobson's organ and nasal cavity of tree frog. (From *Biology of the Amphibia* by Noble.)

c p, cartilage plate; c p i, interior process from septum; c p s, superior process from septum; c s, cartilaginous septum; d j, Jacobson's duct; d n, nasal duct, d ol, olfactory passage; gl j, Jacobson's gland; gl n l, nasolabial gland; mx, maxillary; os n, olfactory nerve; p i, inferior passage; r m, maxillary recess.

olfactory folds, become most elaborate in mammals, nearly all of which depend heavily on the sense of smell; the ethmoturbinals are outgrowths of the ethmoid, on the inner wall of each nasal cavity, while the maxilloturbinals are from the maxillaries, on the lateral walls. They are lost secondarily in porpoises and toothed whales. We have alluded already to the separation of oral from nasal cavities in (1) Crocodilia, and (2) mammals and some of the therapsid reptiles, by a secondary hard palate.

Jacobson's organs are a pair of sensory sacs in the posterior part of the nasal cavities of many tetrapods (Fig. 294), whose function is related to, and probably derived from, that of the olfactory organs. Among birds, bats, and primates they are absent, as well as in aquatic reptiles and mammals, while they enter the mouth, rather than nasal cavities, in Squamata.

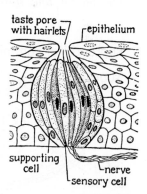

Fig. 295. Section through taste bud in man. (Redrawn from Parker, *Smell, Taste and Allied Senses in the Vertebrates,* Lippincott.)

The part of the olfactory tract and lobes innervating these organs is somewhat separated from the rest.

Taste buds (**gustatory organs**) are small clusters of sensory epithelial cells inside, and sometimes outside, the mouth; external taste buds occur in many fishes (but not Chondrichthyes) and in some aquatic Amphibia. They develop from ectoderm except in the deeper portions of the pharynx, and in some fishes the esophagus, where they are presumably endodermal. To them go fibers from the appropriate cranial nerves: seventh if external or in the buccal cavity, ninth and tenth if in the pharynx. Although more widely dispersed in fishes, taste buds are most specialized in mammals (Fig. 295), which give their food a more careful investigation before swallowing it than is customary in other groups. The tongue and soft palate, epiglottis, and opening of the larynx are the usual locations.

Organs Detecting Pressure Change and the Movement of the Medium (Neuromast System)

This group of organs has in common a structure, the **neuromast,** of sensory epithelial cells ending outwardly in hairs, which are affected by motion of a liquid medium covering them. Fibers of sensory cranial nerves meet these cells at their deep ends. The motion of the medium may be either a slow current or vibration caused by pressure waves of high frequency; the medium itself may be water, slime, or endolymph (in the inner ear).

The *lateral line system* is a series of neuromasts arranged over the

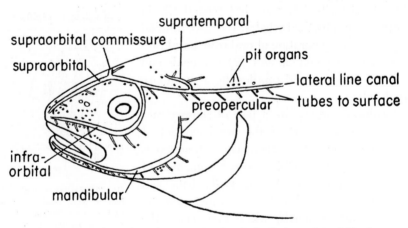

Fig. 296. Head canals and pit organs of pollack. (Redrawn form Bridge.)

head and body of fishes and aquatic amphibians in linear patterns (Fig. 296), and supplied by cranial nerves VII, IX, and X. (See also the Mauthnerian apparatus, page 312.) In the earliest known fishes, some armored ostracoderms, these organs apparently occupied canals in the skin, the impression of which shows on the dermal bones of the head, or which were buried in the dermal bones, just as in most of the bony fishes today. The canals open to the surface by pores at short intervals (Fig. 297) so that water circulates freely within them in contact with the neuromasts. Usually one lateral line canal runs the length of the body, on each side, perforating one row of scales (Fig. 298); in a few teleosts

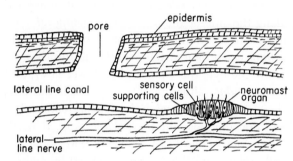

Fig. 297. Section along lateral line canal in fish, showing pore and neuromast organ.

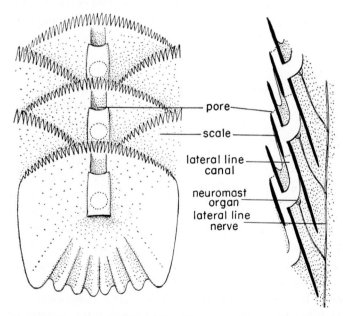

Fig. 298. Lateral line scales of yellow perch, external view and longitudinal section.

there are several such canals, and occasionally none. Of course the relationship between the canals and the dermal bones (or scales) no longer holds when the bones and scales are absent or too deep beneath the skin. The canals may then, as in most Chondrichthyes, modern Dipnoi, and many smooth-skinned teleosts, lie embedded in the skin alone, or form simply an open groove (Holocephali, Fig. 17, and the frilled shark, *Chlamydoselachus*), or disappear, allowing the neuromasts to lie openly on the surface (modern cyclostomes, some advanced teleosts, and the modern aquatic Amphibia).

The pattern of the lateral line canals is remarkable constant (Fig. 296). A horizontal line runs back from the snout above each eye (*supraorbital*), along the side of the otic region (*temporal*), and continues on the side of the body (lateral line proper). It receives from below, en route, a *postorbital* canal behind the eye; this in turn has picked up the *infraorbital* below the eye, the *mandibular* (lower jaw), and sometimes a *hyoid* or *preopercular,* although this may reach the temporal canal separately. There is also an *occipital* or *supratemporal* canal which crosses the head dorsally, near the back of the skull. It would seem that the canals on the sides of the head originally bore some relationship to the series of gill arches, and this is also suggested by embryological evidence.

The *pit organs* of elasmobranchs and bony fishes are neuromasts at the bottom of separate pits in the skin of the head, differing from lateral line organs mainly in the absence of a canal from one to another. Frequently they lie in rows, suggesting that a canal was formerly present. *Ampullae of Lorenzini* are more elaborate, compound neuromast organs, common on the heads of elasmobranchs (Fig. 299).

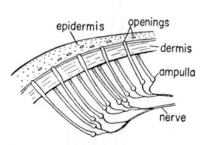

Fig. 299. Sensory ampullae in snout of shark, *Scyllium.* (Redrawn from Goodrich.)

The skin of aquatic larval Amphibia, and of some adult forms which remain in the water, is provided with pores in rows, with a pattern on head and body similar to those in most fish, but without a canal. From one to three parallel rows can be seen on the trunk and tail of salamander larvae, supplied by a corresponding number of branches of the vagus nerve. In the newt, *Diemictylus viridescens,* these lateral line pores are functional in the larva, temporarily obliterated in the land-dwelling "eft," and again functional in the aquatic adult.

If we imagine a pair of primitive neuromast organs sinking deeply into the head from the dorsal side until they lie near the posterior end of the brain, and each then becoming specialized inwardly into a group of canals and hollow vesicles with neuromasts, we will have the plan of the *inner ears*. In one of the most ancient ostracoderms there is a pair of open dorsal pits in the skull which may represent the earliest stage in the evolution of ears. In sharks and rays the *endolymphatic ducts* by which these organs connect with the surface are visible externally even in adults, but in all other known vertebrates they close early in development or do not appear as openings at all. This suggests that the presence of an opening in sharks is not primitive but due to a delay in development.

The inner ear of a cyclostome contains a small *endolymphatic sac,* out of which open an *anterior* and a *posterior vertical semicircular canal* (in hagfishes there is only one, apparently the posterior); no horizontal canal is known in cyclostomes. Each canal is actually a complete ring, with an *ampulla* (bulb) containing a *crista* of neurosensory hair cells, from which extends a twig of the auditory nerve. Presumably the crista is stimulated by the relative movement of endolymph within the canal as the head tips, owing to the inertial lag of the fluid. There is some difficulty in seeing how this can work in cyclostomes, where the lining of the sac bears vibrating cilia which may cause some turbulence in the endolymph, and even in the higher forms a fluid within cavities as small as these is undoubtedly hampered in its free flow by its own viscosity.

There also emerge from the endolymphatic sac in lampreys two pouches, anteriorly a *sacculus,* posteriorly what is perhaps a *lagena,* and each of the three contains a neuromast organ (*macula*) in which minute crystalline grains (*otoconia*) cling to the distal ends of the hair cells. This device, persisting in most vertebrates from fish to man, is presumed to sense the position of the head, rather than its motion, because the weight of the granules is directed differently according to the plane in which the maculae lie.

The semicircular canals, three in gnathostomes (Fig. 300), and the associated vesicles, all filled with endolymph, comprise the *membranous labyrinth.* The cartilaginous or bony case enclosing it is the *otic capsule.* The membranous labyrinth is separated from the walls of bone or cartilage around it by a slight gap filled with a similar fluid, *perilymph* (Fig. 301).

In sharks fine grains of sand enter the inner ear by way of the open endolymphatic ducts and apparently serve the purpose of otoliths (ear stones) in stimulating the maculae. Of the three semicircular canals, the anterior vertical and the horizontal emerge from the upper end of a *utriculus,* while the posterior vertical enters it lower down. The utriculus expands ventrally, joining a sacculus, and out of this in turn comes a very small lagena; in each of these chambers is a *macula* (neuromast organ with a nerve).

The same parts, differing in details, occur generally in fishes and amphibians. The teleosts often develop large calcareous otoliths, a *lapillus* for the utriculus, *sagitta* (the largest) for the sacculus, and *asteriscus*

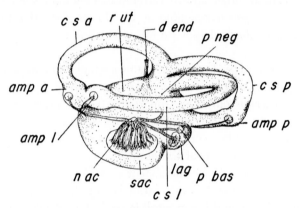

Fig. 300. Inner ear of salamander, *Megalobatrachus.* (From *Biology of the Amphibia* by Noble, after Okajima.)

amp *a,* ampullae of anterior canal; amp *l,* ampullae of lateral canal; amp *p,* ampullae of posterior canal; c s *a,* anterior semicircular canal; c s *l,* lateral semicircular canal; c s *p,* posterior semicircular canal; d end, endolymphatic duct; lag, lagena; n ac, acoustic nerve; r ut, utriculus; sac, sacculus.

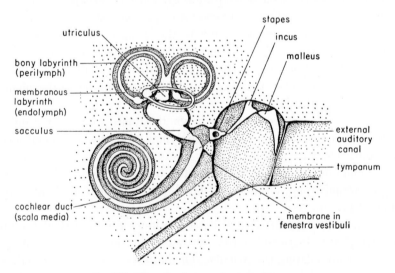

Fig. 301. Diagram of parts of mammalian ear.

for the lagena; the form of these stones is sufficiently complex and constant to serve as a useful aid in classification.

The lagena is still small in Amphibia (Fig. 300, *lag*) and reptiles, but the birds and mammals, with their greater acuity of hearing, have enlarged the lagena into a *cochlea* (Fig. 301), probably independently of each other. This is a bent but not coiled structure in birds. In mammals it becomes a snail-like spiral, the microscopic structure of which is amazingly complex. There are three

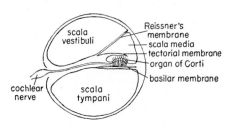

Fig. 302. Cross section of cochlea.

parallel cavities within the cochlea, one of which, the *cochlear duct* or *scala media* (Fig. 302) is the original lagena, extended but still communicating with the sacculus, and therefore containing endolymph. The other two, *scalae tympani* and *vestibuli,* are the original perilymphatic space between the membranous labyrinth and the bone surrounding it, drawn out in the form of a loop, for at the distal end of the cochlea they connect with each other. The fluid in them is, of course, perilymph. At the proximal (large) end of the cochlea the scala vestibuli meets the foot of the stapes in the fenestra ovalis, while the scala tympani meets an elastic membrane at the fenestra rotunda. Thus vibrations induced in the perilymph by the stapes are transmitted through a fluid column of steadily diminishing diameter. The sensory part of this apparatus is the *organ of Corti* (Fig. 302) in the cochlear duct, resting upon a *basilar membrane* and overhung by a shelf, the *tectorial membrane.* The organ of Corti is a highly specialized neuromast in the form of a ribbon (since it extends the length of the cochlea); its hair cells, like those of a macula, are stimulated by contact, in this case against the tectorial membrane. At their bases they communicate with neurons of the cochlear nerve, which becomes the main portion of the auditory nerve. Sound waves of any particular pitch are believed to induce sympathetic vibrations in the basilar membrane at a point where the wave length corresponds with the length of fibers, comparable to harp strings, in the basilar membrane. This causes the organ of Corti at this point to tremble against the tectorial membrane. (It should be recalled that sound waves in a liquid medium are very short as compared with those in air.) It seems, then, that birds and mammals must have obtained a considerable adaptive advantage in perfecting this organ for distinguishing between sounds of different frequencies. In many cases (bats, dogs), they perceive sound of far higher pitch than is audible to us.

While it is likely that fishes hear some sounds, at least, carried through water and through the tissues of their bodies, the reception of atmospheric sound calls for a mechanism which will translate relatively long waves of low energy into the short waves in a liquid medium which we have seen to activate the organ of Corti, or its equivalent. Such a mechanism was developed in the earliest labyrinthodont amphibians, where the spiracular canal of lobefinned fishes became converted into a middle ear cavity by closing its outer end with a *tympanic membrane,* leaving the inner end as a **Eustachian tube** to the pharynx, and at the same time the hyomandibular bone of the fish was transformed into the *stapes* (Fig. 303). The stapes, or columella, therefore bridged the gap from the tympanic membrane to the wall of the inner ear, where presently it came to fit a small opening, the *fenestra ovalis,* and vibrations of the eardrum were thus transmitted to the perilymph of the inner ear.

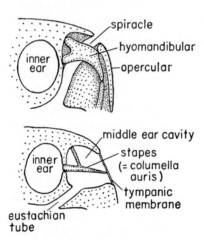

Fig. 303. Diagram of relationship between hyomandibular of a bony fish such as a lobefin (upper), and stapes of a primitive amphibian (lower).

Roughly, this is the kind of ear the labyrinthodonts had, and most Salientia still have, but salamanders and caecilians have lost the middle ear cavity, tympanic membrane, and Eustachian tube secondarily. Many of them retain the stapes, which may reach from the fenestra ovalis to the squamosal or quadrate, evidently carrying sound which is received through the jaws as the head rests against the substratum. Also there is a peculiar device, characteristic of most adult salamanders and many frogs, which is thought to transmit sound from the forelegs to the inner ear. This is a straplike muscle, the *opercularis,* extending from the scapula to a small flat *operculum,* which is a separate portion of the posterior wall of the otic capsule, adjacent to the stapes.

With reptiles and birds the middle ear has made no fundamental change, except that the eardrum withdraws into a pit, the *external auditory canal* (not so in turtles, where it remains at the surface, nor in snakes, where it is lost). But in mammals two more small bones, the *quadrate* (of the reptilian upper jaw) and *articular* (of the lower jaw), have joined the stapes in transmitting sound across the middle ear cavity

(Figs. 162, 301). The quadrate becomes the *incus,* the articular the *malleus,* and the latter is now in contact with the eardrum. The external auditory canal tends to hide beneath the swelling mass of the cranium, and the *external ear* (*pinna*), is added as a sound trap. This reaches its highest efficiency in bats. With the help of certain facial muscles it becomes highly mobile as a device for locating the source of sound without turning the head (carnivores, ungulates, elephants); the large ungulates often use their external ears as switches to shoo away insects from the canal and neighboring parts. In aquatic orders, however, it is reduced or lost.

Organs of Vision, the Median and Paired Eyes

Paired eyes of vertebrates are cameralike organs of marvellous construction, usually fitted to focus a clear image of the surroundings upon a film of sensory cells, the *retina,* and these cells collectively start impulses toward the brain, giving their specific interpretations of intensity, color, or movements in their own parts of the image. But there are also, in some primitive vertebrates, two different median organs which serve as receptors for light, although not necessarily to obtain visual images.

According to Walls (1942, p. 338), "There are indications, from elasmobranch embryology, that the provertebrate possessed a metameric series of paired visual organs on the roof of the head. Most of them rapidly disappeared as the lateral . . . eyes became perfected; but two pairs of dorsal eyes still hung on almost to the cyclostome level . . ." In the lamprey one member of each of these supposed pairs may be seen as a small bulb attached by a stalk to the roof of the brain (diencephalon). The anterior one (*parietal stalk*) does not quite reach, but the posterior (*pineal eye*) does reach a semitransparent spot in the skin of the head. Possibly both bodies were present in primitive Amphibia, for in frogs the pineal is found, nearly reaching the skin, yet in some modern reptiles (*Sphenodon* and a number of lizards) a parietal "eye" is present, with the pineal reduced. Among early vertebrates the evidence of these organs is simply a foramen in the roof of the skull in ostracoderms, some placoderms, crossopterygians, primitive Amphibia, and some of the early orders of reptiles, including many Therapsids. It usually lies between the parietal bones. The parietal eye of *Sphenodon* is well covered, and no function has been demonstrated, but it contains a retina and lens; the neurosensory retinal cells synapse with neurons which go directly down the stalk. In birds the pineal stalk is reduced but often distinct and with a complex structure distally. Mammals have a minute *epiphysis* (pineal organ) which has been suspected to have an endocrine function; there is no satisfactory evidence.

Not related to these, but of entirely different origin, are the *lateral eyes,* present and much alike in all vertebrates except a few that dwell in the deep sea, in caverns, or in underground burrows. A brief description of the human eye will provide certain landmarks to use in studying its development and comparative anatomy (Fig. 304). The eye is a nearly

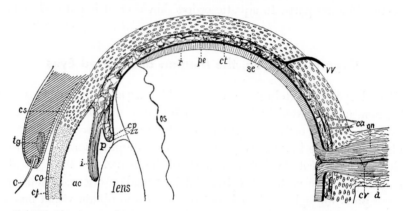

Fig. 304. Partial section through a mammal eye. (After Kingsley, *Outlines of Comparative Anatomy of Vertebrates,* 3rd ed., Blakiston.)

ac, anterior chamber; c, eyelash; ca, ciliary arteries; cj, conjunctiva; co, cornea; cp, ciliary process; cs, conjunctival sac; ct, choroid coat; cv, central vein and artery of retina; d, dura (sheath) of optic nerve; i, iris; on, optic nerve; os, ora serrata (edge of retina); p, posterior chamber; pe, pigmented epithelium; r, retina; sc, sclera, tg, tarsal gland; vv, vorticose vein; zz, zonula zinii.

spherical ball, movably supported in the *orbit* (socket), and connecting with the diencephalon by the *optic nerve.* A set of six *extraocular muscles* moves the eye (see Chapter VI). Three *tunics* or *coats* form its wall: (1) the outer, which is fibrous and composed of the *sclera* (opaque) and *cornea* (transparent, in front); (2) the middle, which is vascular and made of the *choroid, ciliary body,* and *iris,* the last coming partly from the retinal layer; (3) the inner, which is sensory and nervous, the *retina.*

The cornea admits light to the *anterior chamber* where, by passing through the *pupil* in the center of the *iris,* it meets the *lens.* Both the cornea and the lens contribute to refracting the light rays and hence focusing an image on the retina, but in aquatic animals only the lens can do this, since the cornea has little refractive property when under water. Behind the lens is the *vitreous body,* a clear, slightly viscous fluid transmitting light to the retina. This light has to pass between capillaries on the inner (anterior) surface of the retina, then between nerve fibers and two layers of neurons (Fig. 305) before it reaches the photosensory cells, the *rods* and *cones.* The place of greatest concentration of visual cells, at the optical center of the retina, is the *fovea centralis.* Behind the

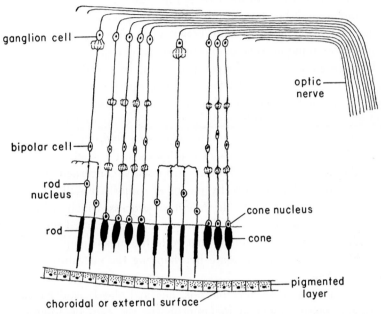

Fig. 305. Diagram of section of retina. (Modified from Best and Taylor, Holt.)

retina comes the darkly pigmented choroid, and finally the thick fibrous sclera. Through these two coats the optic nerve passes; its fibers have converged over the inner surface of the retina to a point near, but not interfering with, the fovea.

Fishes have the eyeball flattened outwardly, as a rule, and since the cornea cannot aid in focusing, the lens is more nearly spherical than in land animals, in order to perform the whole of this function. Since there is no need to keep the surface of the eye moist, there are no movable lids; the so-called "lids" in a shark cannot cover the eye. Likewise there are no lacrimal glands or nasolacrimal canals (tear ducts). In the sclera are commonly found thin *sclerotic bones,* arranged as a ring. These may well have been present in the primitive vertebrate eye, but are absent in modern lungfishes, modern Amphibia, and mammals.

In lampreys the sclera is fibrous, and a transparent spectacle of skin covers the eye. The hagfish eye is degenerate, unable to perceive light, without muscles, lens or pigment; it is hidden under the skin. Elasmobranch fishes, on the other hand, especially those of the deep sea, have eyes that are large but that lack visual acuity. There is a firm cartilaginous sclera. In most types there is a fibrous cartilage rod, the *optic pedicel* (Fig. 213), which holds the eyeball out from the cranial wall within. This group is an exception to the fish rule of flattened eyes, for the cornea is strongly convex. In most cases the retina has only rods, not cones.

Actinopterous fishes typically have a cartilaginous sclera in which are developed two or more sclerotic bones, giving additional strength. This reaches an extreme in some of the big, swift, pelagic fishes, as shown by the bony ring enclosing the eyeball of a tuna or swordfish. On the other hand a few teleosts have neither cartilage nor bone in the sclera. The *myodome* is another common feature, a deep funnel-shaped pit in the posterior wall of the orbit, occupied by the elongated rectus muscles. *Amia* and the teleosts have a unique *choroid gland,* which is not a typical gland but a U-shaped mass of capillaries in the back of the eye, between the retina and the choroid, supposedly concerned with adjustments of intraocular pressure by means of osmosis. Finally, the floor of the eyeball supports a ridge, the *falciform process,* which in turn carries the *retractor lentis* muscle, used to move the lens inward for accommodation. This is, of course, an alternative to the means employed in other vertebrates, which accommodate by changing the curvature of the surface of the lens.

With Amphibia come movable lids, lacrimal glands, and nasolacrimal canals, but these appear at metamorphosis; the eyes of aquatic stages are essentially fishlike. The modern types have a *retractor bulbi* muscle, evidently derived from the external rectus. It serves not only to protect the eye by suddenly withdrawing it, but as an aid in swallowing food, since the eye can press down the roof of the mouth. The eyes of Apoda are reduced, and a tactile tentacle has partly substituted for them, even using two of the eye muscles for its own movements. Scleral cartilage is often absent in frogs; the lens is very large, nearly filling the cavity of the eyeball. Accommodation in most land vertebrates is done by marginal pressure on the lens, either to bulge or flatten it. In mammals the contraction of the ciliary muscle releases the tension in the marginal ligament which tends to hold the lens a bit flattened, and its own elasticity causes it to become rounder.

A new structure appearing in reptiles, especially lizards, is the *conus papillaris* (Fig. 306), a process resting on the head of the optic nerve and pointing forward in the vitreous chamber. It serves as a source of nutriment for the retina, since the latter lacks capillaries. The snakes, derived perhaps from a burrowing type of monitorlike lizard, show in their eyes a remarkable set of reconstructed features, evidently following a period in which the eyes had partly degenerated. Instead of lids, a spectacle of skin covers the surface; the conus has apparently been rebuilt from mesoderm instead of ectoderm, and the lacrimal gland, of course, has disappeared.

The bird's eye is based on that of reptiles (Fig. 307). The conus has

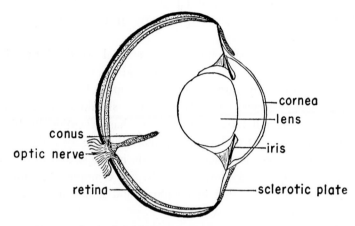

Fig. 306. Lizard eye, showing position of conus, diagrammatic. (Reproduced by permission from *Comparative Anatomy* by L. A. Adams and S. Eddy, published by John Wiley & Sons, Inc., 1949.)

become a complex folded or pleated **pecten,** serving the same function and occupying the same place. A **nictitating membrane** supplements the action of the lids, being far more rapid in blinking. The eyes are relatively very large, nearly meeting each other midway in the head, and the eyeball usually has a ring of scleral ossicles besides the cartilage cup. The extraordinary abundance of cones in the retina is responsible for the acute vision of most birds. The cones are estimated to number one million per square millimeter in the fovea of a hawk, *Buteo,* which gives it about eight times the resolving power of human vision.

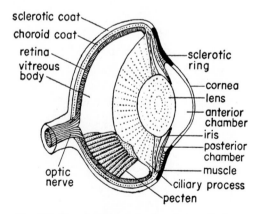

Fig. 307. Eye of chicken, showing pecten. (Redrawn from Adams and Eddy.)

The eye of mammals has no scleral cartilage except in the monotremes, ordinarily is spherical, possesses a retractor bulbi in most types, and has a distinctive pulleylike arrangement for the superior oblique, by which this muscle passes through a ligamentous loop in the anterior wall of the orbit before it goes to the eye. The conus of reptiles persists in a few marsupials, but otherwise is missing. All three major groups of living mammals show evidence of present or past nocturnal adaptation in the fact that cones are either absent (in most primitive types) or redeveloped in several modern lines independently. In this case they are probably modified rods.

The only mammals in which eyes are vestigial are the burrowing insectivores (moles) and a few Old World rodents of similar habit, such as Spalacidae and Bathyergidae, but the nocturnal types generally have small eyes (bats, shrews, etc.). Perhaps this should be qualified by a note that the nocturnal tarsier (a Primate) has exceptionally big eyes, as do the kangaroo rats and jumping mice. But the eye, like the inner ear and the brain, does not increase its bulk in proportion to the size of the head and body in very large animals. For example, the human eye is *relatively* smaller than that of a mouse, and it becomes smaller still in a rhinoceros, elephant, or whale.

CHAPTER XI

Nervous System

THE NERVOUS system is an incredibly complex arrangement of communicating cells, having relationship, first, to the receptors considered in the previous chapter, and second, to the effectors, which are muscles, glands, and contractile pigment cells. For convenience we make three divisions: the *central nervous system* (brain and spinal cord), *peripheral nervous system* (cranial and spinal nerves), and *autonomic system* (sympathetic and parasympathetic nerves). The central nervous system develops as a tube of ectoderm in the embryo, folded in from the neural plate as described in Chapter II. The other two divisions grow out more or less directly from this tube, their cells migrating to the final locations. We shall not attempt to consider the many fiber tracts and centers in the cord and brain, for these involve histology and physiological experiment beyond the scope of a general comparative anatomy (see Chusid and McDonald, 1956).

In the neuromuscular cells of the lower invertebrates, such as *Hydra*, the functions of receptor, conductor, and effector are often combined, and these cells are not localized but generally distributed. Later specialization produces receptors, conductors (neurons), and effectors (Fig. 308). Animals which are sessile (attached to a surface) tend to distribute each of these types radially, and the nervous system becomes a ring with branches. Animals which travel habitually in one direction, and so have a head, tend to group their receptors at the anterior end, and as a

305

result the bulk of the nervous system is also anterior, with nerves going back to the effectors. If the body shows metameric segmentation (annelids and arthropods), there is serial repetition of parts, including the

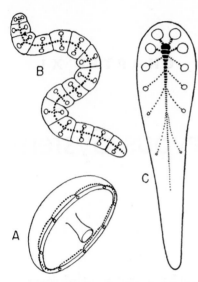

receptors and effectors, and consequently a repetition of both sensory and motor nerves. But such animals also have a head end (cephalization), especially the advanced arthropods; therefore the series of nerves and nerve centers is not uniform but is strongly developed in the head and diminishes from there back. The body acts increasingly as a unit and less as a chain of organs.

In the chordates the nervous system has a segmental relationship to the muscular system by way of paired nerves, but at the same time it shows pronounced cephalization. The brain of the most primitive known vertebrates is not large, but it is unmistakably a brain and not a series of fused nerve centers. The nervous system of

Fig. 308. Diagram of receptors (o) and nervous system (. . . .) in (A) radial, (B) metameric, (C) strongly cephalized animals.

vertebrates does not appear to be derived from segmental nerve chains of invertebrates, and it differs also in being dorsal instead of ventral.

The walls of the embryonic neural tube grow until they are much thicker than the cavity of the tube, and the cells transform into (1) *neuroglia* cells, and (2) *neurons,* many of which extend their fibers outward in the peripheral nerves, while others grow lengthwise along the tube itself. Neuroglia cells are those with other functions than conduction of impulses: some form an interstitial tissue for support, some contribute to the cellular sheaths surrounding nerve fibers, and some are left as a ciliated epithelium, the *ependyma,* lining the inner cavity of spinal cord and brain. The cell bodies and fibers of neurons as they grow take up a specific arrangement. In the spinal cord, cell bodies are internal, while the fibers lie in tracts along the outer part of the wall. In the cerebellum, hemispheres, and optic lobes of the brain the reverse is true. Since most nerve fibers are enclosed in a white myelin sheath, while the cell bodies are not, it follows that the white matter of the cord and brain is composed of fibers, while the gray matter is the region of cell bodies.

A *neuron* (Fig. 309) is peculiar in having its nucleus and most of its cytoplasm confined to a small cell body, out of which run, typically, two or more branching fibers. In one direction goes a *dendrite* or a cluster of them; their function is to bring an impulse *to* the cell body. The impulse is carried on, *away* from the cell body, by the other type of fiber, the

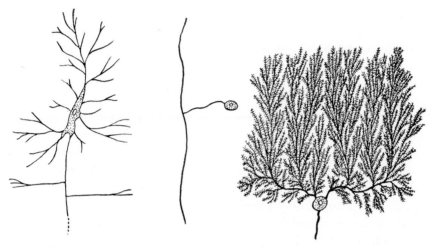

Fig. 309. Examples of neurons.

axon. Sometimes, as in motor neurons, the axon is much longer than the dendrite (Fig. 310), but the opposite may be true, as with most sensory neurons. Thus no fundamental difference exists between the two, except in the direction in which they carry an impulse. It follows, too, that nor-

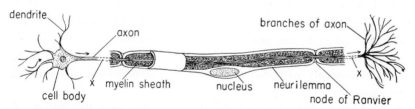

Fig. 310. Neuron with medullated (myelinated) fiber. Direction of impulse indicated by (→); gaps where most of length of fiber is omitted indicated by (X).

mally an impulse can go in only one direction along a neuron, because only the dendrite receives it.

Here it is necessary to keep in mind a distinction between a *stimulus*, which is received by a sense organ or nerve ending; an *impulse*, which is a wave of negative charges spreading along a fiber; and a *sensation*, which is something perceived, something experienced. The latter is a subject for psychology and has no place, as yet, in functional anatomy.

Since both axons and dendrites may branch at their tips and communicate with the fibers of other neurons, the nature of this connection, the *synapse,* is important. The fibers contain cytoplasm, covered by the plasma membrane of the cell, and this covering is complete, even at the end. Therefore a synapse is like the meeting of any two cells, the contact or proximity of two plasma membranes. It has been shown, in the case of many motor nerves, at least, that the end of an axon produces a secretion, acetylcholine, as the result of each impulse that comes to it, and that this induces the response of an effector organ, such as a pigment cell, a gland, or a muscle. That this may be the means of bridging a synapse is at least likely.

Most nerve fibers in gnathostomes are *myelinated* (Fig. 310); that is, enclosed in a white fatty sheath of *myelin.* Around this in turn is a sheath made of cells, the *neurilemma,* each cell of which wraps around its section of fiber much like a roll around a hot dog. Where one neurilemma cell meets the next one there is a notch or constriction (interrupting the myelin layer also), called a *node of Ranvier.* Presumably these sheaths maintain the functional isolation of fibers from one another, as well as provide their nutrition.

Central Nervous System

PROTOCHORDATES

In the development of any chordate the central nervous system begins, as we have said, by the folding in of an area of dorsal ectoderm, the *neural plate,* to form a *neural tube.* This closes first along its middle, and last of all at its anterior end, where the persistent opening is called the *neuropore.* Posteriorly the tube closes over, but often remains connected temporarily with the archenteron; this connection is the *neurenteric canal.*

Among protochordates, Amphioxus and the tunicates follow this scheme, and in both of them the neuropore remains open for a while in larval life. When it closes, the cells adjacent to it form, in Amphioxus, the *olfactory pit,* and in tunicates the *neural gland.* The neural tube of Amphioxus becomes nearly as long as the body, supplying dorsal and ventral segmental nerves to the muscles, but fails to develop a brain. On the other hand, in tunicates the spinal cord is present to supply the body muscles only during the brief free-swimming stage of the larva, and then degenerates when the tail and its muscles disappear, leaving only a *dorsal ganglion* in the position of a brain.

The wormlike hemichordates have a short neural tube only in the collar. From it extend peripheral nerves, and, unlike any other chordates, a nerve ring around the mouth, with a median ventral nerve going back beneath. The small, sessile Pterobranchia, however, do not develop far enough to have a neural tube, but the neural plate remains external. This may not be a primitive condition, but the result of an extreme delay in development.

VERTEBRATES

In all vertebrates the brain forms an enlarged bulb of the central nervous system in the head, while the spinal cord emerges posteriorly and continues down the trunk. Reflex arcs concerned with body and limb muscles are centered, of course, in the cord, but longitudinal fiber tracts run to the brain, where action is coördinated and directed. Besides this, the brain contains the centers of the innumerable sensory and motor functions of the head.

Both brain and cord are wrapped in membranes of connective tissue, the *meninges*, lying between the brain and skull and between the cord and the walls of the neural canal in which it lies. Fishes have a single meninx, but amphibians, reptiles, and birds split this into two, an outer *dura mater* and inner *pia mater*, the latter in contact with the brain and cord. A third meninx, the *arachnoid*, appears in mammals as a fibrous web over the surface of the pia mater. Cerebrospinal fluid occupies the space between the meninges, as well as the cavity of the cord and the ventricles of the brain.

The brain, during its development, grows unevenly, forming at first three divisions: *prosencephalon, mesencephalon, rhombencephalon.* (Since the prosencephalon becomes distinct a little before the mes- and rhombencephalon, the latter two are sometimes lumped as *deuterencephalon.*) These first parts are only temporarily recognizable, for the prosencephalon (forebrain) makes two, the *telencephalon* and *diencephalon*, while the rhombencephalon (hind brain) similarly makes the *metencephalon* and *myelencephalon.* Thus, with the mesencephalon (midbrain) remaining undivided, there are five major parts (see Fig. 82).

The cavity within also expands unevenly (Fig. 311), so that the telencephalon comes to harbor the first two *ventricles*, the diencephalon the third ventricle, and the fourth ventricle lies in both met- and myelencephalon, becoming restricted to the latter in animals above fishes; all these connect with one another and with the lumen of the cord. Now the ventricles are spaces inside the brain, but at two places, the roof of the diencephalon and roof of the myelencephalon, they are covered by nothing but a thin loose membrane, continuous with the ependyma of the ventricles. The membrane in each case is folded into the ventricle and carries with it a network of small blood vessels, a *choroid plexus.* Thus the *anterior* choroid plexus hangs into the third ventricle (pushing also into the first and second), and the *posterior* into the fourth.

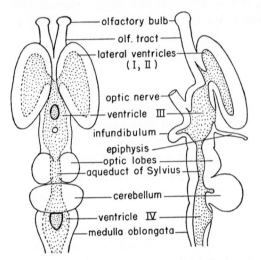

Fig. 311. Generalized diagram of vertebrate brain, as transparent object, from above (left) and from side (right).

Connecting right and left walls of the brain, especially in its floor, run crosswise tracts of fibers, the *commissures,* coördinating motor and sensory functions of the two sides. Three parts of the brain roof are especially well developed: the *cerebellum* (roof of the metencephalon, for motor coördination), the *optic lobes* (roof of the mesencephalon, for visual center), and *cerebral hemispheres* (roof of the two halves of the telencephalon, for association and presumably consciousness, if any).

The discussion so far applies to vertebrates in general. Next we shall look at features of the brain and spinal cord in each major group.

Brain and Spinal Cord

CYCLOSTOMES

The brain in cyclostomes (Fig. 312, A, B) is narrow, elongate, emphasizing the olfactory lobes (ventral part of the telencephalon) and optic lobes (dorsal part of the midbrain). The *pallium* or roof of the telencephalon is thin and does not form cerebral hemispheres in any proper sense of the word. Underneath the diencephalon is a ventral pouch, the *infundibulum,* which forms the posterior lobe of the *pituitary gland* in all vertebrates. But the anterior lobe, the *hypophysis,* is at least partly represented in cyclostomes by an open pouch running down under the front of the brain from the nasal sac to the infundibulum; this is not, of course, a part of the nervous system. The cerebellum is very small, as the brain takes no great part in motor coordination.

The brain and cranial nerves of the ancient ostracoderm, *Cephalaspis*, have been restored by Stensiö (1927), who showed that they were much

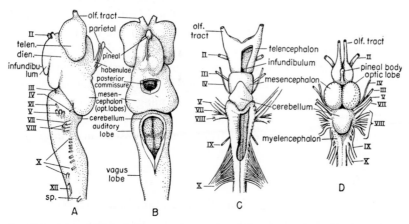

Fig. 312. Brains of fishes. A, lamprey, *Petromyzon*, from side; B, same, dorsal; C, shark, *Heptanchus*; D, pike, *Esox lucius*. (A, B, C after Kingsley; D after Goodrich.)

like those of the modern lamprey except for one or two features. The skull, being massive, enclosed the brain and all ten pairs of cranial nerves which are associated with it in fishes. But in modern lampreys and hagfishes the skull has been so much shortened that the last two pairs (glossopharyngeal, IX, and vagus, X) are left outside it, although they are present and perform the same functions as in any fish. Thus some authors refer to cyclostomes as having eight pairs of cranial nerves instead of ten.

The spinal cord in cyclostomes is a flattened, thick-walled tube in which the gray matter occupies the middle part, showing in cross section as an indistinct horizontal band. There are no longitudinal grooves (*fissures*) such as appear in most vertebrates.

GNATHOSTOME FISHES

With fishes above cyclostomes the pallium remains little developed, but there is generally an enlargement of the optic lobes, since the eyes are important (Fig. 312, C, D). With strong development of the lateral line system the lateral lobes of the *medulla* (myelencephalon) may become much swollen. The cerebellum is moderately large in the most active fishes, especially teleosts. The pituitary gland is fundamentally as in higher vertebrates, for the hypophysial pouch closes early in embryonic life and becomes the small, round anterior lobe. The spinal cord usually, but not always, has dorsal and ventral fissures.

This is a convenient place to call attention to the **Mauthnerian apparatus,** a pair of giant neurons whose cell bodies and dendrites lie in the medulla, one on each side, and whose axons, after crossing to the opposite side, extend down the spinal cord. The Mauthner cells are present in those fishes and aquatic Amphibia which (1) use the tail actively in swimming, and (2) have lateral line organs. The dendrites in the medulla synapse with sensory neurons from the lateral line on their side of the body, while the axons, crossing over, synapse along the spinal cord with successive motor fibers to swimming muscles of the opposite side. Experiments show that the Mauthner cells act as regulatory centers for the wavelike flexor action of trunk and tail muscles in swimming.

AMPHIBIA

The most notable change from the fish brain is the thickening of the pallium to make the beginning of cerebral hemispheres. It becomes occupied by neurons and their synapsing fibers, but still lacks the cortical layer of associative fibers. The olfactory and optic lobes are still the most

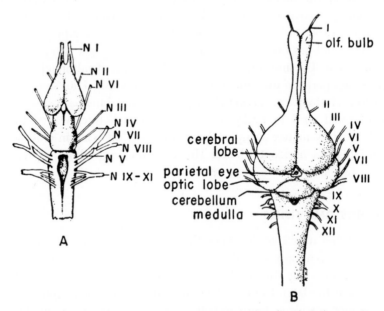

Fig. 313. Brain of (A) a primitive frog, *Pipa pipa;* (B) a lizard, *Sceloporus.* (A from *Biology of the Amphibia* by Noble; B reproduced by permission from *Comparative Anatomy* by L. A. Adams and S. Eddy, published by John Wiley & Sons, Inc., 1949.)

conspicuous parts of the brain, however. The cerebellum is relatively small (Fig. 313A).

We may note here the question of the posterior limits of the brain, as marked by the number of cranial nerves included in the skull. With *modern* Amphibia the number is ten, as in fishes. But they have arrived at this number by reduction, for in ancestral Amphibia, the labyrinthodonts, 12 pairs were included, just as we find in reptiles, birds, and mammals. Consequently the presence of 10 pairs in frogs and salamanders does not indicate relationship to fishes, but a shortening of the skull.

REPTILES

The brain now grows bulbous anteriorly on account of the swelling of the hemispheres with far more neurons than they contained before (Fig. 313B). The cerebral hemispheres are thus well established, although their surfaces remain smooth and they do not conceal the olfactory lobes in front. In some reptiles we find the beginning of a new associative area in the hemispheres, the *neopallium.* The optic lobes are big, for most reptiles have good eyes. The cerebellum remains modest, although larger than in Amphibia. While the reptilian brain in recent types is quite uniform, yet it is known (Edinger, 1949, p. 21) that "the pterosaurs developed birdlike brains, and mammal-like reptiles had long cerebra with large olfactory bulbs." The reptiles have twelve pairs of cranial nerves, a heritage, as we have said, from the labyrinthodont Amphibia.

It would hardly be correct to regard the modern reptilian brain as ancestral to that of either birds or mammals, as contemporary groups cannot be precisely ancestors or descendants of one another. Rather, all three of these are built upon a previous type met in the earliest reptiles. Therefore the superficial resemblances we may find between bird and mammal brains are quite independent, and go back into the remote past.

There are both dorsal and ventral fissures in the spinal cord of Amphibia and reptiles, but not as deep as in birds and mammals. The gray matter forms an H or X in cross section.

BIRDS

A bird has big eyes, complex behavior which includes a certain amount of learning, and remarkable motor coördination. But the sense of smell is unimportant. All these facts are reflected in the form of its brain (Fig. 314). The cerebral hemispheres (neopallium) are big, but the olfactory lobes are reduced. The optic lobes are broad and conspicuous, while the cerebellum has become greatly expanded, with a convoluted surface. In a dorsal view the midbrain and diencephalon are largely hidden under the cerebrum, but this has no convolutions. It is worth pointing out that

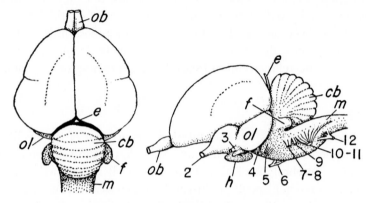

Fig. 314. Brain of goose, dorsal and lateral. (Redrawn after Kingsley, Outlines of Comparative Anatomy of Vertebrates, 3rd ed., Blakiston.)
cb, cerebellum; ec, epiphysis; f, flocculus; h, hypophysis; m, medulla; ob, olfactory bulb; of, olfactory lobe; 1–12, cranial nerves.

these characteristics were slower to arise in birds than those of wings, feathers, and beak, for the brain of *Archeopteryx* was scarcely birdlike at all, and that of the Cretaceous toothed birds was only part way along.

Associated with the flexible jointing of the head on the neck, the medulla shows a bend, present also in reptiles and mammals, the **nuchal flexure.** In embryonic life, in these three groups, the brain grows relatively fast at the beginning, and to help it fit the cramped space available

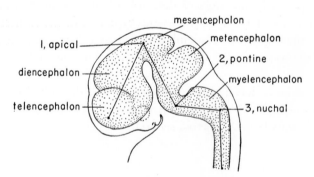

Fig. 315. Flexures of human brain at seven weeks.

tively fast at the beginning, and to help it fit the cramped space available for it, two other flexures also appear, the **pontine** (an upward bend of the metencephalon against the medulla), and the **apical** (a downward bend of the anterior parts of the brain, beginning with the midbrain). These flexures become less marked later on (see Fig. 315).

MAMMALS

Although monotremes have a simple, reptilian brain (Fig. 316), the marsupials and especially the placentals show great progress. A char-

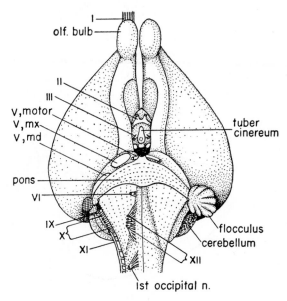

olf. bulb
I
II
III
V,motor
V,mx
V,md
pons
VI
IX
X
XI
tuber cinereum
flocculus
cerebellum
XII
1st occipital n.

Fig. 316. Brain of monotreme, *Ornithorhynchus*, ventral view. (After Parker and Haswell.)

acteristic mammalian feature is the *pons,* a belt of transverse fibers across the ventral side of the metencephalon. In progressive modern orders the cerebral hemispheres become the largest parts of the brain (Figs. 317C, 318), although they were not so in the early members of these orders. For instance the Eocene horse, *Eohippus,* had a brain much like that of an opossum (Fig. 317, A, B; Edinger, 1948). The hemispheres become convoluted in modern ungulates, proboscideans, carnivores, and primates, thus increasing the *cortex* enormously, allowing room for vast numbers of neurons and connections. The folds (ridges) are *gyri,* and the grooves or creases between folds are *sulci.* Crossing between the hemispheres is a thick, flat commissure, the *corpus callosum,* connecting the cerebral cortex of one side with that of the other. The lobes on the roof of the midbrain, in all other classes numbering two, the *corpora bigemina,* now become four (*corpora quadrigemina*). This is associated

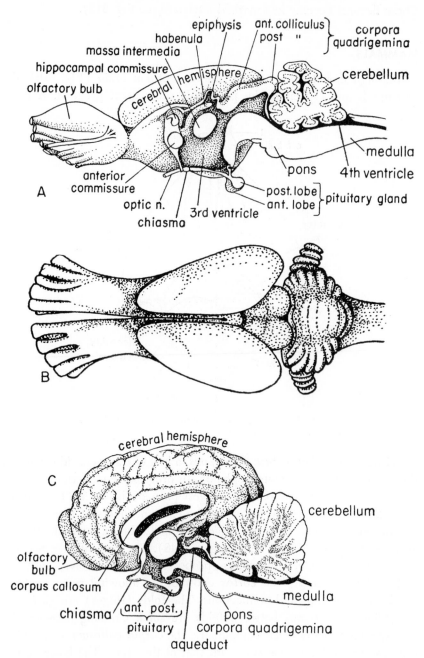

Fig. 317. Brain of opossum. A, sagittal view; B, same, dorsal view; C, brain of horse, sagittal view. (Redrawn from Edinger.)

with two other important changes: (1) Most of the optic fibers, instead of terminating in the corpora bigemina (optic lobes), are diverted into the cerebrum and reach new visual centers in the posterior parts of the hemispheres. This leaves the reduced anterior pair of lobes of the mid-

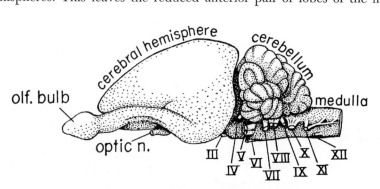

Fig. 318. Brain of hare, *Lepus*. (From Parker and Haswell.)

brain simply as centers for some visual reflexes. (2) Auditory nerve fibers are brought forward into the midbrain, where the posterior pair of lobes in the corpora quadrigemina constitute centers for auditory reflexes; this feature is so strongly developed in bats as to distinguish a bat brain from that of any other mammal. The cerebellum is convoluted, as in birds, but broader, and increased by two lateral lobes; its sagittal section shows a treelike branching of the fibrous interior, the **arbor vitae.**

The spinal cord fails to reach the end of its bony canal in mammals. In fact the spinal nerves emerge from the cord farther anteriorly than the level at which they leave the vertebral column. This is especially evident at the posterior end, where the canal is filled with roots of spinal nerves for some distance below the end of the cord. This cluster of roots, looking like a horse's tail, is the **cauda equina.**

Spinal Nerves

It is an advantage to treat the spinal, cranial, and autonomic nerves as essentially segmental nerves. Of these the spinal nerves serve as the best illustration, for they provide a type, probably primitive, and the relationships of the others to this type can then be explained (Fig. 319).

In Amphioxus and lampreys a segmental nerve has two separate parts, which do not connect with each other. The dorsal one is really an intersegmental nerve, going out from the cord along a myoseptum. It has a dorsal root ganglion in all vertebrates (but not Amphioxus), in which are the cell bodies of sensory neurons whose dendrites bring impulses from the skin and the segmental organs (muscles, etc.) in front of that myoseptum. These fibers are grouped, functionally, as the **somatic sensory component.** Also the dorsal nerve contains a *visceral sensory component* of fibers from the unsegmented part of the body adjoining, such as digestive organs and peritoneum. Finally, the dorsal root in primitive vertebrates (lampreys) carries a *visceral motor component* to (1) the visceral muscles (if located in the head) which are striated, skeletal muscles, and (2) smooth muscles of the viscera and elsewhere, including heart, arteries, skin, iris, etc. This latter group of nerves comprises the *autonomic system,* primitively connected with the **dorsal** root.

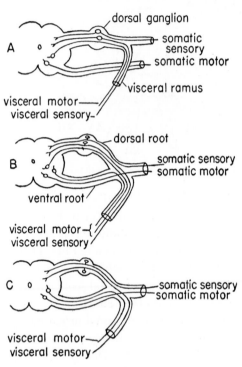

Fig. 319. Components of spinal nerves. A, lamprey; B, many lower gnathostomes; C, mammals. (Adapted from Romer.)

The ventral nerve is strictly segmental and motor, entering the myomere in front of the corresponding dorsal nerve. It is said to be a *somatic motor* nerve, and its cell bodies are in the gray matter of the cord.

Now in hagfishes and all vertebrates above cyclostomes each dorsal segmental nerve emerging from the spinal cord joins the corresponding ventral nerve to form a common **spinal nerve** in which the dorsal root bears a ganglion and the ventral root does not. The visceral motor component (autonomic) now abandons the dorsal root and uses the ventral root instead, along with the somatic motor component. But in the head (cranial nerves) there is no such union of a dorsal with a ventral nerve, and the visceral motor component remains dorsal; in this respect the cranial nerves retain a more primitive arrangement than the spinal. We shall deal with the autonomic system farther on.

The number of pairs of spinal nerves usually agrees, or nearly so, with the number of vertebrae in the column, even though some of these may be fused. The nerves are virtually identical down the series in fishes, except that those in the region of the gill basket have to bend back and downward to reach the pectoral fin, and their lower ends then stretch forward again to supply the hypobranchial muscles. Since the fin muscles in fishes are direct outgrowths of the myotomes, each slip of a fin muscle receives a branch from its appropriate spinal nerve. In the fins of sharks, and even more conspicuously in the pectoral fins of rays (Fig. 320), the

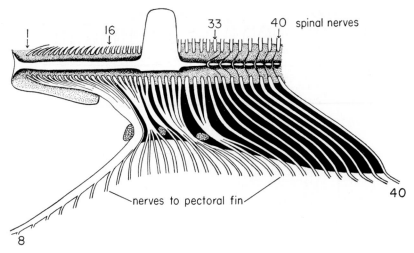

Fig. 320. Spinal nerves entering pectoral fin in ray, *Raja*, left side (anterior end is to left.)

nerves gather together into two or three large trunks as they pass through the foramina in the girdle, and then fan out again into the same number of distal divisions as there were nerves involved.

With land animals the same principle holds, but the limb muscles no longer can be associated individually with myotomes. A few spinal nerves combine to form the **brachial plexus** and the **lumbar** (or **sacral**) **plexus,** and then enter the fore or the hind limb as one or more large nerves. When the limb is extended laterad with the thumb or first toe forward, the innervation of muscles and skin in it follows this general pattern: the more anterior nerves of the plexus serve the parts nearest the body and along the anterior margin of the limb, while the posterior nerves run to the more distal and posterior parts. The fact that any such pattern exists indicates that the limb architecture keeps some of its primitive relationships to the body segments.

Cranial Nerves

There is a great deal of difference, not due entirely to function or position, between cranial nerves and spinal nerves. It is probable that some, but not all, cranial nerves represent what were once separate dorsal (Figs. 321, 322) or ventral nerves belonging to particular head segments. One pair of cranial nerves, the optic, are actually lobes of the brain, and

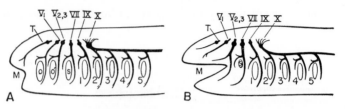

Fig. 321. Distribution of branchial (dorsal root) cranial nerves. A, hypothetical primitive condition; B, condition in jaw-bearing fishes. (From Romer.)

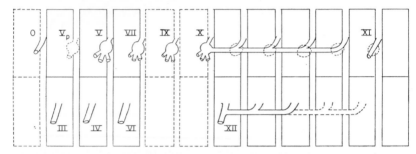

Fig. 322. Diagram of probable segmental relationships of cranial nerves and ganglia; anterior direction to left. Note that the dorsal nerves are intersegmental, the ventral ones segmental in position. A typical dorsal nerve, such as V, VII, IX, or X, carries three functional components: somatic sensory, visceral sensory, and visceral motor. A ventral nerve is somatic motor only. Nerves I and II are not shown, being concerned with lobes of the brain and not related to the others. Nerve VIII is probably derived from VII, as a part of its somatic sensory component, so is not shown separately. The first somite (dotted line) is hypothetical; the next three give rise to muscles of the eye; the two following (dotted lines) do not develop in vertebrates above cyclostomes; the remainder may be called postotic somites.

hence not comparable with the others. Between one class of vertebrates and another there are few major differences in cranial nerves, so we need not treat the classes separately (but see Fig. 323).

O. TERMINAL NERVE

The nervus terminalis is not one of the familiar twelve, but is a pair of small sensory nerves lying along the inner or anterior side of the olfactory lobes. It occurs in fishes, except cyclostomes, is easily found in a shark, but is present only as a temporary or inconspicuous thread in higher animals. This is why it was unknown until recently. It may represent a vestigial sensory nerve for a premandibular segment.

I. OLFACTORY

From the anterior end of each lobe of the telencephalon goes a white *olfactory tract,* ending forward in the *olfactory bulb.* These structures, apparently a big nerve, are actually a lobe of the brain, stretching for-

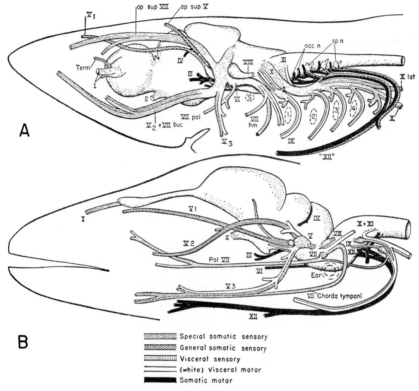

Fig. 323. Distribution and components of cranial nerves. A, a shark, *Squalus;* B, a lizard, *Anolis.* (From Romer.)

ward almost to the olfactory organ. The true *olfactory nerve* is simply an aggregation of short sensory fibers reaching from the olfactory epithelium back to the bulb. In those animals which have a Jacobson's organ, namely the majority of Amphibia, reptiles, and mammals, a division of the olfactory nerve supplies this. Ascending the scale of vertebrate life, we find olfactory tracts prominent in fishes, amphibians, and most reptiles, because the olfactory sense is important in the life of these animals; the tracts are conspicuous because not overhung by the cerebral hemispheres. With birds the sense of smell is much less important, while among mammals it varies from a remarkable development in many carnivores to almost complete atrophy in Cetacea.

II. OPTIC

The optic nerves grow out from the walls of the embryonic diencephalon, first as hollow vesicles, then becoming narrow stalks. The nerve fibers grow back from the retina to the brain. The presence of optic nerves and their degree of development depends on the functional importance of the eyes in particular animals, and this we have dealt with.

A notable feature is the *optic chiasma,* meeting place of the two optic nerves, seen as a white X on the ventral side of the diencephalon just in front of the pituitary body. In the chiasma of lower vertebrates, to and including birds, the fibers from each eye cross to the opposite side of the brain before following the internal tracts to the optic lobes or tectum of the mesencephalon. But in mammals the visual centers are in the cerebral hemispheres; perhaps this is related to the psychological complexities of stereoscopic vision, which call for exceedingly intricate associative pathways among the neurons. In mammals, too, some of the fibers from each retina separate from the rest at the chiasma and go to the same side of the brain as that of the eye from which they came. This is called *incomplete decussation* (incomplete crossover). It apparently is necessary for binocular vision, and occurs progressively with mammals in which the visual fields increasingly overlap. When decussation (crossover at the chiasma) becomes only about 50 percent, so that the fibers from the right side of each retina go to the right side of the brain, and those from the left to the left side, it remains at this proportion, even though the overlap of visual fields of the two eyes may (as in higher Primates) approach 100 percent. This simply means that a stereoscopic image, perceiving depth, is constructed in the right half of the brain, showing the left half of the visual field, and is fitted, so to speak, against a stereoscopic image of the right half of the visual field made in the left half of the brain.

III. OCULOMOTOR

Nerves III, IV, and VI should properly be considered together, since they are motor nerves supplying the eye muscles which develop from the first three head myotomes of the embryo. The oculomotor runs from the floor of the midbrain to the superior, anterior, and inferior recti and the inferior oblique. There are with it parasympathetic motor fibers (autonomic system) which go to the smooth ciliary and iris muscles.

IV. TROCHLEAR

Arising in the midbrain just behind the oculomotor, this nerve supplies only the superior oblique muscle, a product of the second myotome.

V. TRIGEMINAL

Just as nerves III, IV, and VI have a close relationship to each other, so have V, VII, IX, and X. It is sometimes difficult to separate V and VII at the base in dissection, and all four are mixed nerves with quite comparable distribution of their branches.

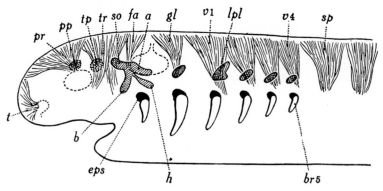

Fig. 324. Diagram of origins of segmental ganglia in gnathostome. (From Goodrich, *Studies on the Structure and Development of the Vertebrates*, The Macmillan Company.)

a, auditory branch; *b,* buccal branch; *br5,* fifth branchial slit; *eps,* epibranchial placode; *fa,* facial; *gl,* glossopharyngeal; *h,* hyoid branch; *lpl,* lateral line placode of vagus; *pp,* profundus placode; *pr,* profundus; *so,* superior ophthalmic; *sp,* spinal accessory; *t,* terminalis; *v1-v4,* vagus roots; *tp,* trigeminal placode; *tr,* trigeminus.

The trigeminal in fishes has four main branches, one of which, the *profundus* (deep ophthalmic, or ramus ophthalmicus profundus), arises a little separately from the rest and is primitively a distinct nerve. On the reasonable assumption that the eye-muscle nerves represent ventral, motor roots of segmental nerves, which also had dorsal roots, it is thought that the profundus is the dorsal (sensory) nerve of the first segment; hence, that it belongs with the oculomotor. It arises from the side of the metencephalon, and has its own ganglion, the *profundus ganglion,* just outside the brain. It goes to the skin of the snout. Among higher vertebrates the profundus ganglion unites with the Gasserian ganglion of the trigeminal proper, and the profundus nerve combines with the superficial ophthalmic; this is why it was not originally numbered as a separate member of the series (Figs. 321, 322, 324).

The remaining branches of the trigeminal arise from the **Gasserian** (trigeminal, or semilunar) **ganglion,** and probably represent a dorsal root of the second segment, belonging with the trochlear. At the same time they are to be regarded as the nerves of the upper and lower jaws; that is, the first visceral arch. The **superficial ophthalmic** (ramus ophthalmicus superficialis) runs through the orbit above the eye, supplying the skin of the upper part of the head. The **maxillary,** also sensory, goes to the upper jaw and its teeth. The **mandibular** nerve supplies (1) the lower jaw and its teeth, as a sensory nerve, and (2) the jaw muscles, as a visceral motor nerve.

How can a dorsal root nerve carry a motor component? We have to remember that primitively the dorsal roots carried the visceral motor fibers for all segments, and that the jaw muscles are visceral, arising from the hypomere, not from myotomes. Thus, as we shall see, cranial nerves V, VII, IX, and X all have such visceral motor divisions, because they represent dorsal segmental roots.

VI. ABDUCENS

This is the motor nerve of the third myotome, innervating the external rectus muscle and, in those animals that have one, the retractor bulbi. The name "abducens" comes from the function of the external rectus in man, to abduct or turn outward the eye.

VII. FACIAL

As the trigeminal is associated with the first visceral arch, the facial is related to the second, the hyoid arch. It is also thought to be the dorsal root for the third segment, and therefore belongs with the abducens. Emerging from the medulla, the facial nerve bears the **geniculate ganglion,** often very difficult to separate from the Gasserian.

The first branch of the facial nerve is the **ophthalmic,** hardly separable from the superficial ophthalmic of nerve V, with which it combines. Its destination is the more dorsal sensory canals and ampullae of the head. The **palatine** is also a sensory nerve, to the roof of the mouth. The **buccal** serves the external surface of the upper jaw, especially its sensory canals.

The *hyomandibular* branch, emerging on the posterior side of the spiracle, in lower vertebrates, supplies (1) sensory canals and ampullae of the lower jaw, by means of the *internal mandibular,* and (2) muscles of the hyoid arch. This motor branch becomes even more important in tetrapods than in fishes because of the elaborate specialization of muscles formerly connected with the hyoid arch. Thus in mammals the facial muscles, the platysma, part of the digastric, and others are served by the facial nerve. A branch running through the middle ear, the *chorda tympani,* carries sensory fibers from the taste buds and motor (parasympathetic) fibers to the salivary glands. This chorda tympani, found in reptiles, birds, and mammals, is derived from the internal mandibular branch in fishes.

VIII. AUDITORY

This nerve is sensory only, going to the end-organs of the inner ear. It has three branches to the ampullae of the semicircular canals, others to the maculae of utriculus, sacculus, and lagena, and a larger division in higher vertebrates to the organ of Corti in the cochlea. Thus it is a nerve of both equilibrium and hearing. We cannot say definitely that it is a part of any primitive segmental nerve, but it is a member of a group of lateral-line nerves (VII, IX, X), and embryology suggests that it may have originated from VII; we have seen already how the inner ear develops as a part of the sensory canal system.

IX. GLOSSOPHARYNGEAL

This nerve is associated with the third visceral arch (first branchial), the one behind the hyoid. It has a sensory palatine branch serving the same area as the palatine branch of the facial, and usually combining with it. The motor part supplies the visceral muscles of the third arch, and is posttrematic so far as the first functional gill slit of most fishes is concerned. Its ganglion is the *petrosal,* and it is thought to represent a dorsal root for the fourth head segment, for which no myotome and no ventral motor root develop in vertebrates.

X. VAGUS (PNEUMOGASTRIC)

This is the most important and most problematical of all the cranial nerves. In fishes it appears to be a combination of several visceral-arch nerves (all those behind the third arch), supplying to each of its arches a visceral motor component, for the muscles, and two sensory branches. But then it continues into the trunk, as a general visceral nerve with parasympathetic fibers to the digestive organs, lungs, and heart. It has also, in fishes and aquatic Amphibia, a lateralis branch serving the entire lateral line except for the anterior parts already supplied by nerves VII and IX. At its origin there are several roots and a *vagus ganglion.* Embryonically it seems that the various roots have their own ganglia, but the majority of these disappear when the developing nerve comes to depend on the more anterior ganglion.

Probably the vagus represents a dorsal root of the fifth head segment, for which no myotome or ventral root is present, plus the visceral branches from the dorsal roots of about four more segments, whose ventral roots are represented by nerve XII. It has, so to speak, stolen these visceral branches by linking them with its own ganglion, thus taking responsibility for all the visceral arches behind the third. It is generally held that two myotomes are missing between the three which make the eye muscles and the first ones to make segmental muscles behind the head. The dorsal nerves related to these missing segments would then be, as we have said, IX and the first root of X.

In tetrapods, with the exception of aquatic Amphibia, the lateralis division disappears and the visceral arch branches are much reduced, so that the vagus of higher animals is simply a nerve to the viscera, but to a physiologist it is the nerve of greatest interest in the whole body.

XI. SPINAL ACCESSORY

The eleventh cranial nerve is a visceral motor nerve; hence it is dorsal. It has a center in the medulla, and supplies muscles developed from the most posterior branchial arches. This means that in fishes it is really included in the vagus, but in tetrapods it innervates the trapezius and sternomastoid (or their equivalents), for these muscles are derived from the branchial group. In tetrapods, except modern Amphibia, it emerges separately from a foramen in the skull. In mammals parasympathetic fibers from it still accompany the vagus to the viscera.

XII. HYPOGLOSSAL

Again, this nerve is "cranial" only in tetrapods, except modern Amphibia. It corresponds to the motor divisions of at least three spinal nerves and has its center in the medulla. It runs to hypobranchial muscles in the fishes and to corresponding muscles of the tongue in mammals.

To summarize the relationships of cranial nerves:

1. Nerve I is a group of neuroepithelial cells connected to a lobe of the brain, and II is itself a lobe of the brain.

2. Nerves III, IV, and VI may be considered ventral, motor divisions of primitive segmental nerves going to the first three myotomes. This does not imply that they were ever connected with the dorsal divisions.

3. The profundus branch of nerve V may be the dorsal, sensory nerve of segment 1, while nerve O may be similarly related to a still more anterior segment, which no longer appears.

4. Nerves V and VII are probably the dorsal, sensory and visceral motor nerves of segments 2 and 3, respectively.

5. For segments 4 and 5 there are no ventral, motor nerves, since no myotomes develop.

6. For segment 4 the dorsal nerve is IX.

7. Nerve X is the dorsal nerve for segment 5 plus at least 4 more segments. It is primarily visceral.

8. The visceral motor nerve for the most posterior branchial muscles, or their derivatives, is XI, although it is not separate in lower vertebrates.

9. Nerve XII is a combination of motor nerves for at least three segments.

10. Nerve VIII and the sensory-canal branches of VII, IX, and X may perhaps not be related to primitive segmental nerves but belong to a group originally distinct, the lateralis nerves; this question is unsettled.

Autonomic System

We generally call "autonomic" those *visceral motor nerves* which go to smooth and cardiac muscles, to glands, contractile pigment cells, etc., but not to the visceral arch muscles of the head. As we saw, in lampreys the autonomic nerves connect with dorsal divisions of segmental nerves in both head and trunk, but in gnathostomes this connection remains only in the case of cranial nerves VII, IX, X, and XI. Otherwise the visceral motor fibers leave the spinal cord by way of the ventral root. (The oculomotor nerve, incidentally, comes in the same category, as a ventral motor nerve.)

Why this happened is not understood, but presumably the lamprey condition is primitive, and certainly it gives us an anatomical basis for arranging these nerves which is quite different from the functional basis commonly used. To escape confusion let us finish with the anatomy and then come to the function.

In a typical spinal nerve with dorsal and ventral root, then, visceral

motor fibers run out the ventral root and then turn off ventrad to a segmental *sympathetic ganglion* lying against the dorsal wall of the body
cavity. These fibers are *preganglionic* and white, since they are myelinated. So they connect the ganglion to the spinal nerve by a **white
ramus.** In the sympathetic ganglion some of them end, while others go on
through to reach an unpaired **collateral ganglion** among the viscera, or
still farther, in the case of parasympathetic fibers, to the viscera directly.
But in *all* these cases there is a synapse with a second neuron, called a
postganglionic neuron, whose fiber is not myelinated and hence is gray.
Thus autonomic impulses pass through two linked neurons, preganglionic
and postganglionic, before ending in a muscle or gland. Postganglionic
fibers beginning in the paired sympathetic ganglia nearest the spinal cord
may go in three directions: (1) up to the trunk of the adjacent spinal
nerve, by a **gray ramus,** and out with the peripheral branches to the
skin, or in lower vertebrates out to the skin separately; (2) down to the
viscera, passing through collateral ganglia without stopping, or sometimes
by-passing collateral ganglia; (3) through longitudinal trunks connecting
successive sympathetic ganglia, but in this case they go on out to their
destination anyway. (We should add here that visceral sensory fibers
may use the same nerves, returning to cell bodies in the dorsal root
ganglia, but the autonomic system is usually thought of as simply an
outflow or motor system, in which these sensory fibers are only inciden-
tal, not differing from any other sensory fibers.)

Thus in the thoracolumbar region the autonomic system shows as a
double chain of ganglia linked by two parallel trunks, and from each of
the paired ganglia two short rami, gray and white, go to the adjacent
spinal nerve.

The more important unpaired, collateral ganglia in the trunk (Fig.
325), are the **coeliac** (near where the coeliac artery leaves the aorta),
superior mesenteric (next to the artery of the same name, but often fused
with the coeliac ganglion), and **inferior mesenteric,** near the inferior
mesenteric artery. These ganglia receive preganglionic fibers which have
not stopped in the thoracolumbar chain; the postganglionic fibers from
them go to the viscera.

Finally, the autonomic system in the trunk includes **peripheral ganglia**
and a number of **plexi** in or on the surfaces of visceral organs and arteries. This includes the heart, aorta, and arterial walls, the digestive organs
and lungs, spleen, gonads and kidneys, etc. The "**solar plexus**" (coeliac
plexus) is a cluster of sympathetic nerves associated with the coeliac and
superior mesenteric ganglia. The plexi of **Auerbach** and **Meissner** lie in
the intestinal walls, taking part in control of peristalsis.

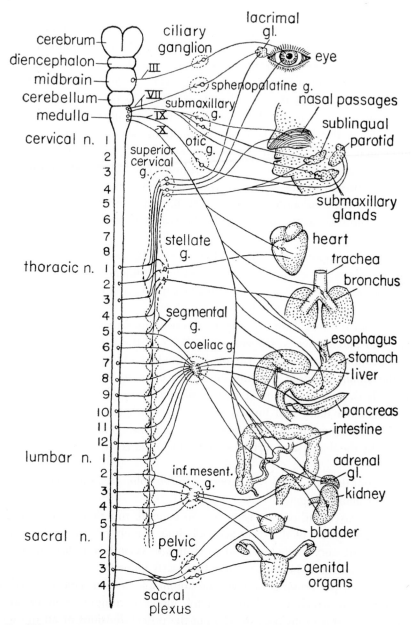

Fig. 325. Autonomic nervous system. Diagram based on man, showing ganglia and neuron pathways of craniosacral (parasympathetic) and thoracolumbar (sympathetic) divisions.

In the head there are peripheral or collateral ganglia, but the segmental chain does not continue, and autonomic motor fibers emerge from the brain in the apparently primitive manner, along dorsal root nerves with the exception of III, which is ventral.

Here we may turn to the physiological separation of autonomic nerves into two types: *sympathetic* (*thoracolumbar*) and *parasympathetic* (*craniosacral*). The sympathetic division includes the fibers coming from thoracic and lumbar spinal nerves (Fig. 325), as just described, to the paired ganglia along the dorsal wall of the body cavity and thence to unpaired ganglia among the viscera. From these, fibers go to virtually all parts of the body. Their motor functions are those which can be duplicated by the drug *adrenalin* (epinephrin, or "sympathin"). That is, they accelerate heart action, activate sphincter muscles, and inhibit most smooth muscles of the digestive tract. Wherever they supply an organ which has parasympathetic nerves as well, their function is the opposite; only in the case of the pancreas do the two have the same effect, stimulating secretion.

The parasympathetic outflow (Fig. 325) consists of fibers in the following places (in each case the preganglionic fibers reach to the organ concerned, where they synapse with postganglionic fibers, the cell bodies of which may or may not lie in a ganglion):

1. From the midbrain, by way of the oculomotor nerve, to the *ciliary ganglion* and thence to the smooth muscles of the iris and ciliary body.

2. From the medulla, by way of: (a) the facial nerve, palatine branch, to the *sphenopalatine ganglion* and thence to the lacrimal gland; also through the chorda tympani to the *submaxillary ganglion* and thence to the submaxillary and lingual glands; (b) the glossopharyngeal nerve to the *otic ganglion* and thence to the parotid gland; (c) the vagus nerve to the heart and arteries, digestive organs (except colon), and lungs.

3. From the first three sacral nerves to the colon, rectum, bladder, and external genital organs.

This parasympathetic division has, in general, functions which can be duplicated by use of the drug acetylcholine, namely to inhibit the action of the heart and sphincters, and to stimulate smooth muscle action and glandular secretion in most of the other parts named.

Nearly all the remarks here on the autonomic system have referred to mammals, in which it is known much more thoroughly than in other classes. Visceral branches extend from the dorsal divisions of all the segmental nerves in Amphioxus, to the viscera, but without ganglia or synapses on the way; thus its autonomic system is like the parasympathetic only. Fishes are in an intermediate stage of separating the sympathetic from the parasympathetic; sharks have a few paired subvertebral ganglia from which postganglionic (sympathetic) neurons supply the walls of arteries. In teleosts we find such ganglia more numerous, linked by longitudinal trunks, and supplying viscera as well as arteries; gray rami carry sympathetic fibers also to the skin.

CHAPTER XII

Panorama

TODAY the distinctions between one biological "subject" and another are breaking down rapidly, and a student needs to see why this is so. The study of *form* (morphology), of *function* (physiology), of *development* (embryology), of *classification* (taxonomy, or systematics) and of the *fossil record* (paleontology) all contributes to the "subject" of comparative anatomy. No field of biology is richer in ideas or carries wider significance.

The Rise of Comparative Anatomy

First, none of these studies sprang up over night. The curiosity of countless men during more than two thousand years has brought into being, a little at a time, the orderly, reasonable system of modern science. Not wishing merely to catalog names or dates, we ought to meet a few of these people and find out what they thought, and what difference their thinking made in the world. We need not consider their contributions to other branches of biology, but only those that have a bearing on comparative anatomy as it is now. It is misleading to say as little as we must here, because many of these men were far bigger in accomplishment and wider in understanding than we give them credit for being. Our view is broader, perhaps, than theirs simply because we stand on their shoulders.

One need not go back to Aristotle (384–322 B.C.) to learn about the developing parts of an embryo chick, although he described them, nor do we need today his accounts of some 540 kinds of animals known to him (Fig. 326). But it is a measure of his stature that more than eighteen hundred years after his death he was still the leading authority on natural science, as well as on much else in human thought. The idea at the center of morphology today, that form develops to its highest perfection out of matter which is formless, was his; he related it both to the development of an individual (*ontogeny*) and to that of the world of living things (*phylogeny*). That something without form can of itself accomplish this involves another of his ideas, *potentiality.*

Fig. 326. Aristotle.

By gathering all contemporary knowledge of animal life and arranging animals in a system according to their ways of living, actions, habits, and bodily parts, and finally by considering that this system showed the rise of life toward its ultimate perfection in man, Aristotle can be said to have produced a workable theory of evolution, which is thus far from being an upstart notion of our day.

Although anatomical dissection was done in Italian universities from the thirteenth century on, it was not with the idea of learning anything new. Medical professors pointed out the organs as surgeons toiled with the dissection; they used the writings of Galen (A.D. 131–?210), who had dissected animals but not human bodies, for authority, while the ever-present philosophy professors quoted Aristotle. It is true that even the use of ancient authorities represented an advance in Europe, where virtually no activity of this sort had taken place before.

Like a fresh breeze through this murky medieval atmosphere came the work of two great men, Leonardo da Vinci (1452–1519) and Andreas Vesalius (1514– ?). Totally unlike and unknown to each other, both held the novel belief that experience, not classical authority, is the source of knowledge. Leonardo began his study of anatomy because of its relationship to painting, but he made numerous comparisons between human anatomy and that of animals. He realized that fossils were the remains of animals once living, and that marine shells found embedded in the rock of mountains proved the former submergence of land beneath the sea. (This was also held by Xenophanes, about 500 B.C., but has been considered heresy by almost all thinkers up to the nineteenth century.) Because most of Leonardo's studies remained in private notes and drawings, unpublished almost to the present time, he had relatively little effect on the scientific practices of his day.

Vesalius, on the other hand, was a medical man, remarkable for his skill in dissecting and teaching (Fig. 327). While still in his twenties he saw that he must escape from Galen's authority and describe the hu-

Fig. 327. Vesalius.

Fig. 328. Harvey.

man body as he found it, with correct illustrations instead of fanciful diagrams. With the strength of his convictions he published the first thorough-going anatomy in the modern spirit. Eventually this work won its place against tremendous opposition from the old-timers.

Still, this was only a beginning. William Harvey (1578–1657), by years of the most careful work, proved that blood circulates through the body in arteries and veins, that the heart is muscular and pumps actively, not merely filling passively, and that the valves control the direction of flow (Fig. 328). He did not see the capillary connections because his work was done just a little before microscopes became available. In his studies of embryology he arrived at the view that the source of every living creature is an egg, yet this was really a confirmation of Aristotle's theory that life perfects its form, so far as it can, out of a formless beginning.

With the advent of the Dutch school of lens makers in the seventeenth century a large number of workers began to explore the fine details of animals, plants, and the human body. Antony van Leeuwenhoek (1632–1723) made out the capillaries and saw blood cells pouring through them. He studied the spermatozoa of several kinds of animals. Marcello Malpighi (1628–1694) likewise applied the lens to everything he could find. He, too, saw capillaries, and he distinguished the kidney tubules. Many other men like these were making discoveries to which their names are still given. Probably more fundamentally new details were seen in the seventeenth century than at any earlier or later time. But with this came a good deal of fantastic speculation and dogmatism, which only more recently has disappeared. The work of Emmanuel Swedenborg (1688–1772) on the brain shows both the progress and the fallacies of the age in ample measure.

In the eighteenth century men worked, still in a pioneering way and still on somewhat unfamiliar ground, but with an attitude more like that of the present. Georges L. L. de Buffon (1707–1788) had probably the greatest influence on later biology. He succeeded in uniting biological knowledge in a comprehensive "natural history," which treated man also as a natural object, and showed that animals and plants are subject to physical laws, to be learned by experiment and observation. Realizing what fossils are, and seeing in part the meaning of geological strata, Buffon rejected the biblical story of creation and inferred instead a series of epochs to cover the past history of the earth. His most direct relationship to comparative anatomy comes in the work of his collaborator, Louis Daubenton (1716–1800), who carried out the anatomical part of the natural history under Buffon's plan. Anatomies of many different animals were compared for the first time.

The studies of a few other eighteenth-century men will illustrate certain advances in thought which took place then. Charles Bonnet (1720–1793) originated a theory of preformation based in part on his work on aphids; he discovered parthenogenesis (reproduction without males) in these insects, and inferred that the females carry within themselves, minute but already formed, the young of succeeding generations. This belief, even though extended to other animals, was not so unreasonable as it seems now to us, and it served to stimulate much other work. Bonnet carried further Buffon's idea of prehistoric epochs, which he thought had ended with violent catastrophes such as world-wide floods, new life developing each time out of eggs or seeds that somehow escaped destruction.

Caspar Friedrich Wolff (1733–1794) by his embryological work put an end to preformation theories, demonstrating (as Aristotle and Harvey had believed) that development makes new structures where none had been before. Petrus Camper (1722–1789) made special anatomical studies of some of the larger animals—rhinoceros, elephant, reindeer, orangutan; he discovered air sacs and their connection with the hollow limb bones in birds. Felix Vicq D'Azyr (1748–1794), studying mammals more extensively, pointed out the functional correlation between parts of the body as used in a particular way of life; for instance, sharp claws, cutting teeth, and a simple kind of stomach go together in meat-eaters.

Fig. 329. Lamarck.　　　　　　　Fig. 330. Cuvier.

The famous German poet, Johann Wolfgang von Goethe (1749–1832) has a place in eighteenth-century anatomy because of his studies on the skeleton of mammals. He supported (but did not originate) the theory that the skull resulted from a fusion of separate vertebrae. He also saw in a human skull the unfused premaxillary bones, at a time when their absence was thought to be an absolute distinction between man and animals.

Every biology student knows the name of Lamarck (Jean B. P. A. de M. de Lamarck, 1744–1829), and the relationship between his theory of the inheritance of acquired characters and the natural selection theory of Darwin and Wallace (Fig. 329). But here we should notice his arrangement of the animal kingdom in a linear series according to the degree of specialization; that is, the presence or absence of organs, and their complexity. He attributed these characters to the habits of animals and the conditions in which they and their ancestors lived. Although this arrangement implied evolutionary descent, we may note that Lamarck was the last to use a single line to express the relationships of all animals.

To Marie François Xavier Bichat (1771–1802) we owe the very important recognition of tissue types, and the categories of organs and systems. Considering that he worked in human anatomy without the help of a microscope, and that he died before he was 31, his contributions were among the foremost of his time.

Georges Cuvier (1769–1832) was a man of extraordinary ability, to whom we owe the creation of both comparative anatomy and paleontology, because no one before him had tied together anatomical studies in so comprehensive a manner (Fig. 330). We have seen, up to this time, either isolated, disconnected work or a submergence of anatomy in efforts which were primarily something else. Cuvier began in a new way, dissecting marine animals, which had scarcely been investigated before. He went on to some special work on large mammals, and was the first to compare in detail the bones of fossil vertebrates with those of their modern relatives. He developed the correlation principle beyond the place where Vicq D'Azyr left it, to the point where it was thought possible to reconstruct the whole of an unknown animal from the structure of one part. Thus he could "restore" an extinct animal from an incomplete skeleton.

Cuvier denied, however, that any species of animal evolved from, or into, different ones. He objected to the linear-series scheme of Lamarck and others, and used instead a system of four primary types of animals (vertebrates, molluscs, articulates, and radiates), four major themes upon which all animal structure could be based. To account for the obvious differences between extinct and living species he used the catastrophe theory of Bonnet, supposing that after each destructive event a new population arose from some remote part of the world that had been spared.

Thus the nineteenth century began with controversy over the principle of evolution, in which the ablest man, who had himself contributed more evidence than any other, stood on the opposing side. Perhaps the resulting delay of general acceptance was not actually time lost, because Cuvier set an example of critical thoroughness and accuracy which was badly needed.

Richard Owen (1804–1892) was the best-known English anatomist of the nineteenth century. His comparative studies of teeth, of the anatomy of lungfishes, of *Archeopteryx,* of the extinct moas in New Zealand, and the apes, have permanent value. The concepts of homology and analogy, as usually explained, are due to him. He meant by **homology** a relationship between corresponding organs of different animals, whether superficially alike or not, the relationship being due to derivation from a single "archetype"; for example, a bird's wing, a whale's flipper, and a horse's foreleg are homologous. **Analogy,** of course, refers to a similarity of form and function between parts which are not derived from one archetype, as the analogy between a bird's wing and an insect's wing. Naturally these

Fig. 331. Huxley.   Fig. 332. Cope.

ideas have undergone a great deal of discussion and some change, especially within the last 25 years.

Mentioning two or three more eminent European figures will bring us close to our own period. T. H. Huxley (1825–1895), known for his mastery of written and spoken English and his powerful support of Darwin, was also important in comparative anatomy and paleontology (Fig. 331). Among other things he was able to show that the skull does not develop by a fusion of vertebrae, and thus to lay a sound basis for the embryological studies made shortly after. Carl Gegenbaur (1826–1903) was typical of the German morphological school, thorough and single-minded. Taking part in the general enthusiasm over Darwinism that followed publication of *The Origin of Species* (1859), Gegenbaur made phylogenetic study his sole aim, especially basing it on the skeleton. Thus he compared limb bones of vertebrates until he found what he thought was the primitive type, the "archipterygial" fin of lungfishes. He believed that gill arches are comparable with ribs. His work, although not free from errors of interpretation, was essential at the time.

Two of the notable generalizations made by Ernst Haeckel (1834–1919) were his principle of recapitulation, or "biogenetic law," and his theory of the germ layers. Both of these have needed qualification in recent years, but the original idea of recapitulation, that embryos repeat in abbreviated manner the ancestral history of the race, is sometimes very nearly true. The most striking examples may not be found among vertebrates, and we can see that usually immature stages possess their own adaptations without reference to whether these occurred in the adults of remote ancestors, but for many anatomical details the concept has value. In these days of "debunking" earlier work it is a common fault to throw overboard *in toto* a great generalization when we find that newer evidence calls for partial revision, and then to dismiss all thinking on the subject as "mere speculation."

The germ-layer theory that primitive animals possessed ectoderm and endoderm, presently enclosing mesoderm between, and that organs in all higher animals develop only from the germ layers with which they were originally associated, has borne abundant fruit in the field of comparative embryology, even if recent students are finding it impossible to keep the original definitions intact.

In the United States the most productive work of the nineteenth century in our field was probably that with a slant toward paleontology, because here, more than in the Old World, a vast store of undiscovered fossil vertebrates awaited the explorer. First to exploit these riches were Joseph Leidy, Edward D. Cope (Fig. 332), Othniel C. Marsh, Henry Fairfield Osborn, and their colleagues. All were able scholars (most opinion puts Cope foremost), and all described quantities of hitherto unknown forms, primarily among Mesozoic reptiles and early Cenozoic mammals, as well as encouraging numerous other students. Theories of the evolution of mammalian teeth, the specialization of limbs and toes in ungulates, and the detailed family trees of modern orders and families come largely from them, although greatly improved by later students.

It would serve no useful purpose to try to evaluate the labors of men still living, for anyone may consult their books and papers. But it is worth emphasizing that the *method of evolution*, as well as its course, is under intense investigation by men who, trained in systematics, genetics, anatomy, or paleontology, see over the boundaries that formerly separated these fields. They are trying, with notable success, to reach agreement on principles, for the documentary groundwork is now pretty well laid.

Origin of the Vertebrates

The question of the origin of vertebrates is also a question of the relationship between Chordata and the invertebrate phyla. We shall present here certain evidence which must be considered, and some of the difficulties in the way, adding that the matter is still obscure.

Now quite generally zoologists lean toward the echinoderms as the nearest relatives of Chordata. Resemblances which have been shown between Chordata and Echinodermata, as probably indicating relationship, include these:

1. The microscopic, ciliated tornaria larva of the acorn worms (Hemichordata) very strikingly resembles the corresponding stage of many echinoderms (Fig. 333).

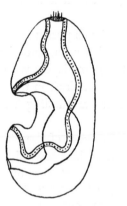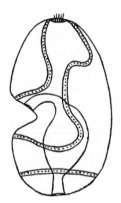

Fig. 333. Resemblance of the tornaria larva of a hemichordate (right) to an echinoid larva (left).

2. The embryos of hemichordates and of Amphioxus produce mesoderm in the form of paired coelomic pouches from the archenteron, just as in echinoderms.

3. The early history of cleavage, gastrulation, and the formation of the anus in the position of the blastopore is essentially the same in the two phyla.

4. Between the most primitive echinoderms (the early Paleozoic carpoids) and the oldest known vertebrates (the ostracoderms, also early Paleozoic) there are surprising similarities (Fig. 334), which of course cannot be found between *modern* echinoderms and *modern* vertebrates.

5. Serological comparisons show a quantitative likeness between the two phyla; such measurements, of course, simply indicate a degree of chemical similarity.

Now merely to enumerate resemblances and differences will get us nowhere unless we see whether they lead us to a possible picture of the
origin of chordates. While the modern echinoderms (see urchins, star-
fishes, sea lilies, and sea cucumbers) are very nearly radial in their
symmetry, the primitive Paleozoic carpoids and cystoids were not. The
cystoids had a flexible stem with ringlike joints and were usually but not
always attached to a surface. Their feeding mechanism was a series of
grooves on the surface of the body which by ciliary action brought microscopic food to the mouth. *Carpoids,* on the other hand, do not show the
food grooves. Each section of the stalk
had two or four plates instead of a
ring; the animals were evidently not
sessile; the stalk and body were distinctly bilateral, and the body was
somewhat flattened above and below,
the plates being different on the two
surfaces. It is probable that they propelled themselves by jerking the
"stalk," like a tail, from side to side.
They may well have lain with the
stalk embedded in mud much of the
time, yet able to bend the body on it.
Some carpoids show clear evidence of
paired muscles entering the expanded

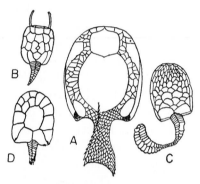

Fig. 334. Resemblance of an early ostracoderm, *Drepanaspis* (A), to several early
carpoid echinoderms (B, C, D). (Redrawn
from Gregory, *Quarterly Review of Biology*,
Williams & Wilkins, Vol. 21 (4), 1946.)

hollow basal part of the stalk from within the body, and in some the stalk
is vertically flattened at the distal end. The dermal armor plates resemble,
both superficially and in microscopic structure, those of certain ostracoderm fishes (Caster and Eaton, 1956), but as yet we know almost nothing of the internal anatomy of carpoids.

It has been our habit to consider the soft protochordates as somehow
primitive types. But with all the immense amount of work which has been
done on them, it is impossible to imagine how any of them gave rise to
an armored primitive fish. The tendency now is to see the process in reverse; the acornworms, tunicates, and Amphioxus are more easily understood as having diverged from the line ancestral to vertebrates, and survived by becoming specialized in their own peculiar ways. And only by
supposing this could a connection between carpoid echinoderms and
ostracoderm fishes be imagined.

DeBeer (1951) has described many instances of a process which he
was among the first to recognize, *pedogenesis,* by which a general retard-
ing of the rate of bodily development in the course of evolution results in

adults of later types showing features of the larvae or young of their ancestors. Thus among Amphibia several species of salamanders fail to complete the usual metamorphosis, but become sexually mature while keeping a larval structure (e.g., *Necturus*). This phenomenon is very widespread in the animal kingdom, and it would seem to fit the problem of the protochordates, for they begin, but fail to complete, many of the structures of vertebrates.

The Enteropneusta, starting out like larval echinoderms, never reach the point of having a stalk or external armor, but become specialized for burrowing instead. The position of Pterobranchia, although they are undeniably related to Enteropneusta, seems ambiguous, for on the one hand they are remarkably simple, sessile, and colonial (which we might expect to be a specialized, degenerate condition), and on the other hand there can be little doubt of their close connection with the extinct graptolites, which are colonial Paleozoic marine animals well established already in the Cambrian period. This could mean (1) that much evolution of early chordates had taken place *before that,* or (2) that animals fitting our present conception of chordates and echinoderms are derived from *more than one line* leading back to forms not definable as either Chordata or echinoderms. The latter possibility seems much more likely.

Amphioxus, developing as a rapid swimmer, fails to put on any armor or produce any hard parts, but takes refuge in the sand, and depends on an elaborate pharyngeal mechanism for feeding. Tunicates, even in their most generalized form, make only a brief, hasty approach to the form of Amphioxus, and then, as it were, change their minds and become sessile, completely making over their bodies to fit the new situation; and this obviously has no connection with the sessile habit of echinoderms.

While we cannot deal here with the matter in enough detail, it will be clear that the approach involves several different methods of study. At every step one must be prepared to meet exacting criticism; for instance, many of those who study modern fishes do not agree that armored ostracoderms really were primitive, but believe there must have been soft-bodied, "normal" types from which the armored ones were derived. This, if true, would push the connections of echinoderms and chordates back beyond reach of any direct evidence, which might, after all, be correct.

Two other theories are that the ancestors of chordates were **annelid worms** (Dohrn, 1875; Minot, 1897), and that they were **arthropods** (Gaskell, 1896; Patten, 1912). A remarkable accumulation of evidence was presented with these views, especially the second one, and on reading Patten's work, at least, a student feels attracted and almost persuaded.

Patten's connecting links were, in arthropods, the arachnids (such as *Limulus*, the horseshoe crab), and, in chordates, the early placoderm fishes, such as *Bothriolepis;* he did not make the recent distinction between placoderms and ostracoderms. Both the annelid and the arthropod theories require a broad assumption which cannot be supported by evidence, namely the inversion of the animal as a whole (Fig. 335). For in those two phyla the central nervous system is ventral (except the brain), and blood is pumped forward on the dorsal side. So if a vertebrate is descended from an arthropod or annelid, it must have turned upside down. Moreover it must have abandoned its old mouth (as well as eyes) and developed a new one, because otherwise the brain would be below

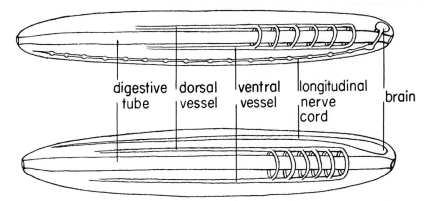

digestive tube | dorsal vessel | ventral vessel | longitudinal nerve cord | brain

Fig. 335. Comparison of the annelid-arthropod body plan (above) with the vertebrate plan (below).

the mouth. These changes were granted by the authors of the theories, but few others are willing to do so, and it is doubtful, with the present knowledge of early fishes, that even they would still hold such a view.

Other groups which perhaps should be mentioned as possible ancestors are *Sagitta* (the arrow worm) and Bryozoa. E. B. Wilson once commented that every invertebrate phylum except the molluscs has been regarded as ancestral to the chordates—"and I think I could make out a case for the molluscs!" The student should not take this to mean that the problem is insoluble, even at the present time, or that it does not need to be solved.

Panorama of the Vertebrates

On the grounds of ignorance, we shall say no more about the first wave of chordate evolution, which established the characters of the phylum, but go on to what looks like a second wave. In the remote ages when no fish swam in the sea, and the dry land was virtually barren, and no insect had ever yet buzzed or crawled, there lived in fresh water early types of jawless armored fishes, the ostracoderms. Their unknown larval stages must have been like those of modern lampreys, feeding on microscopic food by a mechanism of ciliated bands in the mouth and pharynx. To help counteract the tendency of their body fluids to absorb water from outside, these fishes developed a pronephric kidney, which maintained a fairly rapid outflow of water from the coelom.

Evidently, for their time, they had produced a successful "basic patent," for they persisted in four or five orders through the Silurian and Devonian periods, spread into the sea, and made, apparently, more than one experiment with paired fins and speedier locomotion. By the time their wave subsided they must already have given rise to the two parasitic naked orders, Petromyzontia (lampreys) and Myxinoidea (hagfishes), and these lived until today simply because other fishes of more modern type were available to them as prey. Also it is quite evident that during the Silurian period some ostracoderm was able to equip its mouth with jaws and so set in motion a third great wave, based on this new patent.

Again, it is as if nature were experimenting with the earliest gnathostomes, for curious armored forms appeared. Some of the arthrodires were of enormous size and were built quite unlike any other fishes before or since. In one of the Antiarchi, *Bothriolepis,* there is an indication of paired lungs and a spiral valve type of intestine. It seems as if the first step in producing jaws is shown by the little freshwater acanthodians, in which the conversion of a gill arch into an upper and lower jaw had not yet gone far enough to eliminate the gill which it still carried.

By the middle Devonian period, fishes representing the modern classes Chondrichthyes and Osteichthyes had appeared, and seemingly their success spelled the doom of the two major groups that preceded them. Sharks, having made their way down from the fresh water, flourished during the next few million years in the sea, producing many new families and orders. While they came from bony ancestors, their skeletons were considerably reduced and all trace of bone finally was lost. Their ability to meet the new physiological environment of sea water was at least partly due to retention of urea in the blood, to the point where it brought an osmotic balance between the body and the water outside. The Carboniferous seems to have been the golden age of sharks, for since then they have remained a minority among fishes. Two different specialized branches diverged from sharks during the Mesozoic, the rays and the chimaeras, but the latter barely survive today while the former are abundant and varied.

The really progressive vertebrates of the Devonian period were the modern bony fishes, Osteichthyes. One subclass of these, the Actinopteri, took as its fundamental innovation the freely movable fin with jointed fin rays and a thin membrane between. Starting with a scaly armor much like that of acanthodians, they thinned it gradually, made innumerable changes in bodily proportions, and eventually occupied almost every conceivable situation in both fresh and salt water. The whole story of the rise of teleosts and their relatives would take another book to tell, but certainly we should mention the conversion of air-breathing lungs into a hydrostatic swim bladder, the reduction of kidney glomeruli in marine types to conserve water in the body, and the diversity of feeding and reproductive habits, as among the essentials of that history.

Turning to the other subclass, Choanichthyes, we can justly regard it as the forerunner of a fourth great wave of evolution, the terrestrial vertebrates. This was a transformation more important to us than any previous one, for it brought to the animal a new set of characters fitting it to live out of water, breathing air, supporting the weight of the body by its own structure for the first time, and withstanding physical conditions far more rigorous than an aquatic animal is likely to meet. Therefore we need to picture this transformation, which in previous chapters we mentioned only in relation to particular systems, as a whole.

Fossil evidence shows that a freshwater lobefin (crossopterygian) of the late Devonian was in all probability the type from which amphibians arose. Although this lobefin was a fish, with all the equipment it needed for remaining a fish, it already possessed certain features that could be turned to advantage in venturing out of water. One, of course, was a pair of lungs, the common heritage of lobefins, lungfishes, and the primitive ray-fins as well. But this lobefin also had a pair of nostrils, barely raised above the rim of the mouth, so that possibly it was a part-time air breather as an adult, although its gills still bore the brunt of respiration. For leisurely swimming it used the curious appendages that give the name "lobefin" to the group: the paired fins like paddles, having a narrow, bony, muscular base, and broadening out distally to a flat undulating lobe.

Whatever crisis provoked the original attempt to leave the water, we may be sure that only the adults made it, and that the immature stages for a very long time remained aquatic. A life history then was obliged to repeat, each time, the whole sequence of changes that had been accomplished, and to a large degree the modern amphibians still do so. These changes were: loss of gills; reduction of gill-bearing arches and their accompanying muscles and arteries; closing of the external gill openings, with loss of the operculum which covered them; closure of the spiracle (cleft between jaw and hyoid arch), with the very remarkable development of a middle ear in the same location, using the hyomandibular bone now as the stapes for sound transmission; loss of fin membranes and of all the median fins because they were useless out of water; conversion of the basal parts of the paired fins into fore- and hind legs with appropriate digits and joint mechanisms; development of dorsal processes of the pelvis to connect with a pair of sacral ribs in order that the belly should be lifted from the ground during locomotion; reduction of the dermal shoulder girdle so that the head became freely movable; and, finally, the gradual replacement of scales by a glandular, naked skin.

In rivers and lakes of the late Paleozoic era, and around their swampy shores, there lived a diversity of amphibians, some of them apparently reluctant to leave the water at all, others venturing farther away to places from which they might not return even for breeding. These labyrinthodonts were ancestors of reptiles; early in the Pennsylvanian period this break was made. Again a new class, emancipated from certain shortcomings of its forefathers, outweighed the latter in competition for a place in the world, and the last labyrinthodonts died in the Triassic. Only the little, specialized frogs, salamanders, and caecilians remained to hold the amphibian niche.

Producing a reptile (to judge by those still living) required certain fundamental changes, but not as many as took place in the origin of Amphibia. First was the problem of reproduction without going back to water, solved by (1) internal fertilization, using copulatory organs; (2) depositing eggs in the ground, each enclosed in a tough skin which would not easily let water evaporate; (3) provision of a large yolk in the egg, allowing the embryo to develop far beyond the stage corresponding to the amphibian larva, so that when hatched the young reptile was ready for terrestrial life; (4) formation by the embryo of a sac, the amnion, to hold a watery reservoir around its body, and thus free it, during its delicate early stages, from pressures or contacts hampering growth in any direction. From this primitive requirement of a fluid medium no vertebrate has ever wholly escaped.

A scaly epidermis then made it possible for the animal to come and go with little regard for relative humidity. A new type of kidney was introduced, the metanephros, which carried on filtration of fluid from the plasma and its reabsorption into the blood more rapidly than in aquatic animals, leaving a smaller proportion to be lost, and the formation of a urinary bladder (also present in some fishes and Amphibia) permitted control of the release of urine. The effect of temperature, however, could not be directly overcome; the rate of nervous and muscular activity remained high in a warm climate or during warm seasons, but cold brought torpor.

Climate seems not to have stood in the way of the rise of reptile life during the mild Mesozoic ages. Little ones and giants, herbivores and carnivores, soft delicate bodies and armored fortresses, runners, jumpers, swimmers, and fliers, all found opportunity during more than a hundred million years of reptile supremacy.

But, unknown to any of them, two new classes meanwhile came into being, both provided with an answer to the temperature problem, and both with improved brains enabling them to profit a little by experience. Birds had, in addition to this, a spectacular new locomotor mechanism, the feathered wing. They must have been remarkably agile even in the beginning, back in the Jurassic jungles, for they were undoubtedly arboreal reptiles before they were birds. The circulatory system made progress, for the right aortic arch came to be used alone, and the left disappeared, as the heart became four-chambered. In females only the left ovary and oviduct remained. All bones became thin and light, the sacrum stiffened by a fusion of many vertebrae, and the hollow limb bones in most cases received extensions from the air sacs branching out of the lungs. The eyes grew relatively large, and more acute than in any other vertebrates.

With wings, then, and an increasingly effective motor coördination, birds found much of the world free. We know little of the Mesozoic kinds, but enough to show that they did not wait for extinction of the dinosaurs before undertaking their adaptive radiation. Finally they dispensed with teeth and during the Cenozoic era helped themselves to every environmental situation in the world except under ground and in deep water. Thus today they outnumber all classes of vertebrates except the bony fishes.

We may now review, in this setting of the whole vertebrate story, the arrival of mammals, and last consider man's place among them. We find the first mammals already appearing at the end of the Triassic. They remained of minor importance during a full two-thirds of their entire history. The transformation of a line of therapsid reptiles into authentic mammals involved a series of details which we may summarize here:

Already present was the heterodont dentition, the single temporal fossa on each side, the beginning of a hard palate, division of the occipital condyle into two, and elevation of the body off the ground by vertical legs. The lower jaw bones became reduced to a dentary alone as a part of the process of remodeling the middle ear, for when the reptilian *quad-*

rate bone (upper jaw) withdrew from its share in jaw articulation to become the *incus*, the *articular* (lower jaw) came along with it as the *malleus*, and finally the *angular*, just below, got involved in the auditory canal as the *tympanic*. This left the dentary by itself, hinging against the squamosal. The latter, in man and many other mammals, fuses with the bones of the ear capsule to constitute the *temporal* bone. The middle ear now has three sound-transmitting units, the stapes, incus, and malleus.

Soft parts, the evolution of which cannot be traced directly in the fossils, also changed, and their manner of doing so can often be made out in the embryonic stages of mammals. There is no reason to suppose that all mammalian features arose at the same time. The skin became hairy, only gradually losing its scales, and sweat glands began to assist in regulation of temperature. Mammary glands, apparently derived from sweat glands, must have come later, but were, nevertheless, earlier in origin than the viviparous habit, as shown by monotremes. The nasal passages developed folds supported on the turbinal bones, increasing the area of olfactory epithelium.

In a mammal at rest or asleep, one notices little movement of the ribs in breathing, but a considerable movement of the abdominal wall. This is because the principal agent for reducing pressure within the thorax, the diaphragm, pushes down (or back) on the viscera below it, and they in turn press outward on the abdominal wall. Muscles in this wall are therefore indirectly antagonists to the diaphragm, compressing the viscera which in turn thrust the diaphragm upward as it relaxes. This action cannot be carried on effectively in animals whose abdominal walls are confined by ribs. Thus the loss of ribs in the lumbar region must have preceded, or accompanied, the development of a diaphragm and this mammalian mechanism of respiration. But efficient respiration is necessary, in turn, for maintaining a constant high temperature and high metabolic rate; so also is the division of the heart into four chambers, separating the pulmonary from systemic circulation. Probably these interrelated changes in physiology were developed in many experimental patterns during the Mesozoic era, and they need not all have been perfected in any single group at one time.

Remains of Mesozoic mammals are rare and fragmentary. But by the close of the Cretaceous, when dinosaurs disappeared, there were several orders of mammals, including two still living, the marsupials and insectivores. Therefore the reproductive habits of modern mammals must have been initiated by then. Evidently egg-laying monotremes lived somewhere in the world, since they are still with us, but so far none of their fossil progenitors have been found, earlier than the Pleistocene.

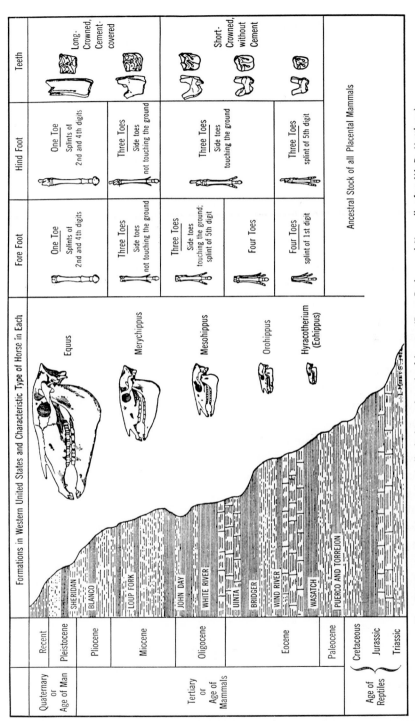

Fig. 336. Progressive changes in skulls, limbs, and teeth of horses. (From Parker and Haswell, after W. D. Matthew.)

Now, just above the Cretaceous rocks, we come to those of the Paleocene, and at once we step into the age of mammals. From then on, order after order appears, and they deploy into all available habitats. We select from among them, as we could from any large group of animals, illustrations of two or three principles not mentioned specifically before.

1. Comparing the structure of a full series of horses, from the little Eocene "dawn horse," (*Eohippus,* or *Hyracotherium*) to the modern *Equus* (horses, donkeys, zebras), one is at first impressed with the *regularity* of their change of proportions (Fig. 336). Three principal modifications keep step with each other: the increase of total size, the gradual reduction in number of toes (*Eohippus,* four in front and three behind; *Equus,* one), and the development of complex enamel ridges on the molar teeth. This apparent straight-line evolution has been called **orthogenesis;** Osborn and others have supposed that it indicates a continuous uncontrollable change in the genetic make-up of the animals, leading in some cases (as titanotheres) to a maladjustment that brought about extinction. Actually the appearance of steady, straight progress is false, for with increasing study of horses it has been shown that (1) numerous side branches were produced in the family tree, with specializations of their own, and (2) there were recessions, delays, and deviations in the evolution of each of the progressing characters. It is clear now that natural selection, under the circumstances in which animals are living, and not a mysterious inherent force, accounts for this and other examples of "orthogenesis."

2. With a great number of different families and orders going their own ways, fitting into new situations from time to time, it often happened that similar adaptations arose independently. If two or more lines go through a corresponding series of changes, arriving at quite similar results, this is called **parallelism;** for instance, the history of camels has been much like that of horses, and even more so has the history of the litopterns, an extinct South American group which became one-toed. If from very different ancestors nearly identical forms evolve, we call it **convergence;** e.g., the true moles (Insectivora), the marsupial "mole," and certain molelike rodents.

Man Among Mammals

In this concluding section we shall try to picture the origin of man, for one of the prime values of comparative anatomy is to give a modern perspective of man as a part of nature. The order Primates arose from insectivores in the Paleocene epoch, some 60 million years ago. Indeed, one of the foremost students of mammals (Simpson, 1945) considers the "tree shrews," previously called Insectivores, to be Primates. Within this order the basic habit is tree-climbing, and therefore the distinctive structural and functional characteristics of Primates are associated, directly or otherwise, with arboreal life. The grasping form of hands and feet, the flat nails instead of claws, the binocular vision, the enlargement of the brain, all probably contributed to arboreal adaptation.

Apes (family Pongidae) and man (Hominidae) come next to the Old World monkeys (Cercopithecidae) in the zoological scheme. Modern apes certainly stand closer to man in their structure than do any other living animals, but they do not represent exactly the form which gave rise to man in the early Pliocene or Miocene. It is fairly certain that the human line diverged at least as long ago as that. Among the known fossil apes of that age, none are as large as either the modern apes or man, but their tooth and skull characters are distinctly more manlike than are those of gorilla, chimpanzee, orang, or gibbon. Evidently the latter have diverged strongly in one direction, man in another. *Oreopithecus*, of the lowest Pliocene in Europe, may be a Hominid.

The adaptive emphasis among apes was toward increasing length of arms and agility in "brachiating" (swinging by the hands from branch to branch) through an unbroken and permanent forest. Therefore the legs are relatively short and of little use for an upright posture. The massive, prominent jaws, sagittal crest of the skull, and heavy supraorbital ridges of adult apes are not seen to the same degree among Miocene and Pliocene types.

The emphasis among human ancestors (at that time) must have been upon erect locomotion, on the ground. In all known Hominidae the legs are relatively long and powerful, the great toe aligned with the others, the heel prominent for leverage, and the arms only moderately good for acrobatics. This suggests that earliest man was adapted for open country, not forest.

Direct evidence of prehistoric man shows that he has lived in the Old World throughout the Pleistocene (a million years) but that he did not become established in the Western hemisphere until some time during or just after the last glacial age, roughly 20 to 30 thousand years ago. Further, there are no indications of apes or Cercopithecoid monkeys of any kind in the western hemisphere. But from Europe, Asia, and Africa we possess partial or complete skeletal remains of a number of kinds of men different from any living now. Indirect evidence of man in the Pliocene epoch, more than a million years ago, has been found in the form of primitive implements of stone and deer horn near Ipswich, England, beneath layers of fossils of known Pliocene age.

All men living today are of the genus *Homo*, species *sapiens*. In order to make comparison with the extinct kinds we must use characters regarding which the fossils will give some evidence, such as the bones and teeth, but we cannot compare skin color, hair, voice, language, etc., since the fossils do not preserve these. In *Homo sapiens*, then, the face is nearly vertical in profile, with a forehead that stands upright for some distance above the eyes, and there are but slight thickenings of the bone at the eyebrow level, or none at all. The nose has a distinct bridge, so that it stands out from the face. The teeth do not project forward on extended margins of the jaw bones but stand vertically, within the contour of the face. The chin makes a right angle or a prominence, as seen in side view. Finally, the skull is smoothly rounded in upper and posterior parts, almost a globe, and rests with easy balance on the atlas vertebra of the neck. This is because the center of gravity of the head is but little in front of the two occipital condyles. The volume of the brain (essentially the same as **cranial capacity**) averages about 1400 cubic centimeters, with normal extremes of roughly 1100 and 2200 cc., between which we have no evidence that intelligence of an individual varies with the size of the brain. Correlated with the erect head is the double curvature of the vertebral column (convex at the thorax and pelvis, concave at the neck and lower back), and the nearly straight shaft of the femur.

Tentatively it seems reasonable to recognize two subfamilies of Hominidae (Robinson, 1953), in one of which, Homininae, we place *Homo*, *Pithecanthropus*, and the inadequately known *Telanthropus;* the other, Australopithecinae, will serve for the remarkable South African finds of recent years, *Australopithecus* and *Paranthropus*. Regarding two or three more types which have been named, no definite allocation can be made for want of sufficient material.

It is clear now that our own species has lived through the last glacial age (there were four of these in the Pleistocene) and a major part, at least, of the long third interglacial age preceding it. Included in *Homo sapiens* are the famous cave-dwelling artists of southern Europe, the Cro-Magnon men, who left relics of their culture during the last part of the glacial period and a few thousand years thereafter. These men were taller than the average European of today, with a slightly larger cranial capacity. But long before their time, and for probably not less than 150 thousand years, men with skulls much like our own have lived in Europe, as shown by discoveries in the cave of Fontéchèvade in France.

In the meantime, however, throughout most of this long, little-known history, another type also dwelt in Europe and a part of Asia, the Neanderthal man. He lacked the double spinal curvature, and his neck hung forward, the condyles of the skull being a little farther back than ours; his face sloped, his forehead was low but overhung by bulging eyebrow ridges, and he lacked a chin (Figs. 62, 337C). The average height was not much over 5 feet. Although the cranial capacity had reached that of modern man, the frontal lobes of the brain were smaller, and the wall of the cranium thicker. Without further information we would suppose that the Neanderthal was a different and more primitive species, but there is no evidence that he was older than *H. sapiens,* and in caves of Mt. Carmel in Palestine there have been found skeletons of individuals showing various intermediate characteristics, yet by no means as old as some of the remains elsewhere. It is certain, then, that interbreeding occurred, and it is thought by some anthropologists that the Neanderthal type was a divergent race rather than a separate species.

Heidelberg man, from either the first or the second interglacial age, is known only from a massive lower jaw found in a gravel pit in Germany, sufficiently distinct to warrant a specific name, *H. heidelbergensis.* Other probable species of *Homo* include *soloensis* from Java and *rhodesiensis* from Africa, similar in some ways to the Neanderthal race. It was shown in 1953 that the so-called "Piltdown man" of Sussex, England, was not authentic but a fake.

In 1894 Eugene DuBois discovered human fragments, including a calvarium (skullcap), jaw, and part of a thighbone, in early Pleistocene gravel along a riverbank in Java, which he named *Pithecanthropus erectus* ("upright ape-man"). Further intensive work, especially by von Koenigswald, has unearthed other pieces to which the name *P. robustus* has been applied, although it is not impossible that all belong to one species. There is no doubt that *Pithecanthropus* (Fig. 337B) was human, but extremely primitive, with a cranial capacity of about 835 to 940 cc. The eyebrow ridges were particularly prominent, the face sloping, and the canine teeth, at least in the male, projected slightly beyond the others.

Peking man, originally named *Sinanthropus pekingensis* by Davidson Black, is now well known from the bones of both young and adults found in middle Pleistocene cave deposits a few miles from Peking (Peiping), China. The brain was somewhat larger than that of the Java man, varying from a little over 900 to about 1200 cc., but other characteristics were so nearly the same that a separate genus cannot be sustained, and it is now called *P. pekingensis.*

Widely publicized in recent years are two other important discoveries by von Koenigswald, represented by fragments only, of primitive giant men of the early Pleistocene. *Gigantopithecus blacki* is based on some molar teeth from an apothecary's shop in southeast China, supplemented very recently by other pieces from a cave, and *Meganthropus paleojavanicus* on a bit of a jaw with teeth, from Java. (This oriental island looks like the happy hunting ground for anthropologists.) If the rest of the bodies of these creatures were as large, porportionally, as the teeth, they stood at least 10 feet high. But this is not necessarily the case, since the

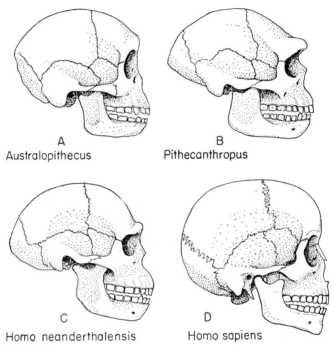

A
Australopithecus

B
Pithecanthropus

C
Homo neanderthalensis

D
Homo sapiens

Fig. 337. Skulls of (A, B, C) early, and (D) modern man.

jaws and teeth may well have been much exaggerated in mechanical adaptation. There is no doubt, however, that these were men and that they were large.

South Africa has given us several remarkable forms of apelike men. Two genera and species can be distinguished with assurance, *Australopithecus africanus* (Fig. 337A, a child's skull) and *Paranthropus robustus*, both known from many specimens, and both separated (Robinson, 1953) into races. While definitely human in tooth characters, they show apelike faces (depressed nasal region, massive jaws, and, in the adults of *P. r. crassidens*, a sagittal crest, not known in any other kind of man). The cranial capacity was intermediate between that of the larger apes and modern man, ranging from about 500 to over 1000 cc. The skeletons show that they were upright and entirely human in body and limbs. The greatest difficulty in their interpretation is the question of age. We know that they are old, but whether middle or early Pleistocene, or even Pliocene (as Robert Broom, discoverer of most of these, believed), is uncertain, since there is no clear correlation between South African cave deposits and those of Europe. It is entirely possible that they stand near the line of human descent, and that when the picture becomes more complete we shall see just such a mixture of progressive and primitive features in our remote ancestry.

Obviously the history of fossil men cannot yet be expressed in correct sequence, but it has involved growth of the forebrain, increasing height of the forehead and corresponding reduction of the supraorbital ridges, shortening of the jaws and tooth rows so that the facial profile becomes steeper and the chin more prominent, and a balancing of the rounded skull more nearly upon its center of gravity. The modern average cranial capacity was reached more than a hundred thousand years ago.

On comparing adult skulls with those of children and infants, especially in such types as *Australopithecus,* it seems probable that the round cranium, vertical face and reduced jaws can be explained as a consequence of the delay of individual development in human beings; with these we can include the scantiness of hair and the relatively immense brain. It takes a man far longer to reach maturity than any other animal, even whales and elephants. The physical features just mentioned can be found in a fetal ape. By drawing them out through a prolonged period of infancy, a human being has time to learn immensely more than any animal on earth, and his brain continues its functional development much longer. It is as if the human line finally attained the advantages of superior intelligence by sacrificing those of early maturity, early reproduction, and early physical vigor, which mean life or death to other species.

Bibliography

Comprehensive Modern Books Pertaining to Comparative Anatomy

Adams, L. A., and Eddy, Samuel, *Comparative Anatomy. An Introduction to the Vertebrates*, John Wiley & Sons, 2nd ed., 1949.

Arey, L. B., *Developmental Anatomy*, P. Blakiston's Son & Co., 6th ed., 1954.

Bolk, L., *et al*, *Handbuch der vergleichende Anatomie der Wirbeltiere*, Berlin, Vienna, 1931–1938, 6 vols.

DeBeer, G. R., *Embryos and Ancestors*, Oxford, Clarendon Press, 2nd ed., 1951.

Colbert, E. H., *Evolution of the Vertebrates*, John Wiley & Sons, Inc., 1955.

Goodrich, E. H., *Studies on the Structure and Development of Vertebrates*, The Macmillan Company, 1930.

Grassé, Pierre-P. (Ed.), *Traité de Zoologie*, Tome XI, *Echinodermes, Prochordés*, 1948; Tome XII, *Vertébrés*, 1954; Tome XV, *Oiseaux*, 1950; Tome XVII, *Mammiféres*, 1955; Masson et Cie, Paris.

Gregory, W. K., *Evolution Emerging*, The Macmillan Company, 1951.

Hyman, L. H., *Comparative Vertebrate Anatomy*, University of Chicago Press, 1942.

Kendall, James I., *Microscopic Anatomy of Vertebrates*, Lea & Febiger, 3rd ed., 1947.

Kerr, J. G., *Textbook of Embryology*, Vol. II, *Vertebrata with the Exception of Mammals*, The Macmillan Company, 1919.

Kingsley, J. S., *Outlines of Comparative Anatomy of Vertebrates*, P. Blakiston's Son & Co., 3rd ed., 1926.

Lull, R. S., *Organic Evolution*, The Macmillan Company, rev. ed., 1948.

Maximow, A., and Bloom, W., *A Textbook of Histology*, W. B. Saunders Co., 6th ed., 1952.

Neal, H. V., and Rand, H. W., *Comparative Anatomy*, P. Blakiston's Son & Co., 1936.

Nelsen, O. E., *Comparative Embryology of the Vertebrates*, P. Blakiston's Son & Co., 1953.

Newman, H. H., *The Phylum Chordata*, The Macmillan Company, 1939.

Nordenskiöld, E., *The History of Biology*, Tudor Publishing Co., 1935.

Parker, T. J. and Haswell, W. A., *A Textbook of Zoology*, Vol. II, The Macmillan Company, 6th ed., 1940.

Quiring, Daniel P., *Functional Anatomy of the Vertebrates*, The McGraw-Hill Book Co., 1950.

Romer, Alfred S., *Vertebrate Paleontology*, University of Chicago Press, 2nd ed., 1945.

Romer, Alfred S., *The Vertebrate Body*, W. B. Saunders Co., 2nd ed., 1955.

Sisson, S., and Grossman, J. D., *The Anatomy of the Domestic Animals*, W. B. Saunders Co., 3rd ed., rev., 1943.

Spemann, Hans, *Embryonic Development and Induction*, Yale University Press, 1938.

Weichert, C. K. *Anatomy of the Chordates*, The McGraw-Hill Book Co., 1951.

Young, J. Z., *The Life of Vertebrates*, Oxford, Clarendon Press, 1950.

Zittel, Karl A. von, *Text-book of Palaeontology*, Vol. II, 2nd English ed., The Macmillan Company, 1932.

Older Books and Papers Cited in Text

Dohrn, Anton, *Der Ursprung der Wirbelthiere*, Leipzig, W. Engelmann, 1875.

Gaskell, W. H., "The Origin of Vertebrates," *Proceedings of the Cambridge Philosophical Society*, Vol. 9, pp. 19 ff., 1896.

Goodrich, E. S., *Vertebrata Craniata. First Fascicle. Cyclostomes and Fishes*. Part IX of E. R. Lancester (ed.), *A Treatise on Zoology*, A. and C. Black, 1909.

Huxley, T. H., "Classification of Birds," *Proceedings of the Zoological Society of London*, 1867.

Minot, C. S., "Cephalic Homologies: a Contribution to the Determination of the Ancestry of Vertebrates," *American Naturalist*, Vol. 31, pp. 927 ff., 1897.

Patten, William, *The Evolution of the Vertebrates and Their Kin*, P. Blakiston's Son & Co., 1912.

Important Sources in Limited Fields

Berg, Leo S., *Classification of Fishes both Recent and Fossil*, Edwards Bros., Ann Arbor, Michigan, 1947.

Chusid, J. G., and J. J. McDonald, *Correlative Neuroanatomy and Functional Neurology*, Lange Medical Publications, 8th ed., 1956.

Clark, W. E. LeGros, *The Fossil Evidence for Human Evolution*, University of Chicago Press, 1955.

Cott, Hugh B., *Adaptive Coloration in Animals*, The Macmillan Company, 1940.

Daniel, J. Frank, *The Elasmobranch Fishes*, University of California Press, 3rd ed., 1934.

Davison, A., and Stromsten, F. A., *Mammalian Anatomy, with Special Reference to the Cat*, P. Blakiston's Son & Co., 7th ed., 1947.

DeBeer, G. R., *The Development of the Vertebrate Skull*, Oxford University Press, 1937.

Francis, E. T. B., *The Anatomy of the Salamander*, Oxford University Press, 1934.

Greene, E. C., "Anatomy of the Rat," *Transactions American Philosophical Society* (N.S.), Vol. 27, pp. 1 ff., 1935.

Gregory, W. K., "Fish Skulls: a Study of the Evolution of Natural Mechanisms," *Transactions American Philosophical Society*, Vol. 23, pp. 75 ff., 1933.

Hartman, C. G., and Straus, W. L., Jr., *The Anatomy of the Rhesus Monkey*, Williams & Wilkins Co., 1933.

Howell, A. B., *Anatomy of the Wood Rat*, Williams & Wilkins Co., 1926.

Jordan, D. S., *Fishes*, D. Appleton Co., 1925.

Moy-Thomas, J. A., *Palaeozoic Fishes*, Chemical Publishing Co., 1939.

Noble, G. K., *Biology of the Amphibia*, The McGraw-Hill Book Co., 1931. (Republished by Dover Publications, Inc., 1954.)

Norman, J. R., *A History of Fishes*, A. A. Wyn, Inc., 1951.

Reighard, J. E., and Jennings, H. S., *Anatomy of the Cat*, Henry Holt & Co., 3rd ed., 1935.

Romer, Alfred S., *Osteology of the Reptiles*, University of Chicago Press, 1956.

Scott, W. B., *A History of Land Mammals in the Western Hemisphere*, The Macmillan Company, 2nd ed., 1937.

Simpson, G. G., *The Principles of Classification and a Classification of Mammals*, Bulletin American Museum of Natural History, Vol. 85, 1945.

Simpson, G. G., *Horses*, Oxford University Press, 1951.

Smith, Hobart M., *Handbook of Lizards*, Comstock, 1946.

Smith, Homer W., *Physiology of the Kidney*, Oxford University Press, 1937.

Stensiö, E. A., *The Downtonian and Devonian Vertebrates of Spitzbergen. I. Family Cephalaspidae*, Skrifter om Svalbard og Nordishavet, No. 12, 1927.

Walls, Gordon L., *The Vertebrate Eye and its Adaptive Radiation*, Cranbrook Institute of Science, Bulletin 19, 1942.

Watson, D. M. S., "The Evolution and Origin of the Amphibia," *Philosophical Transactions of the Royal Society*, B., Vol. 214, 1926.

Watson, D. M. S., "The Acanthodian Fishes," *Philosophical Transactions of the Royal Society*, B, Vol. 228, 1937.

Watson, D. M. S., and Romer, A. S., "A Classification of Therapsid Reptiles," *Bulletin Museum Comparative Zoology*, Vol. 114, 35–89, 1956.

Weber, M., and others, *Die Säugethiere*, Jena, 2 vols., 2nd ed., 1927–1928.

Special Studies and Short Papers

Atz, James W., "Narial Breathing in Fishes and the Evolution of Internal Nares," *Quarterly Review of Biology*, Vol. 27(4); 1952, pp. 366 ff.

Barrington, E. J. W., "Observations on Feeding and Digestion of Glossobalanus minutus," *Quarterly Journal of Microscopical Science*, Vol. 82, 1940, pp. 227 ff.

Bellairs, A. d'A., and G. Underwood, "The Origin of Snakes," *Biological Reviews*, Vol. 26, 1951, pp. 193 ff.

DeBeer, G. R., and Moy-Thomas, J. A., "On the Skull of Holocephali," *Philosophical Transactions of the Royal Society*, B, Vol. 224, 1952, pp. 287 ff.

Caster, Kenneth E., and T. H. Eaton, Jr., "Microstructure of the Plates in the Carpoid Echinoderm Paranacystis," *Journal of Paleontology*, Vol. 30, 1956, pp. 611–614.

Denison, R. H., "The Soft Anatomy of Bothriolepis," *Journal of Paleontology*, Vol. 15(5), 1941, pp. 553 ff.

Eaton, T. H., Jr., "Skeletal Supports of the Median Fins of Fishes," *Journal of Morphology*, Vol. 76(3), 1945, pp. 193 ff.

Eaton, T. H., Jr., "Origin of Tetrapod Limbs," *American Midland Naturalist*, Vol. 46, 1951, pp. 245 ff.

Eaton, T. H., Jr., "Pedomorphosis, an Approach to the Chordate-Echinoderm Problem," *Systematic Zoology*, Vol. 2, 1953, pp. 1 ff.

Edinger, T., "Evolution of the Horse Brain," *Geological Society of America Memoir 25*, 1948.

Edinger, T., "Paleoneurology versus Comparative Brain Anatomy," *Confinia Neurologica*, Vol. 9, 1949, pp. 5–24.

Evans, F. Gaynor, "The Morphology and Functional Evolution of the Atlas-axis Complex from Fish to Man," *Annals New York Academy of Science*, Vol. 39(2), 1939, pp. 29 ff.

Fraser, E. A., "The Development of the Vertebrate Excretory System," *Biological Reviews*, Vol. 25, 1950, pp. 159 ff.

Gregory, W. K., and Raven, H. C., "Studies on the Origin and Early Evolution of Paired Fins and Limbs," *Annals New York Academy of Science*, Vol. 42(3), 1941, pp. 273 ff.

Jarvik, E., "On the Fish-like Tail in the Ichthyostegid Stegocephalians," *Meddelelser om Grønland*, Vol. 114(12), 1952, pp. 1 ff.

Jarvik, E., "The Oldest Tetrapods and Their Forerunners," *Scientific Monthly*, Vol. 80, 1955, pp. 141 ff.

Jones, F. R. H., and Marshall, N. B., "The Structure and Functions of the Teleostean Swimbladder," *Biological Reviews*, Vol. 28, 1953, pp. 16 ff.

Kozlowsky, R., "Les affinités des Graptolithes," *Biological Reviews*, Vol. 22, 1947, pp. 93–108.

Leach, W. J., "The Archetypal Position of Amphioxus and Ammocoetes and the Role of the Endocrines in Evolution," *American Naturalist*, Vol. 78, 1944.

Reynolds, T. E., "Hydrostatics of the Suctorial Mouth of the Lamprey," *University of California Publications in Zoology*, Vol. 37, 1931, pp. 15 ff.

Robinson, J. T. "The Genera and Species of the Australopithecinae," *American Journal of Physical Anthropology*, Vol. 12, 1953, pp. 181–200.

Romer, Alfred S., "The Braincase of the Carboniferous Crossopterygian Megalichthys nitidus," *Bulletin Museum Comparative Zoology*, Vol. 82, 1937, pp. 1 ff.

Romer, Alfred S., "Cartilage an Embryonic Adaptation," *American Naturalist*, Vol. 76, 1942.

Romer, Alfred S., "Notes on Certain American Paleozoic Fishes," *American Journal of Science*, Vol. 240, 1942, pp. 216 ff.

Romer, Alfred S., "The Development of Tetrapod Limb Musculature—the Thigh of Lacerta," *Journal of Morphology*, Vol. 71, 1942, pp. 251 ff.

Romer, Alfred S., "The Development of Tetrapod Limb Musculature. The Shoulder Region of Lacerta," *Journal of Morphology*, Vol. 74, 1944, pp. 1 ff.

Romer, Alfred S., and Witter, Robert V., "Edops, a Primitive Rhachitomous Amphibian from the Texas Red Beds," *Journal of Geology*, Vol. 50, 1942, pp. 925 ff.

Sawin, H. J., "The Cranial Anatomy of Eryops megacephalus," *Bulletin Museum Comparative Zoology*, Vol. 88, 1941, pp. 407 ff.

Schaeffer, Bobb, "Evolution of the Tarsus in Amphibians and Reptiles," *Bulletin American Museum Natural History*, Vol. 78, 1941, pp. 395 ff.

Straus, W. L., "The Riddle of Man's Ancestry," *Quarterly Review of Biology*, Vol. 24, 1949, pp. 200 ff.

Westoll, T. S., "The Origin of the Tetrapods," *Biological Reviews*, Vol. 18, 1943, pp. 78 ff.

Westoll, T. S., "The Origin of the Primitive Tetrapod Limb," *Proceedings Royal Society London*, B, Vol. 131, 1943, pp. 373 ff.

Zangerl, R., "Contributions to the Osteology of the Skull of the Amphisbaenidae," *American Midland Naturalist*, Vol. 31, 1944, pp. 417 ff.

Biological Abstracts and the *Zoological Record* are periodical compilations of references and abstracts of the current literature indispensable for the student doing original work; they are arranged in convenient systematic order.

Index

Italicized page numbers mean that the item is illustrated on the page, although not necessarily labeled in every case.

Abdominal muscles, 187
Abdominal ribs, 156–157
Abducens nerve, *320, 321,* 324
Abomasum, *215*
Acanthodii (Acanthodian), 3, *15, 160,* 344
  fins, 159, *160*
Acetylcholine, 308, 330
Acinous glands, *83*
Acipenser sturio, *18*
Acrania, *see* Cephalochorda
Acrodont tooth attachment, *102,* 104
Actinopteri, 4, *17–20,* 345
  axial skeleton and fin supports, *162*
  characters, 17
  fin rays, *100, 162,* 163
  members, 17 ff.
  vertebrae, *144–146*
Adipose tissue, 76
Adrenalin, 284, 330
Adventitia of arteries, *231*
Agkistrodon mokasen, *25*
Aglossa, absence of tongue in, 210
Agnatha, 3
  defined, 13
Agranulocytes, 77
Air bladder, in fish, 219–222
  relationship to lungs, *220, 222*
Air sacs, in birds, *222, 223*
  in chameleons, 223
  in frogs, 222, *223*
Albula, fins, *167*
Allantois, 69, *70, 72*
Alligator, American, *27*
  lizard, *see* Gerrhonotus

Alligator—(*Continued*)
  mississippiensis, *27*
  pelvis, *178*
  skull, *133*
Allotheria, 5
Alveolar glands, *83*
Ambystoma punctatum, skull, *129*
Ameloblast, *101,* 102
Amia, 18, 19
  female reproductive and excretory system, *272*
  scales, *98*
  spiracle, 120
  vertebrae, 145
Ammocoetes, 14
  and thyroid gland, 203, *204*
  transformation, 203, 204
Ammodytes, pyloric cecum, 207
Amnion, 69, *70*
  cavity, 69, *70,* 71
Amniota, defined, 69
  development, *69–73*
Amniotic fluid, 69
Amphibia, 4, 22, 246
  characters of, 23, 24
  limbs, 168–170
  members, 22–24
  skull, 125–130
Amphioxus, *see* Branchiostoma
Amphistylic jaw suspension, *118*
Amphitherium prevostii, jaw and teeth, *107*
Amphiuma, erythrocytes, 78
  limbs, 170

Ampullae of Lorenzini, *294*
  of semicircular canals, 295, *296*
Analogy, 338
Anapsida, 4
  type of skull, 132
Anaspida, 3
Anatomy, comparative, history of, 332–339
Angelichthys, fins, *161*
Angler fish, *see* Lophius americanus
Anguilla, fins, *161*
Ankylosauria, 30
Annelid theory, 342, 343
Anolis, male throat fan, *279*
  nerves, cranial, *321*
Anseriformes, 5
Anteater, great, *47*
  spiny, *36*, 37, 84
Anthropoidea, 5
  members, *42*, *43*, 44
Antiarchi, 3, 15, 162, 344
Antlers, 95, *96*
Anura, 4, 23, *24*
        See also Salientia; Frogs: Toads
Anus, in fishes, 209, *210*
  in Urochorda, 12
Aorta, dorsal, *239*, *240*, *241*
  left, *241*, 242
  right, *241*, 242
  ventral, 239, 240
Aortic arches, *239*, *240*, *241*
Apes, 6, *42*, *43*, 351
Aphetohyoidea, *see* Placodermi
Apoda, 4, 23
        See also Caecilia
Appendicular skeleton, 114
Appendix, 216
Apsidospondyli, 4
Apteria, *91*
Apteryx, olfactory organ, 291
  pelvis, *178*
Arachnoid, 309
Arbor vitae, *316*, 317
Arch-elements, *142*
Archenteron, frog embryo, 60, *61*
Archeopteryx, *32*, 33, 90
  vertebrae and ribs, 152, 153
Archeornis, 33
Archeornithes, 4
  defined, 33
Archeria, vertebra, *174*
Archipterygial fin, 166, *167*, 338
Archosargus, fins, *167*
Archosauria, 4
Arciferous pectoral girdle, *156*, 175
Arcualia, *142*
Aristotle, *333*, *334*, 336
Armadillo, 46, 97

Armor, dermal, *97–100*
  special types, *95–97*
Arterioles, 231
Artery (ies), *231*, *232*, 239 ff.
  branchial, *239–241*
  carotid, 233, *236*, *237*, *240*, 242
  celiac, 243
  mesenteric, 243
  omphalomesenteric, 243
  pulmonary, *241*, *243*
  umbilical, *243*
  vitelline, 243
Arthrodira, 3, 15, *117*, 344
Arthropod theory, 332, 333
Articular bone in relation to malleus, 299
Artiodactyla, 6, *48*, *49*, 50
Ascaphus, pectoral girdle, *156*
  tail (extension of cloaca), *266*
  vertebra, *111*
Ascidian, *see* Urochorda
Astroscopus, internal nares, 190
Asymmetron, 9, 10
Ateles ater, *42*
Atlas vertebra, 149, *150*
Atriopore, Branchiostoma, 9, 10, 203
  Urochorda, *11*, 203
Atrium, Branchiostoma, 9, 10, 203
  heart, 233 ff.
  Urochorda, *11*, 203
Auditory nerve, *321*, *323*, 325
Auricle, 233 ff.
Australopithecus, 352, 355
  africanus, skull, *354*
Autodiastylic jaw suspension, 117, *118*
Autonomic nervous system, 327–331
Autostylic jaw suspension, *118*, 123, 129
Aves, 4, *32* ff.
        See also Birds
Axial bones in fins and limbs, *167*, *168*
Axial skeleton, 114
Axis vertebra, 149, *150*
Axolotl, 55
Axon, 75, *307*

Baboon, *42*, 43
Baculum, 268
Baer, K. E. von, 54
Balaeniceps rex, *34*
Balanoglossus, 6, 7, 9, 202
  pharynx, 202, 203
Barb of feather, 91, *92*, 94
Barbules of feather, 91, *92*
Basal (pterygiophore), 163, *164*
Basidorsal, *142*
Basiventral, *142*
Bat, 5
  fruit, *40*
  wing skeleton, *171*

Batoidei, 3
    See also Ray; Raja
Bdellostoma, *13*
Beaks, *87,* 88
Beavers, 6
Bee-eaters, 5
Bichat, 337
Bicornuate uterus, 276
Bidder's organ, 273
Biogenetic law, 54, 339
Bipartite uterus, *276*
Birds, 4, 32 ff., 347
    leg and foot skeleton, 172, *173*
    skull, *135, 136*
    wing skeleton, *171*
Black, Davidson, 353
Bladder, air, *see* Air bladder
    gall, *see* Gall bladder
    urinary, *201,* 259, *260*
Blastocyst, *71*
Blastomeres, frog, 59
Blastopore, Branchiostoma, 66, *67*
    frog, *60*
Blastula, Branchiostoma, *67*
    frog, *60*
Blood, 229 ff.
Bluejay, *35*
Body stalk, *72*
Bone, cancellous, 112
    cartilage, *114*
    compact, 112
    dermal, *114*
    membrane, *114*
    replacing, *114*
    sesamoid, 113
    structure of, 77, 112, *113*
    types, 112, 113
Bonnet, 335, 337
Bothriolepis, 343, 344
    lungs, 220
    spiral valve, 208
Bowfin, *see* Amia
Bowman's capsule, 255
Brachiosaurus, 29
Brachyodont teeth, 109
Brain, Amphibia, *312,* 313
    birds, 313, *314*
    Cyclostomata, 310, *311*
    development, 309, *310*
    fishes, *311,* 312
    flexures, *314*
    mammals, *315–317*
    reptiles, *312,* 313
    Urochorda, 12, 308
    vertebrates, 12, 309–317
Branchiomeric muscles, *184,* 195–199
Branchiostoma, 3, 9, 10
    circulatory system, 230
    coelomic pouches, 67, 225

Branchiostoma—(*Continued*)
    development, *66–69*
    gonads, 254
    larva, *68*
    metapleural folds, 159, *160*
    muscles, 185
    nephridium, *254*
    pharynx, 202
    preoral pit, 284
    relationships, 341
Bronchi, *223,* 224
Bronchioles, 224
Brontosaurus, 29
Broom, Robert, 355
Bryozoa, 343
Buffon, 335
Bufo americanus, skull, *129*
Bulbus cordis, 234
Bunodont teeth, *107,* 108
Bursa omentalis, 227
Buteo, eye, 303
Buzzard, beak, *87*
    stomach, *212*

Caecilia (order), 4, 23
    C. pachynema, *23*
    skull, *128*
Calamoichthys, 18
Camper, 336
Campostoma, intestine, 209
Canal, auditory, external, *296,* 298
    Haversian, *113*
    hyoid (preopercular), *292*
    infraorbital, *292*
    lateral line, *292–294*
    mandibular, *292,* 294
    neurenteric, 308; Branchiostoma, 66,
        67
    occipital (supratemporal), *292,* 294
    postorbital, 294
    temporal, 294
    vertebrarterial, 150, 153
Canaliculi, in bone, 77, 112, *113*
Cancellae, 112, 140
Canine teeth, *102, 106*
Capillaries, 230, *231*
Capitulum, 155
Caprimulgiformes, 5
Capsule, Bowman's, 255
    nasal (olfactory), *114, 115,* 116
    optic, 114
    otic (auditory), 114, *115, 116,* 295
    renal, *see* Bowman's
Cardiac cycle, 238
Cardiac endothelial cells, frog embryo,
    64
Cardiac muscle, 76, *181*
Caretta caretta, 26
Caribou, Newfoundland, *49*

Carnassial teeth, 107
Carnivora, 6
 kinds of, 44, 45
Carp, Weberian ossicles, 224
Carpal bones, origin, 168, 169
Carpoid echinoderms, 340, 341
Cartilage bone, 114
Cartilage, calcified, 77, 112
 elastic, 77, 112
 fibrous, 77, 111, 112
 hyaline, 77, 111
 structure of, 77, 111
 types, 77
Caturus furcatus, vertebrae, 144
Cauda equina, 317
Caudal fin, 157, 158
Caudata, 4
 inner ear, 296
 pelvis, 178
 skull, 128, 129, 130
 spermatophores, 266
 tongue, 210
  See also Urodela
Cebidae, 42, 43
Ceboidea, 5, 42, 43
Cecum, pyloric, in fishes, 207
Cecum, in mammals, 216
 in reptiles, 211
Cement, 102
Centrum, amphicoelous, 144, 145, 153
 amphiplatyan, 145, 152
 birds, 152, 153
 chordal, 143
 cyclospondylous, 144
 Elasmobranch fishes, 143, 144
 heterocoelous, 145, 153
 mammals, 153, 154
 opisthocoelous, 145
 perichordal, 144, 145
 procoelous, 145
 reptiles, 149–152
 shapes of, 145
 tetrapods, 147–154
Cephalaspidomorphi, 3
Cephalaspis, 14
 brain, 311
 skull, 115
Cephalochorda, 3, 9
  See also Branchiostoma
Cephalodiscus, 3, 8, 254
Ceratopsia, 30, 31
Ceratotrichia, 100, 163
Cercopithecoidea, 5, 42, 43
Cerebellum, 310
 embryo, 64
Cerebral hemispheres, embryo, 64
Cetacea, 6, 44, 45, 46, 84
Chalicothere, 89

Chamber (of eye), anterior, 300, 303
 posterior, 300, 303
Charadriiformes, 5
Cheirolepis trailli, skull, 120
Chelidosaurus, vertebra, 142
Chelonia, 4, 26
 beak, 87
 muscles of head and neck, 198
 pectoral girdle, 176
 skull, 131, 132
Chelydra serpentina, muscles of head
  and neck, 198
 skull, 131
Chevron bone, 149, 153
Chiasma, optic, 317, 322
Chick, thoracic (lymph) ducts, 250
Chicken, eye, 303
 heart, 237
Chimaera colliei, 17
Chimaera, pectoral fin, 164
 pelvic fin, 164
  See also Holocephali
Chimaerae, 4
Chimpanzee, 42
Chiroleptes, aglomerular kidney, 259
Chiroptera, 5, 40
Chlamydoselachus, lateral line, 294
 thyroid gland, 203, 281
 tooth, 103
Choanichthyes, 4
 members of, 20 ff., 345
Chondrichthyes, 3, 16, 344
 vertebral column, 143, 144
Chondroblast, 77, 111, 112
Chondrocranium, 117, 119
Chondrocyte, 77
Chondrostei, 4, 17
 skull, 120
 vertebrae, 145
Chorda tympani, 325
Chordae tendineae, 238
Chordamesoderm, 61
Chordata, characters of, 1, 2
 members, 3 ff.
Chorion, in Amniota, 69, 70, 72
Choroid coat, of eye, 300–303
 gland, 302
 plexus, 310
Chromatophores, 81
Chrysochloris, 84
Ciconiiformes, 5
Ciliary body of eye, 300
Ciliated bands, Branchiostoma, 10
Circulation in vertebrates, 232, 233
 embryonic, 243
Cirri, oral, Branchiostoma, 10
Cladodus, 164
Cladoselache, 143
 fins, 159–161

Cladoselachii, 3
Classification, purpose of, 2
Clavicle, *164*, 165, 175, *176*
Claws, 88, *89*
Cleavage, frog egg, *53*, 57, *58*, *59*
  holoblastic, *58*
  mammal egg, *71*
  meroblastic, *58*
Cleithrum, *164*, 165, 175, *176*
Climatius, *15*
Clinus, fins, *167*
Cloaca, *267*, *268*
Coccosteus, skull, *117*
Cochlea, *296*, *297*
Cod, jaw muscles, *197*
Coelacanthini, 4, 22
Coelom, Amniota, 69, *70*, *72*, *226–228*
  Branchiostoma, *67*, 225
  frog embryo, *63*
  structure and development, 224–228
Coelomic pores, 252
Coelomic pouches, Branchiostoma, *67*, 225
  Hemichorda, 225
Collar, Enteropneusta, *6*, *7*
Collateral ganglion, *328*, *329*, 330
Colon, 211, 216
Color, integument, 80, 81
Columba, *see* Pigeon
Columbiformes, 5
Columella auris, *see* Stapes
Colymbiformes, 5
Commissures, brain, 310, 315, *316*
Condor, wing skeleton, *171*
Condylarthra, 6, 39, *44*, 48
Condyle, occipital, in Amphibia, *128*, *129*
  in mammals, *137*, *138*, *139*
  in reptiles, *131*
Cones of retina, *301*, 303
Conies, *see* Hyracoidea
Connective tissue, 76–78
Conus arteriosus, 233, *234*, 235
  papillaris, 302, *303*
Convergence, 350
Cope, *338*, *339*
Copperhead, 25
Coprodeum in birds, 261
Coracoid, *164*, *176*, 177
  anterior, 175, *176*
Cord, epigonal, 270
  spermatic, 268
Cord, spinal, 309–317
  in Amphibia and reptiles, 313
  in cyclostomes, 311
  in fishes, 312
  in mammals, 317
Corium, *see* Dermis
Cormorants, 5

Cornea, *300*, *303*
  optic vesicle as organizer of, *65*
Corneum, stratum, *80*
Coronoid process, 139
Corti, organ of, *297*
Corpora bigemina, 315
  cavernosa, *267*, 268
  quadrigemina, *316*
Corpus callosum, 315, *316*
  luteum, 286
  spongiosum, 268
Corpuscle, renal (Malpighian), *256*
Cortex, of brain, 315
  of hair, 94
Cosmoid scale, 98
Cott, H. B., 81
Cotylosauria, 4, 27
  skull, *132*
Cowfish, *99*
Cranes, 5
Craniata, *see* Vertebrata
Craniosacral nerves, *see* Autonomic
Cranium, components of, *114*
  platybasic, 177
  tropybasic, 177
Creodonta, *44*
Cricotus, *see* Archeria
Crista, 295, *296*
Crocodile, heart, *237*
  vertebrae, *151*
Crocodilia, 4, 27
Crop in birds, 211, 212
Crossopterygii, 4, 20, *21*
  braincase (neurocranium), *125*
  dermocranium, *124*
  fin skeleton, 167, *168*
  pelvis, *177*
  skull, 123–125
  tooth, *103*
  vertebrae, *148*
Crotalus, hemipenis, *267*
      See also Rattlesnake
Crotaphytus, femoral pores, 83
Cryptobranchus, gills, 218
  pelvis, *178*
Ctenoid scales, 98
Cuculiformes, 5
Cuckoos, 5
Cup, optic, *65*
Cuticle of hair, 94
Cuvier, *336*, *337*
  duct of, *see* Vein, cardinal, common
Cycloid scales, 98
Cyclopterus lumpus, muscles, *185*
Cyclostomata, 3, *13*, *14*, 15
  vertebrae, 143
Cynognathus, skull, *133*
Cystoid echinoderms, *341*

Da Vinci, Leonardo, 333, 334
Darwin, 336, 338
Daubenton, 335
d'Azyr, Vicq, 336, 337
De Beer, 55, 341
Decussation, 322
Deer, 6
    mule, skull of, 139
Demibranch, 218
Dendrite, 75, 307
Dendrobates, eggs, 273
    poisonous secretion, 83
Dendrograptus, 8
Dental formula, 105–107
    papilla, 101
Denticles, in catfishes, 99
    in sharks and rays, 97, 98
Dentine, in placoid scales, 98
    in teeth, 101
Dermal fin rays, 100
Dermal spines, 100
Dermatome, frog embryo, 63
Dermis, 79, 80
Dermocranium, 114
    of lobefin, Osteolepis, 124
Dermoptera, 5
Desmognathus fuscus, spermatophore,
    266
    tongue, 210
Deuterencephalon, 309
Development, 53 ff.
    Amniota, 69–73
    Branchiostoma, 66–69
    frog, 59–66
Diapedesis, 230
Diaphragm in mammals, 187, 226, 227,
    228
Diapophysis, 150, 151, 155
Diapsid skull type, 134
Diastema, 106
Dicamptodon, hyoid and branchial
    arches, 130
    muscles, body wall, 187
Diceros bicornis, 47
Didactyla, 173
Didelphis, developing ear ossicles, 137
    pectoral girdle and sternum, 156
    pelvis, 178
    teeth, 106
        See also Opossum
Diemictylus, 278
    spermatophore, 266
Diencephalon, 64
Digestion defined, 200
Digitigrade defined, 44
Digits, origin of, 168
Dimetrodon, neural spines, 152
    pectoral girdle, 176
Dinocerata, 39

Dinosaurs, 4
Diphycercal caudal fin, 158
Diphyodont succession of teeth, 102
Diplodocus, 29
Diplospondyly defined, 144
Diplovertebron, 23
Dipnoi, 4, 20, 21
    external gills, 219
    female reproductive and excretory
        system, 272
    heart, 235
    lungs, 220
    skull, 123
    vertebrae, 146, 148
Diprotodon, 38
Dog larynx, 223
Doliolum, alternation of generations, 254
Dorosoma, gizzard, 207
Dorsal nerve cord, see Nervous system,
    central
Dorsal ribs, 154, 155
Down feathers, 91–94
Drepanaspis, 341
DuBois, Eugene, 353
Duck, 5
    skull, 136
    syrinx, 223
Duckbill, beak, 87
    spur of male, 89, 90
        See also Ornithorhynchus
Duckbill dinosaur, 30
Duct, archinephric, 255, 257
    ejaculatory, 269
    mesonephric, 256
    metanephric, 256, 260
    Müllerian, 256, 271
    pronephric, 255, 256
    sperm, 256, 258, 264, 265
    thoracic, 250, 251
    Wolffian, 256, 257, 264, 265
Ductule, efferent, 256, 258, 265
Ductus arteriosus (Botalli), 241–243
    caroticus, 242
    deferens, 256, 265, 268
Dugong, flipper, 171
Duodenum, birds, 212
    mammals, 216
Duplex uterus, 275
Dura mater, 309
Durodentine, in placoid scales, 98

Ear, external, 299
    inner, 295–298
    middle, 296, 298, 299
    ossicles in mammals, origin of, 137,
        138, 298, 299
Eardrum, 296, 298
    origin of, 298
Ecdysis, 80

Echidna, *36*
Echinoid larva, *340*
Ectoderm, 73
  frog, 61
  products of, 74
Ectosteorhachis, braincase, *125*
Edaphosaurus, neural spine, *152*
Edentata, 6, 46, 47
Edinger, Tilly, 313
Edops craigi, skull, *127*
Egg, frog, *53*, 57–59
  human, *71*, 262
  mammal, cleavage of, *71*
  vertebrates, 269
Elasmobranchii, 3
  vertebrae, *143*, 144
    See also Chondrichthyes
Elastica externa, *110*, 141
Elephant, 50
  African, *50*
  shrew, *39*
Elephantulus rufescens, *39*
Embolomerous vertebrae, 147, *149*
Embryo, defined, 53
  frog, *53*, 59–66
Emu, 4
  feather of, *92*
Enamel, *101*, 102
Enamel organ, 101
End plate, *182*
Endocrine organs, 280–286
Endoderm, 73, *201*
  frog, 61
  products of, 74
Endolymph, 295–297
Endolymphatic ducts, 295
  sac, 294
Endometrium, 286
Endomysium, *181*
Endoskeleton defined, 110
Endostyle, Ammocoetes, 203, *204*
  Branchiostoma, 10
  Urochorda, *11*, 12
Endothelium, 64, 76, *230*, *231*
Enteropneusta, 6
Entosphenus lamottenii, buccal funnel
    and teeth, *87*
  tridentatus, *13*
Eohippus (Hyracotherium), *349*, 350
  brain, 315
Ependymal cells, 75, 306
Epidermal structures, *87–90*
Epidermis, 79, *80*
Epigenesis, defined, 54
Epimere, frog embryo, *63*
Epimysium, *181*, *182*
Epipharyngeal groove, 202
  Branchiostoma, 10
  Urochorda, 12

Epiphysis, of vertebrae, mammals, 153
  pineal organ, 300
Epipubic bones, *178*, *179*
Epithelium, 74, 75
Equus, *48*, *349*, 350
  manus and pes, *174*
Eryops, *23*, 128
  foot (manus), *168*, *169*
  fore limb, *168*
Erythroblasts, 77
Erythrocytes, 77, 230
Esophagus, 205, 207, 211, 214
  in Branchiostoma, 10
Esox, brain, *311*
  vertebra, *147*
Estrogens, 269
Ethmoid bone, human, *290*
Euhyostylic jaw suspension, 122
Eutheria, 5, 39
Eurycea bislineata, tongue, *210*
Eustachian tube, 296, 298
Eusthenopteron, vertebrae, 147, *148*
Exoskeleton defined, 110
Eye, 299–304
  lateral (paired), 300–304
  median (parietal, pineal), 299

Facial muscles, *199*
  nerve, *320*, *321*, 324
Falciform ligament, 226
  process, 302
Falconiformes, 5
Fallopian tubes, *276*
Fang of rattlesnake, *103*, 105
Fascia, defined, 182
Feather, *90–94*
  contour, 91
  development of, *93*
  down, 91, *92*
  flight, 91
  hair, 92
  quill, 91, *92*
  rhachis, 91, *92*
  structure of, 91, *92*
  tracts, *91*
Fenestra ovalis, *296–298*
Fertilization, 56, 57
Ferungulata, 5
Fetus, 71
Fiber, argyrophil, 77
  collagenous, 77
  muscle, 75, 76, *181*
  nerve, 75, *307*, 308
  yellow elastic, 77
Fibroblast, 77
Fibrous sheath, *110*, 141
Filoplume, 92
Fin-fold theory, *159–162*
Fin rays, types of, *100*

Fins, median, 156-159
    paired, 166-168
Firmisternal pectoral girdle, 156, 156, 175
Fissipedia, 44, 45
Flame cells, see Solenocytes
Flamingo, synsacrum and caudal vertebrae, 153
Flexure of brain, apical, 314
    nuchal, 314
    pontine, 314
Flipper, dugong, 171
    Ichthyosaurus, 171
    porpoise, 171
Floating ribs, 156
Flounder, see Lophopsetta maculata
Follicle, feather, 93
    hair, 80, 94
    in human ovary, 71, 262, 269
Foramen ovale, in heart, 237
    of Winslow, 227
Forebrain, embryo, 64
Fovea centralis, 301
Frogs, 4
    development described, 59-66
        See also Rana; Hyla; Pseudacris
Fulcra, 100
Fundus, 214
Funnel, peritoneal, 255

Galen, 333, 334
Gall bladder, Ammocoetes, 204
    fishes, 208
    mammals, 216
Galliformes, 5
Gametes, 56, 57
Ganglion, ciliary, 329, 330
    coeliac, 328, 329
    collateral, 328, 329
    dorsal, in tunicates, 308
    Gasserian, 320, 321, 323, 324
    geniculate, 320, 321, 324
    mesenteric, inferior, 328, 329; superior, 328, 329
    otic, 329, 330
    peripheral, 328, 329
    petrosal, 320, 321, 323, 325
    profundus, 320, 323
    sphenopalatine, 329, 330
    submaxillary, 329, 330
    sympathetic, 328, 329
    trigeminal, 320, 321, 323, 324
    vagus, 320, 321, 323, 326
Gannets, 5
Ganoid scales, 97, 98
Garpike, see Lepisosteus
Gars, 4
        See also Holostei
Gastralia, 156

Gastrophryne carolinensis, tadpole, 24
Gastrula, Branchiostoma, 67
    frog, 60
Gavia immer, skull, 135
Gaviiformes, 5
Gegenbaur, 338
Genital ridges, 262
Geococcyx, feather tracts, 91
Gephyrocercal caudal fin, 158
Germ-layer theory, 339
Germinative layer, 79, 80
Gerrhonotus, scales, 90
Ghostfishes, see Holocephali
Gigantopithecus, 354
Gila monster, 26, 210
Gill bars, Branchiostoma, 10
    primary, 202
    Protochordata, 203
    secondary, 203
Gill clefts, Branchiostoma, 10, 203
    Cephalochorda, 10, 203
    Chordata, 2
    Enteropneusta, 7, 203
    Pterobranchia, 8
Gills, in fishes, 216, 217-219
    external, in fishes, 218, 219; in frog larva, 64, 218, 219; in salamanders, 218, 219
Girdles, pectoral and pelvic, fishes, 163-166
    tetrapods, 175-179
Gizzard, 212
Gizzard-shad, 207
Glands, acinous, 83
    adrenal, 284
    alveolar, 83
    bulbourethral, 269
    choroid, 302
    Cowper's, 269
    digestive, 213-216
    ductless, see endocrine
    endocrine, 280-286
    gastric, 215
    gonads, 285, 286
    granular, 82
    luminous, 85, 86
    mammary, 84
    milk, 84
    mucous, 82, 83
    musk, 83
    neural, in Urochorda, 253
    oil, 85
    pancreas, 285
    parathyroid, 282
    pituitary, 282-284
    poison, 83
    prostate, 269
    salivary, 209, 213
    sebaceous, 85

Glands—(*Continued*)
  shell, 271
  skin, *82–86*
  stink, 83
  sweat, 83, 84
  thyroid, 203, 204, 281, 282
  tubular, 83
  uropygial, 83
  wax, 83
Glans, 268
Glass snake, 26, 90
Glires, 6
Globicephalus, flipper, *171*
Glomerulus, Hemichorda, 252
  vertebrates, 252
Glomus, 257
Glossobalanus minutus, ciliary feeding, 202
Glossopharyngeal nerve, *320, 321, 323,* 325
Gnathostomata, 3
  defined, 15
  digestive organs, 205 ff.
  skull, 116 ff.
Goethe, 336
Gonads, Asymmetron, 11
  Branchiostoma, 10
  Cephalochorda, 10, 11
  Enteropneusta, 7
  Urochorda, 12
  vertebrates, 253, *262* ff.
Gonopodium, 266, *267*
Goose, brain, *314*
Gorgosaurus, 29
Gorilla, pectoral girdle, *176*
Granulocytes, 77
Granulosum, stratum, *80*
Graptolites, 3, 8
Gray crescent, 59, 60
Grebes, 5
Gruiformes, 5
Guanaco, manus and pes, *175*
Guanophores, 81
Guinea fowl, feather, *92*
Gulls, 5
Gymnophiona, *see* Apoda
Gyri, 315
Gyrinophilus porphyriticus, nasolabial groove, *290*

Haeckel, 54, 339
Hagfish, 3
  mouth and nostril, *204*
  See also Myxinoidea
Hair, 94, *95*
Hair feathers, *92*
Halmaturus, uterus, *276*
Hapalidae, 43
Hare, vertebrae of, *154*

Harvey, *334,* 336
Haversian canal, 112, *113*
  system, *113*
Hawk, 5
  See also Buteo
Heart, Amphibia, 235, *236*
  birds, 236, *237*
  Branchiostoma, 10
  early development, *234*
  fishes, 233–235
  lymph, *250*
  mammals, 237–239
  reptiles, 236, *237*
  Urochorda, 12
  Vertebrata, 12, 233 ff.
Heloderma, 26
Hemal arch, 144, 153
  spine, *144*
Hemichorda, 3, 6–8
Hemipenis, 267
Hemispheres, cerebral, *312–317*
Henle's loop, 261
Heptanchus, brain, *311*
Hermaphroditism, in Hemichorda, 254
  in Urochorda, 12, 254
  in Vertebrata, 262, 270
Heron, 5
Herring, jaw muscles, *197*
Hesperornis, *33,* 136
Heterocercal caudal fin, *158*
Heterodont teeth, 105, 212
Heterodontus, teeth, *103*
Heterostraci, 3
Hexanchus griseus, *16*
Hindbrain, embryo, *64*
Hippocampus, male, brood pouch, *278*
His, bundle of, *238*
History, comparative anatomy, 332–339
Hoatzin, claws on wings, 88
Holobranch, 218
Holocephali, 4, *17*
Holonephros, 255
Holostei, 4, *18,* 19
  skulls, 120
  vertebrae, 145
Holostylic jaw suspension, *118*
Homalodotherium, claws of, 89
Hominidae, 6, *43*
Hominoidea, 6, *43*
Homo, 352
  heidelbergensis, 353
  neanderthalensis, *43,* 353; skull, *354*
  rhodesiensis, 353
  sapiens, 352, 353; skull, *354*
  soloensis, 353
Homocercal caudal fin, *158,* 159
Homodont dentition, *107*
Homology, 55, 56, 338
Hoofs, 89

Hormone, 280–286, 287
    adrenalin, 284
    anterior pituitarylike, 286
    estrogens, 269
    estrone, 285
    gonadotrophic, 283
    growth, 283
    insulin, 285
    lactogenic, 283
    parathyroid, 282
    pituitary, 283
    progesterone, 287
    testosterone, 286
    thyroid, 281, 282
Horns, 95, 96
Horse, 6, 49, 50
    brain, 316
    evolution, 349, 350
    manus and pes, 174, 349
    molar tooth, 107, 349
Hummingbirds, 5
Huxley, 338
Hyla, Jacobson's organ, 291
    pectoral girdle, 175
Hyla goeldii, female with eggs, 279
    septentrionalis, 24
Hyoid in mammals, 140
Hyomandibular cartilage (or bone), 118,
        121, 122
    change to stapes, 124, 125, 298
    nerve, 321, 324
Hyostylic jaw suspension, 118
Hypocentrum, see Intercentrum
Hypocercal caudal fin, 158
Hypoglossal nerve, 320, 321, 326
Hypomere, frog embryo, 63
Hypopharyngeal groove, see Endostyle
Hypophyseal sac, 289, 310
Hypophysis, 282–284
Hypsodont teeth, 108
Hyracoidea (Hyrax), 6, 48, 215, 216
Hyracotherium, 349, 350
    manus and pes, 174

Ichthyophis glutinosa, skull, 128
Ichthyopterygia, 4
Ichthyornis, 33
    vertebrae, 153
Ichthyosauria, 4, 31, 32
    forelimb, 171
    skull, 134
Ichthyosaurus, 32
    forelimb, 171
Ichthyostegid, 22
Iguanodon, pelvis, 178
Ileum, birds, 212
    mammals, 216
Impennae, 5, 33
Impulse, 287, 288, 307

Incisor teeth, 102, 105, 106
Incisura angularis, 214
Incus, origin from quadrate, 299
Infundibulum, 282–284
Inguinal canal, 268
    sac, 268
Iniomi, light organs, 85
Insectivora, 5, 39, 40
Insertion of muscle, defined, 182
Integument, general nature of, 79, 80
Interbranchial septum, 217, 218
Intercalary arch, 143, 144
Intercentrum, 142, 148, 149
Interclavicle, 175, 176, 177
Interdorsal, 142
Intermuscular bones, 155
Interneural, see Intercalary arch
Interventral, 142
Intestine, Amphibia, 211
    birds, 212
    Branchiostoma, 10
    fishes, 208, 209
    mammals, 216
    reptiles, 211
    small, layers of wall, 206
    spiral valve, 209
Intima, 231
Iris, 300, 303
Ischnacanthus, fins, 160
Isolecithal eggs, defined, 57

Jacobson's organ, 291
Jamoytius, 97
Jaw suspension, amphistylic, 118
    autodiastylic, 117, 118
    autostylic, 118, 123, 129
    holostylic, 118
    hyostylic, 118
    methyostylic, 118, 121
Jaws, origin of, 116, 117
Jejunum in mammals, 216
Jordan, D. S., 277
Juvenal plumage, 93

Kangaroo, 38
    young in pouch, 84
Kidney, vertebrate, 254–262
    development, 255–257
Kingfishers, 5
Koala, 38
Koenigswald, von, 353

Labyrinth, bony, 296
    membranous, 295–297
Labyrinthodontia, 4, 22, 23
    skull, 125–128
Lacertilia, 25, 26
    cranial nerves, 321
    lung, 221

Lacertilia—(*Continued*)
  muscles, pelvis and thigh, *193;* shoulder and arm, *192*
  skull, *134*
Lacteals, 216, 249
Lacunae in cartilage, 111
Lagena, 295–297
Lagenorhynchus, teeth, *107*
Lagomorpha, 6, 47, 48
Lamarck, *336,* 337
Lamella of bone, 113
Lamprey, 3, *13*
  brain, *311*
  buccal funnel, 87
  horny teeth, 87
  larva, 14, 203, *204*
  pharynx, 203, *204*
  skull, *115, 116*
  spinal nerve components, *318*
  transformation, 204
      See also Ammocoetes; Entosphenus; Petromyzon; Petromyzontia
Langerhans, islands of, 285
Lantern fish, 85
Lanugo, 95
Larva, as a stage in development, 53, 68
  frog, 65
  lamprey, 14, 203, *204*
Larynx, 140, 224
  of dog, *223*
Lateral line system, 292–294
Lateral plate, frog, *62*
Latimeria, *21,* 22, 290
Leeuwenhoek, 335
Leidy, 339
Lemur, 5, *41*
  catta, *41*
  skull, *140*
Lemuriformes, 5
Lens, optic vesicle as organizer of, *65*
Leonardo da Vinci, 333, 334
Leopard, *45*
Lepidosauria, 4
Lepidosiren, 20
  external gills, *219*
Lepidotrichia, *100,* 163
Lepisosteus, *18*
  scales and dermal bones, *99*
  semilunar valves, *234*
  vertebrae, 145
Lepospondyli, 4
Lepus, vertebrae, *154*
Leucocytes, 77, 230
Light organs, 85, *86*
Limb, bud, frog, *66*
  paired, 163, *164*
  shark, *160*
  tetrapod, 167–174

Limnoscelis, *27*
Limulus, 343
Linea alba, 184
  in frog embryo, 63
Lion, tooth replacement, *102*
Liver, Branchiostoma, 10
  fishes, 208
  lamprey, *204*
  mammals, *216*
Lizard, 4
      See also Lacertilia
Lobefin, 4
      See also Crossopterygii
Lobes, optic, *310–317*
  in embryo, 64
Longitudinal (segmental) muscles, *185* ff.
Loon, 5
  skull, *135*
Lophius americanus, *19*
Lophodont teeth, 108
Lophopsetta maculata, *20*
Lorenzini, ampullae of, *294*
Loxodonta africana, *50*
Lungfish, *see* Dipnoi; Neoceratodus; Lepidosiren; Protopterus
Lungs, absent in certain salamanders, 222
  Amphibia, *221–223*
  birds, 222–224
  Bothriolepis (placoderm), 220
  Dipnoi, *220*
  mammals, 224
  Polypterus, *220*
  reptiles, *221,* 223
Lymph, 229
  hearts, *250*
  nodes, 249, *250*
  sinuses, 248
  spaces, 248
  system, 249–251; chick, rat, tadpole, *250*
  vessels, *230*
Lymphoid organs, 249

Macaca, uterus, *276*
Macrolecithal eggs, defined, 57
Macula, 295, *296*
Malacocephalus, 86
Malleus, origin from articular, *299*
Malpighi, 335
Malpighian corpuscle, *see* Renal corpuscle layer, 79, *80,* 95
Mammal-like reptile, *see* Therapsida
Mammalia, 5, 36 ff., 347–350
  eye, 303, *304*
  heart, 236–239
  limbs, 170, *171, 173–175*
  lung, 224
  pelvis, *178,* 179

Mammalia—(*Continued*)
  skull, *137–140*
  spinal nerve components, 318
Mammary glands, *84*
Mammoths, 50
Man, 6, *43*, 350–355
  Cro-Magnon, 352
  facial muscles, *199*
  Java, 353, *354*
  Neanderthal, *43*, 353, *354*
  Peking, 353
  Piltdown, 353
  skulls of early and modern, *354*
Manatee, *49*
Mandible, 116
Mandibular nerve, 321, 324
Manta, 103
Marmosets, 43
Marsh, 339
Marsipobranchii, *see* Cyclostomata
Marsupial bones, *178*, 179
Marsupialia, 5, *37*, 38
  birth of, 84
  pectoral girdle and sternum, *156*
  pelvis, 179
  pouch and nipples, *84*
  reproductive and excretory ducts, 265
  uterus, *276*
Mastodon, 50
  tooth of, *107*
Mauthnerian apparatus, 312
Maxillary nerve, 321–324
Medulla, of brain, *310–317;* in embryo, 64
  of hair, 94
Megachiroptera, 5
Megalichthys, braincase, *125*
Megalobatrachus, gills, 218
  inner ear, *296*
Meganthropus, 354
Megaptera nodosa, *46*
Melanophores, *81*
Meninges, 309
Merychippus, *349*
Mesencephalon, embryo, *64*
Mesenchyme, 76
Mesentery, 224–229
Mesocardium, *234*
Mesocolon, 226
Mesoderm, 73
  frog embryo, 62–64
  products of, 74
Mesoduodenum, 226
Mesogaster, 226
Mesohippus, 349
Mesolecithal, defined, 57
Mesonephric duct, 256–259
Mesonephros, 255–261
Mesopterygium, *164*

Mesorectum, 226
Mesothelium, 76
Mesovarium, 270
Metamorphosis, 54
  of frog, 66
Metanephros, 255, *256*, 260–262
Metapterygium, *164*
Metatheria, 5, 38
  See also Marsupialia
Metencephalon, embryo, *64*
Methyostylic jaw suspension, *118*, 121
Mice, 6
Microchiroptera, 5
Microlecithal eggs, defined, 57
Micropodiiformes, 5
Microsauria, 4
Molar teeth, 105–108
Mole, 84
  golden, 84
  marsupial, 38
Molt in birds, 93
Molting, defined, 80
Monkeys, 5, *42*
Monocytes, 77
Monophyodont teeth, 102
Monotremata, 5, *36*, 37
  brain, *315*
  male excretory and reproductive ducts, *265*
  uterus, *276*
Moropus, claws, 89
Mosasaur, 26
Mouth, Branchiostoma (Cephalochorda), *9*, 10
  Enteropneusta, 6, *7*, *202*
  fishes, 206, 207
  lamprey, *204*
  Urochorda, 11
Mucosa, digestive tract, 205, *206*
Mud puppy, *see* Necturus
Müllerian duct, *256*, 271
Muscle, abductor (abduction), 183
  adductor (adduction), 183
  adductor mandibulae (-aris), 195–*197;*
    operculi, 196
  arrector pili, 94
  branchiomeric, *184*, 195–199
  cardiac, 76, 181
  constrictor, 183; colli, *198*, 199; dorsalis, 195, *196;* of hyoid, 195, *196*
  coracohyoideus, 188
  coracomandibularis, 188
  defined, 181
  depressor, 183; mandibulae, *197*, *198*
  digastric, *198*
  dilator operculi, 196, *197*
  epaxial, *184*
  erector of fin ray, 190
  extensor, 183

Muscle—(*Continued*)
external oblique, *187, 197*
eye, 188–190; development, *189,* 190
facial, *199*
fiber, 75, *181*
fins, in fish, 190, *191*
flexor, 183
functions, 183
geniohyoid, 188
hypaxial, *184*
hypobranchial, *184,* 188
inclinator of fin ray, 190
insertion, defined, 182
intercostal, 187
interhyoid, 195, *197*
intermandibularis, 195–*198*
internal oblique, *187*
latissimus dorsi, 188, *192,* 193
levator, 183, *184;* palpebrae superioris, 189
limbs, in tetrapods, 191–194
longitudinal, 185 ff.; in fishes, 185–187
masseter, *198*
oblique, external and internal, *187, 197*
obliquus, inferioris and superioris, *189,* 190
opercularis, 298
origin, defined, 182
panniculus carnosus, 188
papillary, 238
pectoralis, *192*
pelvis and thigh, *193*
platysma, *199*
pronator, 183
protractor of fin, 190
pterygoid, 198
pyramidalis, 189
quadratus, 189
rectus abdominis, *187*
rectus group, of eye, *189*
retractor bulbi, 189; of fin, 190; lentis, 302
rhomboideus, 188
rotator, 183
segmental, 183–194
serratus, 188
shoulder and upper arm, *192*
skeletal, 76, *181,* 183 ff.
smooth, 75, *181*
sphincter, 183
stapedius, 198
sternohyoid, 188
striated, *181*
supinator, 183
temporalis, *198*
tissue, types of, *181*
transversus abdominis, *187*
Muscularis of arteries, *231*
Musk deer, erythrocytes, 78

Mutica, 6
Myelencephalon, embryo, 64
Myelin, *307,* 308
Myelinated fibers, *307,* 308
Myodome, 302
Myofibrils, 75, *181*
Myomere, Branchiostoma, 9
Myoseptum, 141, *142*
Myotome, frog embryo, *63*
development of first three, 189
relationship to limb bud, *191*
Myrmecophaga tridactyla, *47*
Mysticeti, *46*
Myxinoidea, 3, *13*
Myxipterygium, *16, 264,* 266

Nails, 89
Nasal capsules, *114*–116
Nasal passages, in Apteryx, 291
in fishes, 289
in mammals, 291
in tree frog, *291*
Nasolabial groove, *290*
Neanderthal man, *43,* 353, *354*
Nectophrynoides, oviducts, 272
Necturus, *24,* 55
gills, 218
Neoceratodus forsteri, 20, *21*
archipterygial fin, *167*
skull, *123*
vertebrae, *148*
Neognathae, 5, 33, 34, 136
Neopallium, 313
Neornithes, 4, 33
Neoteny, 55
Nephrocoel, 255
Nephrostome, 255, 257
Nephrotome, 255
Nerve, abducens, *320, 321,* 324
auditory, *321, 323,* 325
autonomic system, 327–331
buccal, *321,* 324
chorda tympani, 325
cranial, 319–327; in lizard, Anolis, *321;* segmental relationships, *320,* 327; shark, Squalus, *321;* summary of, 327
craniosacral, *see* autonomic system
facial, *320, 321,* 324
glossopharyngeal, *320, 321, 323,* 325
hyomandibular, *321,* 324
hypoglossal, *320, 321,* 326
mandibular, *321,* 324; internal, 325
maxillary, *321,* 324
motor, *182*
oculomotor, *320*–322
olfactory, 321
ophthalmic, 324; superficial, *321,* 324
optic, *321,* 322; development, *65*

Nerve—(*Continued*)
  palatine, *321*, 324
  parasympathetic, 329, 330
    See also autonomic system
  phrenic, 228
  pneumogastric, *see* vagus
  profundus, *320, 321, 323*
  spinal, *317–319;* functional components of, *318*
  spinal accessory, *320, 321, 323,* 326
  sympathetic, *329,* 330
    See also autonomic system
  terminal, *320, 321, 323*
  thoracolumbar, *see* autonomic system
  trigeminal, *320–324*
  trochlear, *321, 323*
  vagus, *320–326;* effect on heart, 239
Nervous system, autonomic, 305, 327–331
  central, 305, 306, 309–317; Branchiostoma, 9, *308;* Chordata, *2;* Enteropneusta, 7, *309;* Pterobranchia, 8, *309*
  peripheral, 305, 317–331
Nestling plumage, 92, 93
Neural arch, *143, 144*
  folds, frog, *61*
  gland, Urochorda, 253
  groove, frog, *61*
  plate, 67, *308*
  spine, *144–152*
  tube, frog, *61*
Neurenteric canal, 66, *67,* 308
Neurilemma, *307,* 308
Neurocranium, Crossopterygian, *125*
  defined, *114*
  paleoniscid, *119*
  shark, *119*
Neuroglia cell, 306
Neurohumor, defined, 81
Neuromast organs, *292–299*
Neuromuscular cells, 305
Neuron, 75, 288, 306, *307*
  postganglionic, 328, *329*
  preganglionic, 328, *329*
  retina, *301*
Neuropore, 308
Neurula, frog, *61,* 62
Neurulation, 62
Newt, secondary sex characters. *278*
    See also Caudata; Urodela
Nictitating membrane, 303
Nightjars, 5
Nipples, types of, 85
Node, of Ranvier, *307,* 308
  sinauricular, 238
Nostrils, Amphibia, 124, *290*
  fishes, 298, *290*
Notarium, pterosaurs, 151
Notochord, Branchiostoma, *9*
  Chordata, 1, 2

Notochord—(*Continued*)
  Enteropneusta, 7
  frog embryo, 62, *63*
  structure of, *110, 111,* 141
  Urochorda, 11
Nototrema, egg sac, 279
Notoungulata, 39
Noturus, poison glands, 82
Nuptial plumage, 93

Occlusion of teeth, *106, 108*
Oculomotor nerve, 322
Odontoblast, *101*
Odontoceti, *44,* 46
Odontognathae, 4, *33*
Olfactory bulb, *288,* 321
  capsules, *see* Nasal capsules
  epithelium, *288*
  nerve, *288,* 321
  organ, Apteryx, *291;* Branchiostoma, *9;* vertebrates, *288–291*
  pit, *9*
  tract, 321
Omasum, *215*
Omentum, 226, 227
Omosternum, *156,* 157
Ontogeny, 53, 333
Onychodactylus, claws of, 88
Oöcyte, 57
Operculum, fish, *120–124*
  frogs, salamanders, 298
  tadpoles, 218
Ophidia, 26
Ophisaurus, scales, 90
Ophthalmic nerve, 324
  superficial, *321,* 324
Opossum, 37
  brain, *316*
  developing ear ossicles, *137*
  muscles, pelvis and thigh, *193;* shoulder and arm, *192*
  pouch and nipples, 84
    See also Didelphis
Opsanus tau, skull, *122*
Optic chiasma, *317,* 322
  cup, *65*
  nerve, *321,* 322
  pedicel, *189,* 302
  vesicle, *65;* as organizer, 65
Orbit, *300*
Orca gladiator, *44*
Oreopithecus, 351
Organizer, central nervous system, frog, 61
  dorsal lip of blastopore as, 61
  lens, 65
  optic vesicle as, 65
Origin, of muscle, 182
  of vertebrates, 340–343

Ornithischia, 4, 29, *30, 31*
Ornithorhynchus, 37
   brain, *315*
   pectoral girdle, *176*
   uterus, *276*
      See also Duckbill
Orohippus, *349*
Orthogenesis, theory of, 350
Os priapi, 268
Osborn, H. F., 339, 350
Ossicles, Weberian, 221, *224*
Osteichthyes, 4, 344, 345
Osteoblast, 77
Osteoclast, 113
Osteocytes, 77, 112, *113*
Osteodentine, 102
Osteoderms, 100
Osteolepis, dermocranium, *124*
Osteostraci, 3, *14*
Ostium, 270
Ostracoderms, 3, 13, *14*, 340, *341*, 344
      See also Cephalaspis; Rhyncho-
       lepis
Ostrich, *34;* feather, *92*
Otic capsule, 114, *115, 116,* 295
   ganglion, *329,* 330
Otoconia, 295
Ovarian cords, 269
Ovary, *262,* 269
Oviduct, 270
Oviparous habit, 58, 263
Ovis, uterus, *276*
Ovisac in teleosts, *272*
Ovoviviparous habit, 274
Owen, R., 337, 338
Owls, 5

Paddlefish, *see* Chondrostei
Paired limbs, fishes, 163, *164*
   origin of, 159 ff.
   tetrapods, 166 ff.
Paleognathae, 4, 33, *34,* 136
Palate, hard, 212, *213*
Palatine nerve, *321,* 324
Palatoquadrate, 117
Paleogyrinus decorus, skull, *126*
Paleoniscid, 4, *17*
   neurocranium, *119*
   skull, *120*
Paleoniscus macropomus, *17*
Pallium, Amphibia, 312
   cyclostomes, 310
   fishes, 311
Pan troglodytes, *42*
Pancreas, fishes, 208
   lamprey, 204
   mammals, *216*
Pangolins, 6, 84
Pantotheria, 5, 37, 108

Papilla, dermal, of feather, *93*
Papio hamadryas, *42*
Parabronchial tubes, *222,* 224
Parachordal cartilages, 116
Paracone, *108*
Paraconid, *108*
Parallelism, 350
Paranthropus, 352
   r. crassidens, 354
   robustus, 354
Parapophyses, 144, 150, *151,* 155
Parapsid skull type, 134
Parasympathetic nerves, effect on heart,
   239
   nervous system, *329,* 330
Parathyroid glands, 282
Parexus, fins of, *160*
Parietal mesoderm, frog embryo, *63*
Parrots, 5
Parturition, 73
Passeriformes, 5, 35
Patten, 343
Pecten, *303*
Pectoral fin, Chimaera, *164*
   girdle, 163 ff., 175 ff.
Pedicel, optic, *189,* 302
Pedogenesis, 341, 342
Pelecaniformes, 5
Pelicans, 5
Pelvic fin, Chimaera, *164*
   teleosts, 166, *167*
Pelvis, Amphibia, *177, 178*
   birds, *178,* 179
   fishes, 165, *166*
   mammals, *178,* 179
   renal, *260*
   reptiles, 266, *267*
Pelycosauria, 4, 28
   vertebra, *152*
Penis, birds, 267
   bone, 268
   mammals, *265,* 268
   reptiles, 266, *267*
Perca flavescens, *see* Perch, yellow
Perch, yellow, lateral line scales, *293*
   skull, *121*
   vertebrae and fin skeleton, *146*
Pericardial cavity, *226, 227*
Pericardium, *226, 227*
   frog embryo, 64
Perichondrium, *111,* 182
Perilymph, 295–297
Perimysium, *181,* 182
Periosteum, *182*
Peripharyngeal bands, Ammocoetes, 203
   Branchiostoma, 10
   Urochorda, 12
Peripheral ganglia, 328, *329*

Perissodactyla, 6, *48*, 49
  foot skeleton, *174*
Peristalsis, 216
Peritoneal cavity, frog embryo, 63
  funnel, 255
Peritoneum, *206*, 225
Pessulus, *223, 224*
Petrels, 5
Petromyzon, brain, *311*
  skull, *115*
Petromyzontia, 3, *13*
Petrosal ganglion, 320–323, 325
Phagocytes, 77
Phallichthys, gonopodium, *267*
Pharynx, Branchiostoma, 10, 202
  Enteropneusta, 6, 7, 202
  Urochorda, *11*, 12, 202, *203*
Phenacodus, *44*
Pholidota, 6
Photophores, 85, *86*
Phrenic nerve, 228
Phylogeny, 333
Physoclystous fish, *220*, 221
Physostomous fish, *220*, 221
Pia mater, 309
Piciformes, 5
Pig, 6
  fetal, *48*
Pikas, 6
Pike, brain, *311*
  vertebra, *147*
Pinna of ear, 299
Pinnipedia, 44, *45*
Pipa pipa, brain, *312*
  female with eggs, *279*
Pipidae, absence of tongue, 210
  claws, 88
Pit organs, 292, *294*
Pithecanthropus, 353
  erectus, 353; pekingensis, 353; robustus, 353
  skull, *354*
Pituitary gland, 282–284
Placenta, 73
Placental mammal, male excretory and reproductive ducts, *265*
    See also Eutheria
Placodermi, 3, 15
  spiral valve, 208
Placoid scales, 97, *98*
Plate, lateral, frog embryo, *62*
Platelets, blood, 78
Plates, armadillo, 97
  cowfish, *99*
  fishes, 99
  mammals, 96, 97
Platyrrhina, *see* Ceboidea
Pleural cavities, 228
  ribs, 154, *155*

Pleurocentrum, *142*, 148, *149*
Pleurodont tooth attachment, *102*, 104
Pleuroperitoneal membrane, 228
Plexus, of Auerbach, 328
  brachial, 319
  choroid, *see* Choroid plexus
  of Meissner, 328
  sacral, 319
  solar, 328, *329*
Plover, black-bellied, *35*
Plumage, 93
Pneumatic duct, 221
Pneumogastric nerve, *see* Nerve, vagus
Polar body, 57
Pollack, head canals and pit organs, *292*
Polyphyodont tooth succession, 102
Polypterus, 4, 120
  bichir, *18*
  external gills, *219*
  lungs, *220*
  pectoral girdle and fin, *164*
  ribs, 154
  skull, 120
Pongidae, 6, *42, 43*
Pons, *315, 316*
Pores, abdominal, *264*
  coelomic, 252
  genital, 272
  lateral line, 292–294
  urinogenital, 272
Porichthys, photophore of, *86*
Porpoise, 45, *46*
  flipper, *171*
  stomach, 215
  teeth, *107*
Postcleithrum, *164*, 165
Postnuptial plumage, 93
Potentiality, 333
Pouches, brood, 278
  coelomic, in Branchiostoma, 67, 225
  inguinal, 268
  Rathke's, 282, *283*
Precoracoid, *see* Coracoid, anterior
Preformation, 54
  theory of, 335
Prehallux, *169*
Premolar teeth, 105–107
Prepollex, *169*
Prepuce, 268
Primates, 5, *41* ff., 89
Primitive streak, 72
Pristis, 103
Proatlas, *150*
Proboscidea, 6, 48, *50*
Proboscis, Enteropneusta, *6, 7*
Procellariiformes, 5
Proctodeum, birds, 261
Profundus ganglion, 320, *323*
  nerve, *320, 321, 323*

Pronephros, 255–257, 261
Propterygium, 164
Prosencephalon, embryo, 64
Prosimii, 5, 41
Protocercal caudal fin, 158
Protochordates, 6 ff.
  circulatory system, 232
  digestive and respiratory organs, 201–203
  excretory and genital organs, 253, 254
  muscles, 185
Protocone, 108
Protoconid, 108
Protonephridia, Branchiostoma, 10, 253, 254
Protopterus, 20
  female reproductive and excretory system, 272
  heart, 235
  mucous glands in skin, 82
Prototheria, 5, 37
Proventriculus, birds, 212
Psalterium, 215
Pseudacris clarki, tadpole, horny beak and teeth, 87
Pteranodon, 31, 151
Pteraspidomorphi, 3
Pterobranchia, 3, 7, 8
Pterodactylus, wing skeleton, 171
Pteropus giganteus, 40
  wing skeleton, 171
Pterosauria, 4, 30, 31, 151
  wing skeleton, 171
Pterygiophores, 162, 163
Pterylae, 91
Ptyalin, 213
Ptychodera, 6
Pulp cavity, feather, 93; scale, 98; tooth, 101–103
Pygostyle, 153
Pyloric ceca, 207
  portion of stomach, 214
  valve, 214
Pylorus, 214

Quadrate, in relation to incus, 299
Quill, 91–94

Rabbit, 6
  jaw muscles, 198
Rachis of feather, 92
Radial (pterygiophore), 163, 164
  in archipterygial fin, 167
  in crossopterygian fin, 167, 168
Rails, 5
Raja erinacea, 16
  spinal nerves to pectoral fin, 319
  spiral valve, 209
Rana clamitans, muscles, 197

Rana, kidney, 259
  pectoral girdle, 156
  pelvis, 178
  pipiens, egg, 53; development described, 57–66; larva, 54
  temporaria, heart, 236
Rangifer caribou, 49
Ranvier, node of, 307, 308
Rat, lymphatic vessels, 250
Ratitae, 33, 34
Rattlesnake, fang, 103
  hemipenis, 267
  skull, 133
Ray, 3
  calcified cartilage in skull of, 112
  thorny, 16
    See also Chondrichthyes; Batoidei; Raja
Recapitulation, 339
Receptors, 287
Rectal gland in elasmobranchs, 209
Rectrices, 91
Rectum, in birds, 212
  in fishes, 209
Reflex act, 287
Remiges, 91
Renal corpuscle, 256, 257
  tubule, 255–257
Reproductive organs, female, 262, 269–276
  male, 262–269
Reptilia, 4, 23, 346, 347
  limbs, 172
  skull, 130–135
Resegmentation, 142
Response, 287
Rete testis, 263, 265
Reticulum, 215
Retina, 300, 301
  development, 65
Rhabdopleura, 3, 8
Rhachitomous vertebra, 142, 148
Rhina, 103
Rhineodon, 103
Rhinoceros, 6, 47
Rhipidistia, 4, 22
  skull, 124, 125
Rhombencephalon, embryo, 64
Rhynchocephalia, 4, 26, 28
  skull, 131, 134
Rhyncholepis, 14
Ribs, 154–157, 156
Roadrunner, feather tracts, 91
Rodentia, 6, 47, 48
Rods of retina, 301
Rostrum, Branchiostoma, 9
Rumen, 215
Ruminant, hollow-horned, 96
  stomach, 215

Sabertooth, skull, *140*
Sac, hypophyseal, *289, 310*
   inguinal, *268*
Sacculus, 295, *296*
Sacrum, Amphibia, 149
   birds, 152, *153*
   reptiles, 150, 151
Sagitta, 343
Salamander, 4
   hyoid and branchial arches, *130*
   skull, *129*
      See also Caudata, Urodela
Salamandra atra, viviparous habit, 58,
   273
Salientia, 4, 23, *24*
   skull, *129*
Salivary glands, 209, 213
Salmo fario, pectoral girdle and fin skele-
   ton, *164*
   salar, *19*
Salmon, Atlantic, *19*
   secondary sex characters, 277
Salpa, alternation of generations, 254
Saltoposuchus, 28
Sarcolemma, *181*
Saurischia, 4, 28, *29*
Sauropoda, 28, *29*
Scales, cosmoid, 97, 98
   ctenoid, *98*
   cycloid, *98*
   epidermal, 90
   fish, 97, *98*
   ganoid, 97, 98
   mammalian, 96
   placoid, *98*
   reptilian, *90*
Scapula, *164*, 165, 175–177
Scapulocoracoid, 163
Sceloporus, brain, *312*
   skull, *134*
Schilbeodes, poison glands, 82
Sciurus carolinensis, skull, *138*
Sclera of eye, 300–303
Sclerotic bones, in birds, *303;* in fish, 301
   coat, *see* Sclera
   plate, *303*
   ring, 301
Sclerotome, 141, *142*
Screamer, claws, 88
   spurs, 90
Scrotum, 268
Scyllium canicula, fin development, *160*
Sea cow, *see* Sirenia
Sea horse, *see* Hippocampus
Sea squirt, *see* Urochorda
Seal, fur, 45
Segmental muscles, 183–194
Selachii, 3
Selenodont teeth, *107,* 108

Semilunar valve, *234, 238*
Sensation, 307
Sense organ, defined, 287
Septum, dorsal, 184
   horizontal, *184*
   transverse, 227
Serosa of digestive tract, *206*
Sertoli cells, 263
Sex characters, primary, 263 ff.
   secondary, 263, 275 ff.
Sex hormones, 263
Seymouria, skull, *132*
   vertebra, *142*
Shaft of feather, 91, *93,* 94
Shark, 3
   brain, *311*
   cranial nerves, *321*
   heart, *234*
   hepatic portal system, *247*
   muscles, body, *188;* eye, *189;* head,
      196
   neurocranium, *119*
      See also Chondrichthyes; Elasmo-
         branchii; Squalus
Sheath, elastic, of notochord, *110,* 141
   of feather, *93,* 94
   fibrous, of notochord, *110, 111, 141*
   of penis, 268
Sheep uterus, *276*
Shrew, 39
Simpson, G. G., 351
Sinanthropus, 353
Sinauricular node, 238
   valve, 233
Sinopa, *44*
Sinus, air, 140
   urogenital, *256*
   venosus, *232–235*
Siphon, atrial, *11*
   oral, *11*
   sacs, 266
Siren, external gills, *219*
   limbs, 170
Sirenia, 6, 48, *49, 50,* 84
      See also Dugong
Skeleton, appendicular, 114
   axial, 114
   visceral, *114*
Skull, Actinopteri, *119* ff.
   Agnatha, *115, 116*
   Amphibia, 125–130
   anapsid type, 132
   arthrodire, *117*
   birds, *135, 136*
   Crossopterygii, 123–125
   Cyclostomata, *115, 116*
   diapsid type, *134*
   Dipnoi, *123*
   Elasmobranchii, 117–*119*

Skull—(*Continued*)
  gnathostomes, *116* ff.
  kinetic, reptiles and birds, 132
  mammal-like reptiles, *133*, 135, 137–139
  mammals, *137–140*
  parapsid type, 134
  perch, *121*
  Reptilia, 130–135
  streptostylic, 132, *133*
  synapsid type, 132
  toad fish, *122*
Smilodon californicus, skull, *140*
Smith, H. M., 83
Smooth muscle, 75, *181*
Snake, *see* Ophidia, Rattlesnake
Snake, glass, 26, 90
    See also Ophisaurus
Soft rays, *100*
Solenocytes, Branchiostoma, 10, 253, *254*
Somites, frog embryo, *63*
  vertebrates, 141
Spalacotherium tooth, *107*
Specter, *see* Tarsier
Spemann, Hans, 61
Sperm cell, 57, *262*
Spermatic cord, 268
Spermatid, 57, *262*, 264
Spermatocyte, 57, *262*, *263*
Spermatogonia, *262*, *263*
Spermatophores, *266*
Sphenodon, 4, *266*
  parietal eye, 299
  punctatum, *26*
  skull, *134*
  vertebrae, *150*
Sphenopalatine ganglion, *329*, 330
Spider monkey, *42*
Spinal accessory nerve, *320*, *321*, *323*, 326
Spinal cord, *see* Cord, spinal
Spinax, photophore of, 86
Spiny rays, *100*
Spiracle, fishes, 117; tadpoles, 218
Spiral valve in fishes, 208, *209*
Splanchnic mesoderm, frog embryo, *63*
Splanchnocranium, *114*
Spleen, *247*, 249
Spurs, *89*, 90
Squalus acanthias, arteries of head, *240*
  cranial nerves, *321*
  hepatic portal system, *247*
  muscles of eye (orbit), *189;* of head, *196*
  urinary and genital organs, *264*
  vertebra, 144
Squamata, 4, *25*, *28*
  skull, 131–*134*

Squirrels, 6
  skull of, *138*
Stapes, mamalian, *296*, 297
  origin of, *298*
Stegosaurus, *30*
Stensiö, E. A., 14, 15
Stereospondyli, skull, 126
  vertebrae, 148
Sternal rib, 155
Sternebrae, 157
Sternum, 154–157, *156*
Stimulus, 287, 307
Stomach, Amphibia and reptiles, 211
  birds, *212*
  fishes, 207
  mammals, *214–216*
  Urochorda, 12
Stork, 5, *34*
Stratum corneum, 80
  germinativum, 79, 80
  granulosum, *80*
  lucidum, *80*
Streptostyly in reptiles and birds, 132, *133*
Striae in muscle fibers, *181*
Striated muscle, *181*
Strigiformes, 5
Sturgeon, 4, *18*
Styloid process, 140
Submaxillary ganglion, *329*, 330
Submucosa, digestive tract, *205*, 206
Subpharyngeal gland, 203, *204*
Subunguis, 88, *89*
Sulci, 315
Supracleithrum, *164*, 165, 175
Swedenborg, 335
Swifts, 5
Symmetrodonta, 5, 108
Symmetry in egg, 59
Sympathin, effect on heart, 330
Sympathetic ganglion, 328, *329*
  nervous system, *329*, 330
Synapse, *308*
Synapsid skull type, 132, *133*
Synapsida, 4
Synapticulae, Branchiostoma, 10, 203
  Protochordates, 203
Syncytium, 76, *181*
Syndactyla, 173
Synsacrum, 152, *153*
Synotic tectum, 116
Syrinx, *223*, 224
Systole, 238

Tachyglossus (Echidna), *36*, 37, 84
  mammary pouches, 84
Tadpole, beak and teeth of, 87
  Gastrophryne carolinensis, *24*

Tadpole—(*Continued*)
  lymphatic vessels, *250*
  Rana, *54*
Tail, 156–159
      See also Caudal fin
Tail-bud stage, frog, *62*
Talonid, *108*
Talpa, 84
Tapirs, 6, *48,* 49
  manus and pes, *174*
Tarsier, 5, *41*
Tarsiiformes, 5
Tarsometatarsus, in birds, development,
    173
Taste buds, *214, 291,* 292
Teeth, *101–108*
  acrodont, *102*
  attachment, *102*
  bunodont, *107,* 108
  carnassial, 107
  crossopterygian, *103*
  deciduous, *102*
  development of, *101*
  formula, 105
  horny, in hagfishes, 87; lampreys, 87;
    tadpole, 87
  lophodont, *108*
  molar, 105–108
  occlusion of, *106, 108*
  pattern in lobefins, 104
  permanent, 102
  pleurodont, *102*
  rattlesnake, *103,* 105
  replacement, *102*
  selenodont, *107,* 108
  shark, 102, *103*
  succession, 102
  thecodont, *102*
  tritubercular, *107*
Tegu lizard, 25
Telanthropus, 352
Telencephalon, embryo, *64*
Teleostei, 4, *19,* 20
  female reproductive and excretory sys-
    tems, *272*
  poison glands, 82
  skull, 120–*122*
  vertebrae, *146, 147*
Telolecithal egg, defined, *58*
Temporal bone, origin of, 131
Tendon, defined, *182*
Testis, *262,* 265
  cords, *263*
Testudinata, *see* Chelonia
Tetrapoda, 4, 22
  limbs, 168 ff.
  skull, origin of, 123–125
Thecodont tooth attachment, *102,* 105
Thecodontia, 4, 28

Therapsida, 4, 28, 36
  skull, *133,* 135, 137–139
Theria, 5, 38
Theropoda, 28, *29*
Thinopus antiquus, 169
Thoracolumbar nerves, *see* Autonomic
    nervous system
Thrombocytes, 78
Thymus, 249
Thyroid gland, 203, *204,* 281, 282
Tibiotarsus in birds, development, *173*
Tillodonta, 39
Tinamous, 4, 33
Tissue fluid, 229
  spaces, *230*
Tissues, 73–87
Toadfish, skull, *122*
Toads, 4
  lung, *221*
  pectoral girdle, 175
  skull, *129*
      See also Salientia
Tongue, Amphibia, *210*
  birds, 211
  mammals, *213,* 214
  reptiles, 210
Tonsils, 249
Tornaria larva, *340*
Tortoise, *see* Chelonia
Trabeculae in heart, 238
Trachea, 222–224
      See also Pneumatic duct
Trachodon (Anatosaurus), *30*
Tracts, feather, *91*
Transverse process, 155
Tree shrew, 5, 351
Trematops, hind limb, *168, 169*
Triassochelys, teeth, 105
Triceratops, *31*
Trigeminal ganglion, 320–324
  nerve, 320–324
Trigonid, *108*
Triton cristatus, male and female, *278*
Tritubercular tooth, 107
Trituberculata, 37
Trochlear nerve, *321,* 323
Trophoblast, *71*
Trunk of Enteropneusta, *6, 7*
Trunkfish, *99*
Tubes, Fallopian (uterine), *276*
Tuberculum, 155
Tubular glands, 83
Tubule, renal, 255
  seminiferous, *262, 263*
Tunicata, *see* Urochorda
Tunics of eye, *300*
Turbinal bones, *190, 191*
Turkey, pectoral girdle, *176*
  stomach, *212*

Turtle, *see* Caretta; Chelonia; Chelydra
Tympanic membrane, *296, 298*
Typhlosole, *204*
Tyrannosaurus, 28

Umbilicus of feather, 91, *92,* 94
Uncinate process, 156
Unguiculata, 5
Ungulate, even-toed, *see* Artiodactyla
  odd-toed, *see* Perissodactyla
Ureter, *260*
Urethra, *267, 275*
Urinary bladder, 259, *260*
Urochorda, 3, *11*
  pharynx, *11,* 12, 203
Urodela, 4, 23, *24*
    See also Caudata
Urodeum, 261
Urogenital (urinogenital) pore, *272*
  sinus, *275*
Uropygial gland, 83
Uropygium, *91*
Urostyle, 149
Uterus, *275, 276*
Utriculus, *296*

Vagina, *225, 276*
Vagus ganglion, *320, 321, 323,* 326
Vagus nerve, *320–326*
Valve, auriculoventricular, 234, *236, 238*
  bicuspid (mitral), *237, 238*
  semilunar, *234, 238*
  sinauricular, 233
  tricuspid, 238
Vane of feather, *91–94*
Vas deferens, *256, 258*
Vein, abdominal, 246
  azygos, *244,* 246
  cardinal, *244, 245*
  caudal, *244, 245*
  cerebral, 244
  defined, *231*
  described, 244–248
  hepatic, *244*
  hepatic portal, *244,* 246, *247*
  iliac, *244,* 246
  jugular, *244*
  omphalomesenteric, 248
  postcaval, *244*–246
  precaval, *244, 245*
  renal portal, *244, 245*
  subcardinal, *244, 245*
  subclavian, 245
  subintestinal, *244*–246
  supracardinal, 246
  umbilical, *243*
  vena capitis lateralis, *244*
  vertebral, 246
  vitelline, 248

Velum, Branchiostoma, 10
  lamprey, 204
Venom, snakes, 209
  Gila monsters, 210
Ventral ribs, 154, *155*
Ventricles, of brain, 309, *310*
  of heart, 233–238
Vertebra, Actinopteri, *144–146*
  Amphibia, *147–149*
  birds, 152, *153*
  Chelidosaurus, *142*
  Chondrostei, 145
  Crossopterygii, 147, *148*
  cyclostomes, 143
  development, 141, *142*
  diplospondylous, 144, 145
  Dipnoi, 146, *148*
  Elasmobranchii, *143,* 144
  embolomerous, 147, *149*
  Holostei, *144,* 145
  mammals, 153, *154*
  Polypterus, 144
  reptiles, 149–152
  rhachitomous, *142*
  Seymouria, *142*
  shark, *143,* 144
  Teleostei, *146, 147*
  tetrapods, 147 ff.
    See also Centrum
Vertebral rib, 155
Vertebrarterial canal, 150, 153
Vertebrata, 3, 12 ff.
  origin of, 340–344
  panorama (review), 343–350
Vesalius, 333, *334*
Vesicle, seminal, 269
Vicq d'Azyr, 336, 337
Villi, of intestine, *206,* 216
  of placenta, *70, 72,* 73
Visceral cartilages, *116*
Visceral muscles, *see* Muscles, branchio-
    meric
Visceral skeleton, *114*
Viviparous habit, 58, 263
Vocal sacs in frogs and toads, 223

Wallace, 336
Watson, 15
Weberian ossicles, 221, *224*
Whale, *44–46*
  humpback, *46*
  killer, *44*
Whalebone, 46
Wheel organ, Branchiostoma, 10
Williston's law, 139
Wilson, E. B., 343
Wing, skeleton, *171*
Winslow, foramen of, 227
Wolff, 335

Wolffian duct, *256, 257, 264, 265*
Woodpeckers, 5

Xanthophores, 81
Xantusia, pectoral girdle and sternum, *156*
Xenophanes, 334
Xenopus, absence of tongue, 210
Xiphophorus, 266

Yolk sac, 69, *70*
Ypsiloid cartilage, *178*

Zaglossus, 37
Zebra, *48*
Zygapophyses, in teleosts, *146*
    in tetrapods, *146*
Zygote, frog, 59

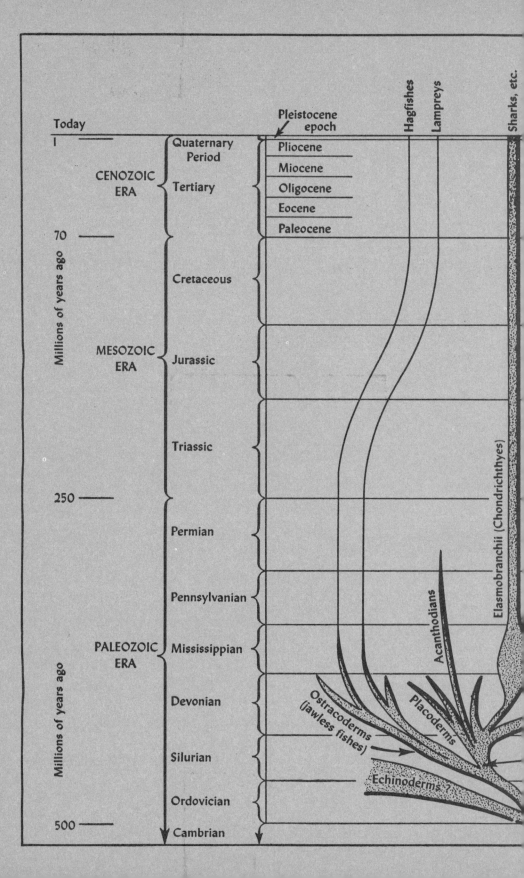